Scott Foresman - Addison Wesley
MATH

Assessment Sourcebook
Grade 3

Scott Foresman - Addison Wesley

Editorial Offices: Menlo Park, California • Glenview, Illinois
Sales Offices: Reading, Massachusetts • Atlanta, Georgia • Glenview, Illinois
Carrollton, Texas • Menlo Park, California

http://www.sf.aw.com

ISBN 0–201–31295–6

Printed in the United States of America

1 2 3 4 5 6 7 8 9 10 – BW – 02 01 00 99 98 97

Table of Contents

Assessing Student Performance in Mathematics

> *"Instead of assuming that the purpose of assessment is to rank students on a particular trait, the new approach assumes that high public expectations can be set that every student can strive for and achieve. . ."*
>
> *—NCTM Assessment Standards for School Mathematics*

Linking Assessment and Instruction

Recommendations made by the National Council of Teachers of Mathematics stress the importance of linking assessment and instruction methods. As teachers employ more diverse methods of instruction, such as hands-on activities, open-ended investigations, and long-term projects, they also need to employ diverse methods of assessment. As we make the goal of mathematics the acquisition of dynamic processes, we strive for methods of assessment that further our goals. Authentic assessment tools require critical thinking and problem solving, not merely mastery of facts and procedures.

Because instruction and its assessment are closely linked, methods of evaluation need to change as instructional methods change. New forms of assessment provide a more authentic way of evaluating the depth of our students' knowledge of mathematics, rather than their ability to memorize facts and procedures. These alternative methods of assessment offer the opportunity for students to display how they approach problem situations, collect and organize information, formulate and test conjectures, and communicate their mathematical insights.

An authentic assessment program contains tasks that are appropriate to the topics students are learning and that provide outcomes that are valuable to the students. Such an assessment program allows for such highly individual factors as a school's curriculum objectives, a teacher's style of instruction, and a student's maturity level. Each individual teacher determines the assessment best suited to the needs of his or her students.

To help teachers select the most appropriate evaluation tools for their classrooms, the *Assessment Sourcebook* provides the following materials.

Informal Assessment Forms
- Student-completed forms, Math Logs (journals), Student Surveys, Self-Evaluations, Portfolio Guides, and more
- Teacher-completed forms for Ongoing Assessment in Problem Solving, Observation, and Cooperative Learning, as well as forms for assessing projects and portfolios

Formal Assessment Instruments
- Free-response chapter tests that cover every objective in the student text chapter and that include an Explain Your Thinking question; Parallel forms A and B of this test are provided.
- Multiple-choice tests for each chapter
- Alternative chapter assessments (Performance Assessment) comprised of several open-ended questions; Each test is accompanied by its own Evaluation Guide.
- Mixed-response chapter tests that include a short performance task
- Mixed-response cumulative chapter test that prepares students for standardized tests and includes items for current chapter objectives along with covering concepts from previous chapters
- Item Analysis management forms that teachers can use to evaluate student comprehension of each chapter objective
- Class record forms

> *"Assessment should be a means of fostering growth toward high expectations."*
>
> *—NCTM Standards for School Mathematics*

Guidelines for Developing an Authentic Assessment Program

Developing an authentic program of assessment is an ongoing process. Some assessment instruments will seem perfectly suited to the teacher and his or her students from the start. Others may be effective only after the teacher has had a chance to experiment with and refine them. Still others may be inappropriate for a given class or instructional situation. The following are some guidelines that may be helpful when choosing the types of assessment for a particular program.

Use an assessment form that serves your purposes.

- For the teacher, assessment yields feedback on the appropriateness of instructional methods and offers some clues as to how the content or pace of instruction could be modified.
- For the students, assessment should not only identify areas for improvement, but should also affirm their successes.
- Traditional forms of assessment yield a tangible score.

Make the assessment process a positive experience for students.

- Use a variety of assessment techniques.
- Provide opportunities for students to demonstrate their mathematical capabilities in an atmosphere that allows maximum performance.
- Emphasize what students *do* know and *can* do, not what they do not know and cannot do.
- Motivate students to achieve by using tasks that reflect the value of their efforts.

Use authentic assessment to focus on higher-order thinking skills.

- Authentic assessment provides a picture of the student as a critical thinker and problem solver.
- Authentic assessment helps to identify how the student does mathematics, not just what answer he or she gets.

Provide assessment activities that resemble day-to-day tasks

- Use activities similar to instructional activities to do assessment.
- Use assessment activities to further instruction.
- Give students the immediate and detailed feedback they need to further the learning process.
- Encourage students to explore how the mathematics they are learning applies to everyday life.

Include each student as a partner in the assessment process.

- Encourage students to reflect on what they have done.
- Encourage students to share their goals.

Making and Using an Assessment Portfolio

For students and teachers alike, portfolios are exciting records of progress. In mathematics, the process of making a portfolio and adding materials to it on an ongoing basis is an extremely effective method for learning and assessment. A math portfolio can contain student work, including projects, reports, drawings, reflections, and formal assessment instruments.

As students review their portfolios, they observe concrete evidence of their growth in skills and confidence. For many students, seeing progress is believing.

> "Large pieces of work like performance tasks, projects, and portfolios provide opportunities for students to demonstrate growth in mathematical power."
>
> —NCTM Assessment Standards for School Mathematics

Getting Started

There are many procedures that students and teachers can use to make and use portfolios. It might be helpful to use a two-stage approach for keeping student portfolios. In this approach, students use a work portfolio, which contains the work they have completed in a period of a few weeks. At designated times, the teacher and student can evaluate the Work Portfolio and transfer materials to the Assessment Portfolio.

At the beginning of the school year, you will want to do the following:
- Provide two file folders for each student.
- Have students label one folder *Work Portfolio* and the other *Assessment Portfolio*.

About the Work Portfolio

The *Work Portfolio* is for "work in progress" and recently completed materials. The student should have access to it on a day-to-day basis and should keep in it all class work, group work, homework, and projects for the current period, including student assessment forms such as *My Math Log*.
- You can periodically review students' *Work Portfolios* to verify that students are completing assignments on time.
- You can write notes to students, commenting on individual items in their *Work Portfolios*.
- Every two to six weeks, students should review their *Work Portfolios* to determine which materials they would like to transfer to their *Assessment Portfolios*. (See below.)
- After transferring selected items to the *Assessment Portfolio*, students complete the *About My Portfolio* and take home all items remaining in the *Work Portfolio*.

About the Assessment Portfolio

- The *Assessment Portfolio* contains materials that will help students and teachers evaluate progress over the course of an interval, such as a marking period or a school year. Some of the materials included in the *Assessment Portfolio* will be chosen by students and some may be chosen by teachers.

You may find it helpful to schedule Portfolio conferences with individual students. In that way, you can work with students to evaluate materials. The following questions may help you choose the items for the *Assessment Portfolios*:
- Does an item illustrate the student's ways of thinking about mathematical processes?
- Does an item show a baseline—a starting point for a given year?

Assessment Portfolio

- Does an item show progress, or growth in understanding, over time?
- Is an item an example of how mathematics connects with experiences outside the classroom?
- Does the item show positive attitudes towards mathematics?
- Does the item show problem-solving processes?

The following list includes some, but not all, of the materials you and your students may want to include in their *Assessment Portfolios*:

- Student-selected items from the *Work Portfolio*
- Letter from the student about the work included in the *Assessment Portfolio*
- Math autobiography
- Other work selected by you and the student, including math surveys, formal assessments, and informal assessments such as interviews and observations.

> *"The opportunity to share mathematical ideas through portfolios can mark a real turning point in student attitudes."*
>
> —NTCM Mathematical Assessment

Evaluating a Portfolio

When you need to evaluate student *Assessment Portfolios*, you may want to use the following tips:

- Keep in mind that portfolio evaluation is a matter of ongoing discussion.
- Set aside time to discuss the *Assessment Portfolio* with the student.
- Use the *Assessment Portfolio* when discussing the student's progress with his or her family.
- Use it as a basis for identifying strengths and weaknesses and for setting group and individual goals for the next period.
- Consider developing your own rubrics or other criteria for evaluating portfolios.

Table of Contents for Assessment Forms

Assessment Forms

Using Assessment Forms

Using Student-Completed Forms

This sourcebook provides eight forms that students can use as aides to self-assessment. Use one or more depending upon students' needs.

Form	Purpose	Suggested Uses
My Math Log	To write about experiences in mathematics	Keep a daily math journal that lets students reflect on how mathematics relates to daily life.
Student Survey	To check student attitudes toward various math activities	Periodically monitor the change in student attitudes toward math.
How We Worked in Our Group	To evaluate student interaction with members of groups	Complete at the conclusion of group projects.
Group Work Log	To keep records of groups assignments	Monitor and evaluate group assignments.
Checklist for Problem-Solving Guide	To organize problem-solving efforts To follow the steps given in the Student Edition	Monitor student use of the problem-solving process.
Student Self-Assessment	To encourage student awareness of independent work	Monitor student progress in working independently.
About My Portfolio	To describe the contents of student's portfolio	Update when student places materials in his or her *Assessment Portfolio*.
My Math Experiences	To summarize attitudes toward and achievement in mathematics	Complete at the end of instructional periods.

© Scott Foresman Addison Wesley 3

Using Teacher-Completed Forms

Eight assessment forms are provided in this sourcebook to help the teacher keep a record of authentic but informal assessments. Some forms are for use with individual students while others are for use with groups of students.

Form	Purpose	Suggested Uses
Assessing Performance in Problem Solving	To assess individual students in problem-solving situations	Describe the level of student performance. Modify instructions to meet individual needs.
Ongoing Assessment: Problem Solving	To assess groups of students in problem-solving situations	Assess the entire class. Assess small groups over time.
Ongoing Assessment: Observation	To observe and assess several students at one time	Provide a mathematical profile of the entire class. Identify common strengths and weaknesses. Modify pace or content. Determine appropriate groupings.
Ongoing Assessment: Cooperative Learning	To assess student ability to work constructively in groups	Assess one or more cooperative groups.
Individual Assessment Through Observation	To determine the student's thought processes, performance, and attitudes	Record observation of a student in the classroom.
Overall Student Assessment	To summarize each student's overall performance	Evaluate student performance over an entire instructional period.
Project/Presentation Checklist	To evaluate oral presentation or extended projects	Prepare students and evaluate presentations or projects.
Portfolio Assessment	To evaluate individual portfolios	Periodically evaluate contents of portfolio. Help students assess process of creating a portfolio.

Name _____

Date _____

My Math Log

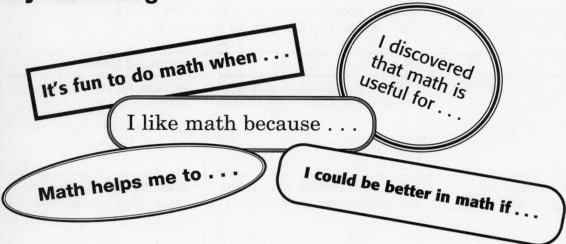

It's fun to do math when . . .

I discovered that math is useful for . . .

I like math because . . .

Math helps me to . . .

I could be better in math if . . .

Use this sheet to help you write about math.

You may use the phrases above to help you get started.

You may use the space at the bottom for math drawings or sample problems.

_____

_____

_____

_____

_____

_____

_____

Name _____

Date _____

Student Survey

For each statement, record a ✔ to tell how you feel.

	Most of the time	Some of the time	Hardly ever
I am good in math.			
I need help on most problems.			
I see how math is used in real life.			
I understand word problems.			
I can solve most problems.			
I like to try new strategies.			
I give up easily.			
I keep an organized notebook.			
I think math is fun.			

Describe a project you would like the class to work on.

_____

_____

What is your favorite kind of math? Explain why.

_____

_____

List some activities outside of school where you have used math.

_____

_____

Name _____

Date _____

How We Worked in Our Group

What we worked on: _____

_____

Group Members: _____

_____

Check the sentences that describe what happened.

_____ We had a new idea or made a suggestion.

_____ We asked for more information.

_____ We shared the information we found.

_____ We tried different strategies to solve the problem.

_____ We helped a group member explain his or her idea more clearly.

_____ We combined our ideas.

_____ We encouraged students who did not understand the task.

_____ Other: _____

Complete each sentence below.

We learned _____

_____

We found an answer by _____

_____

After we found an answer, we _____

_____

By working together, we _____

_____

Name _____

Date _____

Group Work Log

Group Members: _____

_____

List the date, assignment, and page numbers for each group assignment. Describe how the group worked together to arrive at a group solution for the assignment. Mention any techniques that you found helpful in completing the assignment.

Date	Assignment	Description of Group's Work

Name _____

Date _____

Checklist for Problem-Solving Guide

Put a ✔ in the box after you answer each question or complete each part.

━ Understand ━

☐ What do you know? _____

_____

_____

☐ What do you need to find? _____

_____

━ Plan ━

☐ What will you do? _____

_____

_____

☐ What operation or strategy will you use? _____

_____

━ Solve ━

☐ Use your plan. Show your solution.

☐ What is the answer? Give a complete sentence.

_____

━ Look Back ━

☐ Check your work. Is your answer reasonable?

_____

Name _____

Date _____

Student Self-Assessment

Assignment _____

Write about what you did.

What were you trying to learn? _____

_____

_____

How did you start your work? _____

_____

_____

What materials did you need? _____

What did you learn? _____

_____

_____

Check the sentences that describe your work.

_____ I made a plan before I began my work.

_____ I was able to do the work.

_____ I did not understand the directions.

_____ I followed the directions but got the wrong answer.

_____ I found a different way to do this assignment.

_____ I could explain how to do this to someone else.

_____ The work was easier than I thought it would be.

_____ The work was harder than I thought it would be.

_____ Other: _____

Name _____

Teacher _____ Date _____

About My Portfolio

Describe the assignment, giving the page number or project name.

_____

_____

Why is this assignment part of your portfolio?

_____ My teacher chose the assignment.

_____ Everyone else in the class included this assignment.

_____ I chose this assignment.

Complete each sentence.

I began my work by _____

_____

_____

I liked this assignment because _____

_____

_____

Doing this assignment helped me _____

_____

_____

This assignment was . . .   too easy.   _____

                                 easy.   _____

                                 about right.   _____

                                 hard.   _____

                                 too hard.

Name _____

Date _____

My Math Experiences

Math that interests me: _____

_____

_____

_____

My math goals: _____

_____

_____

_____

Math skills I just learned and can do: _____

_____

_____

_____

Math skills I need to work on: _____

_____

_____

_____

Math awards I have received: _____

_____

Assessing Performance in Problem Solving

Student _____ Date _____

Check each statement below that accurately describes the student's work.

━━ Understand ━━

_____ Reads the problem carefully

_____ Studies any tables or graphs

_____ Can restate the problem in his or her own words

_____ Can identify given information

_____ Can identify the question to be answered

━━ Plan ━━

_____ Chooses an appropriate strategy for solving the problem

_____ Estimates what the answer should be

━━ Solve ━━

_____ Works systematically

_____ Shows solution in an organized fashion

_____ Computes correctly

_____ States the answer in a complete sentence, giving correct units

━━ Look Back ━━

_____ Checks to see that the answer is reasonable

_____ Tries other ways to solve the problem

Use the following criteria to assess the student's performance:

Level 4 (11–13 items checked)   The student demonstrates an in-depth understanding of the problem and communicates that understanding in a clear and concise manner. He or she is able to relate the problem to other work previously accomplished.

Level 3 (8–10 items checked)   The student understands the problem and shows a correct solution in a clear and organized fashion.

Level 2 (4–7 items checked)   The student displays an adequate understanding of major concepts, but may commit errors in some of the specific components.

Level 1 (0–3 items checked)   The student has partial or no apparent understanding of the problem. He or she does not complete the necessary work or uses an inappropriate strategy. No answer, an inappropriate response, or an incorrect answer with no work is shown.

Ongoing Assessment: Problem Solving

Date _____

Rate each item with a
- **+** if excellent
- **✔** if satisfactory
- **−** if needs improvement
- **NA** if not applicable

	Reads problem carefully	Studies any tables or graphs	Can restate problem in own words	Can identify given information	Can identify question to be answered	Chooses appropriate strategy	Estimates what the answer should be	Works systematically	Shows solution in organized fashion	Computes correctly	States answer in sentence giving correct units	Checks that the answer is reasonable	Tries other ways to solve problem
1.													
2.													
3.													
4.													
5.													
6.													
7.													
8.													
9.													
10.													
11.													
12.													
13.													
14.													
15.													
16.													
17.													
18.													
19.													
20.													
21.													
22.													
23.													
24.													
25.													
26.													
27.													
28.													

Ongoing Assessment: Observation

Date _____

Rate each item with a
- **+** if excellent
- **✔** if satisfactory
- **−** if needs improvement
- **NA** if not applicable

	Demonstrates knowledge of skills	Understands concepts	Works neatly and systematically	Works well with others	Displays a positive attitude	Considers and uses ideas of others	Shows patience and perseverance	Asks for help when needed	Uses time productively	Tries alternate approaches					
1.															
2.															
3.															
4.															
5.															
6.															
7.															
8.															
9.															
10.															
11.															
12.															
13.															
14.															
15.															
16.															
17.															
18.															
19.															
20.															
21.															
22.															
23.															
24.															
25.															
26.															
27.															
28.															

Ongoing Assessment: Cooperative Learning

Date ______________________________

Rate each item with a
- \+ if excellent
- ✔ if satisfactory
- – if needs improvement
- NA if not applicable

	Demonstrates problem-solving ability	Works systematically	Works with others in the group	Tutors and helps others	Considers and uses ideas of others	Speaks quietly	Initiates questions	Has a positive attitude	Shows patience and perseverance	Disagrees without being disagreeable			
1.													
2.													
3.													
4.													
5.													
6.													
7.													
8.													
9.													
10.													
11.													
12.													
13.													
14.													
15.													
16.													
17.													
18.													
19.													
20.													
21.													
22.													
23.													
24.													
25.													
26.													
27.													
28.													

Individual Assessment Through Observation

Student _____   Date _____

	Frequently	Sometimes	Never
Understanding			
Demonstrates knowledge of skills	_____	_____	_____
Understands concepts	_____	_____	_____
Selects appropriate solution strategies	_____	_____	_____
Solves problems accurately	_____	_____	_____
Work Habits			
Works in an organized manner	_____	_____	_____
Works neatly	_____	_____	_____
Gets work in on time	_____	_____	_____
Works well with others	_____	_____	_____
Uses time productively	_____	_____	_____
Asks for help when needed	_____	_____	_____
Confidence			
Initiates questions	_____	_____	_____
Displays a positive attitude	_____	_____	_____
Helps others	_____	_____	_____
Flexibility			
Tries alternate approaches	_____	_____	_____
Considers and uses ideas of others	_____	_____	_____
Uses mental math and estimation	_____	_____	_____
Uses calculators and other technology	_____	_____	_____
Perseverance			
Shows patience and perseverance	_____	_____	_____
Works systematically	_____	_____	_____
Is willing to try	_____	_____	_____
Checks work without being told	_____	_____	_____
Other			
_____	_____	_____	_____
_____	_____	_____	_____

© Scott Foresman Addison Wesley 3

Overall Student Assessment

Date ______________________

Rate each item with a
+ if excellent
✔ if satisfactory
– if needs improvement
NA if not applicable

	Problem Solving	Cooperative Learning	Math Writing	Class Work	Homework	Participation in Discussion	Quiz Scores	Test Scores					
1.													
2.													
3.													
4.													
5.													
6.													
7.													
8.													
9.													
10.													
11.													
12.													
13.													
14.													
15.													
16.													
17.													
18.													
19.													
20.													
21.													
22.													
23.													
24.													
25.													
26.													
27.													
28.													

Project/Presentation Checklist

This form can be used to evaluate an oral or written student project made by one student or a group of students. This checklist also can be used to discuss successful methods for making presentations, or given to students to help guide them in planning their projects such as mathematical art, scientific experiments, data gathering for charts and graphs, computer demonstrations, skits, or oral and written research projects.

Student(s) _____

_____

Project _____

The Project

```
Rate each item with a
  +  if excellent
  ✔  if satisfactory
  −  if needs improvement
 NA  if not applicable
```

_____ Demonstrates a mathematical concept properly

_____ Communicates math ideas clearly

_____ Shows a connection to another subject

_____ Shows time spent in planning and preparation

_____ Is original and/or creative

_____ Is colorful and neat

_____ Stimulates further investigation of the topic

_____ Includes a written report

_____ Lists resources used

_____ Shows a delegation of tasks among group members

The Oral Presentation

_____ Demonstrates a knowledge of the mathematical concept

_____ Is organized, and includes an introduction, main section, and conclusion

_____ Uses audio-visual props where appropriate

_____ Speaks clearly and paces presentation at proper speed

_____ Answers questions and stimulates further interest in the topic

_____ Demonstrates a positive problem-solving attitude

_____ Mentions resources used

Portfolio Assessment

Student _____ Date _____

	Required	Included	Comments
Table of Contents			
Letter from student • Explanation of contents • Criteria for selection			
Excerpt from Journal			
Working solution to an open-ended question			
Photo or sketch of problem worked with manipulatives			
Mathematical connections • Problems that work with more than one chapter • Problems that work with more than one area of math			
Subject-area connections • Problems that show connections with health, science, art, literature, data collection, social science, history, or geography			
Quiz, test, or homework; corrected or revised homework			
Projects			
Paragraph from student • How making a portfolio has been helpful			

Table of Contents for Test and Quizzes

Table of Contents for Tests and Quizzes *(continued)*

Using the Quizzes and Chapter Tests Forms A, B, C, E, and F

Assessment should be compatible with styles of learning and teaching. The *Assessment Sourcebook* offers several options for formal assessment. As teachers, you set the instructional styles for your classroom. The various forms of chapter tests help you incorporate assessment into whatever instructional styles you choose.

Teachers use written tests for many purposes. Particularly when a test is objective-referenced, it can be an efficient method of diagnosing the scope of a student's mathematical understanding. Tests can also provide valuable instructional feedback. And, of course, grades are a traditional instrument for reporting student achievement to parents, administrators, and the community. You may wish to have students show their work for all test forms. When there is limited space for this on the test page, ask that they include an additional sheet of paper with their work shown, or use the back of the test paper.

Quizzes (one per section)
There is a 1-page quiz for each section of the Student Edition. It covers each objective from the section.

Chapter Tests Forms A and B (free response)
Each test covers all of the objectives in the chapter of the Student Edition in a free-response format. Forms A and B are essentially parallel to each other. You can use Forms A and B together as pre- or post-tests. If you administer Form A and the test results show that students need additional instruction for particular objectives, you can reteach the objectives and then administer Form B.

The Item Analysis for Individual Assessment (in the Management Forms section of this *Assessment Sourcebook*) correlates these test items to objectives from the course, and it provides review options that you may use as needed.

While free-response tests are generally designed for written responses, they may also be used orally with individual students. An oral response approach might be especially helpful with students having special needs and with students who have limited proficiency in English.

Chapter Test Form C (multiple choice)
Test Form C is a 4–5 page multiple-choice test, which includes items that test every chapter objective. Because Test Form C is longer than Test Forms A and B, there are more items per objective. Even though Test Form C has a multiple-choice format, students taking these tests are not limited to performing calculations. Items, including word problems, are designed to assess understanding of concepts. In many school districts, students are required to take standardized tests. Using Test Form C provides students with practice in responding to multiple-choice questions, which are often used in standardized tests. You may want to have students use the Answer Form for Multiple-Choice Tests provided on page 262.

The Item Analysis for Individual Assessment (in the Management Forms section of this *Assessment Sourcebook*) correlates these test items to objectives from the course, and it provides review options that you may use as needed.

Using the Quizzes and
Chapter Tests Forms A, B, C, E, and F *(continued)*

Chapter Test Form D (performance test)

This form is a 1-page performance test. The use of this form and its accompanying Evaluation Guide is discussed on page 29 of this *Assessment Sourcebook*.

Chapter Test Form E (mixed response)

This test is a 2–4 page mixed-response test, which includes free-response and multiple-choice items. At the end of each Test Form E, there is a performance task which requires students to apply mathematical concepts in a real-life application. Because Test Form E includes varied types of test items, you are able to use one test to evaluate understanding for students with varied learning and assessment styles.

The Item Analysis for Individual Assessment (in the Management Forms section of this *Assessment Sourcebook*) correlates these test items to objectives from the course, and it provides review options that you may use as needed.

Chapter Test Form F (cumulative chapter test)

This 2–4 page test is a mixed-response test designed to prepare students for standardized tests. About two-thirds of the test covers all of the objectives from the chapter at hand. The rest of the test covers important objectives from previous chapters. The test items are both free response and multiple choice.

There are three sections on each test. The first section, *Computation,* includes exercises designed to assess student ability to perform calculations. The second section, *Concepts,* assesses student understanding of mathematical ideas. The third section, *Applications,* provides opportunities for students to apply what they have learned in class to real-world situations.

The Item Analysis for Individual Assessment (in the Management Forms section of this *Assessment Sourcebook*) correlates these test items to objectives from the course, and it provides review options that you may use as needed.

Evaluating the Quizzes and Chapter Tests Forms A, B, C, E, and F

For Test Forms A and B, answers are displayed on reduced facsimiles of student pages. These answers begin on page 266. Answers for Quizzes and Test Forms C, E, and F begin on page 279. While many numerical answers are straightforward, it is important to keep in mind that a student may not use the exact wording given for problems requiring written explanations. Also, it is a good idea to refer to students' work and grant partial credit if the work is correct, but the answer is not. A Percent Table for Scoring is found on page 325 of this *Assessment Sourcebook*.

Using Chapter Test Form D (performance test)

> *"Possessing mathematical power includes being able, and predisposed, to apply mathematical understanding in new situations, as well as having the confidence to do so."*
>
> *–NCTM Standards for School Mathematics*

Students often wonder aloud when they will ever need to use a particular concept or skill. By using long term projects and performance tasks, teachers respond to students' need for meaningful learning experiences. As teachers expand their use of projects and other authentic tasks for teaching mathematics, performance assessment becomes a logical choice for assessing student understanding of mathematics.

For each chapter, the *Assessment Sourcebook* provides Test Form D, which is a performance assessment. Many of these tests provide information about a realistic situation and ask students to use new information along with their mathematics power to solve problems. Most of the problems are open ended, with an emphasis on finding meaningful solutions rather than calculating one and only one correct response.

The mathematical tasks included in Test Form D allow students to demonstrate a broad spectrum of abilities. By using performance assessment, you can evaluate how students:
- reason through problems;
- make and test conjectures;
- use number sense to predict reasonable answers;
- utilize alternative strategies.

Performance tests also give a way to assess student qualities of imagination, creativity, and perseverance.

Administering Chapter Test Form D
Managing performance assessment projects may be more difficult than managing other types of assessment. The following tips may help you with classroom management during performance assessment administration.

- Consider having students work in groups to complete a performance assessment.
- Move among students as they work to collect anecdotal information during the test. Ask questions that will give you information about thought processes.
- Spend time at the beginning of the test to be sure all students understand the purpose.
- You may wish to share the evaluation standards on the Evaluation Guide with students before they begin work.

Evaluating Chapter Test Form D
The *Assessment Sourcebook* provides a 1-page **Evaluation Guide** on the reverse side of each Test Form D. This page includes teacher notes that identify the mathematical concepts and skills involved in performing the assessment task.

For each test, a set of task-specific evaluation standards help you evaluate student work. These standards identify four levels of performance. Specific standards were created using the following characteristics of student performance as general guidelines.

Level 4: Accomplishes and extends the task; displays in-depth understanding; communicates effectively and completely.

Level 3: Substantially completes the task; displays minor flaws in understanding or technique; communicates successfully.

Level 2: Partially completes the task; displays one or more major errors in understanding or technique; communicates unclear and/or incomplete information.

Level 1: Makes an attempt; gives little evidence of understanding; communicates little relevant information.

Because performance assessments are open-ended, student responses may be as varied and individual as the students themselves. For that reason, you may find it helpful to use these general standards as well as the task-specific standards when evaluating student performance.

Using the Inventory Test and Quarterly Tests

Inventory Test

A four-page Inventory Test helps assess student skill levels at the beginning of the school year. The Item Analysis for Individual Assessment (in the Management Forms section of this *Assessment Sourcebook*) correlates these test items to objectives from the previous year, and it provides review options that you may use as needed.

Evaluating the Inventory Test

Answers for the Inventory Test are given on page 279. A Percent Table for Scoring is found on page 325 of this *Assessment Sourcebook*.

Quarterly Tests

Four Quarterly Tests (cumulative tests covering chapters 1–3, 1–6, 1–9, and 1–12, respectively) help maintain ongoing assessment of student mastery of the course objectives. The Item Analysis for Individual Assessment (in the Management Forms section of this *Assessment Sourcebook*) correlates these test items to objectives from the course, and it provides review options that you may use as needed.

Evaluating the Quarterly Tests

Answers for the Quarterly Tests are given sequentially after the answers for Test Form F for Chapters 3, 6, 9, and 12, respectively. A Percent Table for Scoring is found on page 325 of this *Assessment Sourcebook*.

Inventory Test

Fill in the ◯ for the correct answer.

Do You Like Kickball or Four Square ?

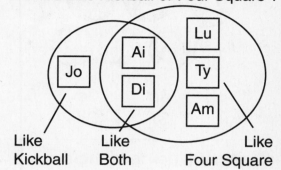

Like Kickball   Like Both   Like Four Square

1. Use the diagram.
How many students
like only kickball?

4	3	2	1
Ⓐ	Ⓑ	Ⓒ	Ⓓ

Solve. Choose the correct number sentence.

2. 6 🚗 are in a parking lot.

1 🚗 drives away.

How many 🚗 are left?

Ⓐ $6 - 1 = 5$; 5 🚗

Ⓑ $6 + 1 = 7$; 7 🚗

Ⓒ $6 - 5 = 1$; 1 🚗

Ⓓ $1 + 7 = 8$; 8 🚗

3. 15 students were in the
classroom. 6 went outside.
How many were still in
the classroom?

$15 - 6 = 9$ $15 - 9 = 6$ $6 + 9 = 15$
　　Ⓐ　　　　　Ⓑ　　　　　Ⓒ

4. What is the correct rule?

3	6
9	12
7	10

Ⓐ Subtract 5

Ⓑ Add 4

Ⓒ Subtract 3

Ⓓ Add 3

5. What is the number?
2 tens 7 ones

7	20	27	72
Ⓐ	Ⓑ	Ⓒ	Ⓓ

6. Which number is greatest?

45	87	21
Ⓐ	Ⓑ	Ⓒ

Name _____

7. How much money altogether?

83¢	78¢	68¢	63¢
Ⓐ	Ⓑ	Ⓒ	Ⓓ

8. What is the ending time?
Roxanne gets on a horse at
4:00. She rides the horse for
2 hours. The time is ___.

4:00	6:00	8:00
Ⓐ	Ⓑ	Ⓒ

9. What time does the clock show?

Ⓐ 10:30

Ⓑ 6:50

Ⓒ 6:10

Add. Regroup if you need to.

10.
$$\begin{array}{r} 18 \\ + 5 \\ \hline \end{array}$$

13	22	23	32
Ⓐ	Ⓑ	Ⓒ	Ⓓ

11.
$$\begin{array}{r} 64 \\ + 25 \\ \hline \end{array}$$

39	99	98	89
Ⓐ	Ⓑ	Ⓒ	Ⓓ

Subtract. Regroup if you need to.

12.
$$\begin{array}{r} 58¢ \\ - 6¢ \\ \hline \end{array}$$

42¢	52¢	54¢	64¢
Ⓐ	Ⓑ	Ⓒ	Ⓓ

13.
$$\begin{array}{r} 82 \\ - 26 \\ \hline \end{array}$$

56	64	66	68
Ⓐ	Ⓑ	Ⓒ	Ⓓ

14. Compare the numbers.
572 ● 527

>	>	=
Ⓐ	Ⓑ	Ⓒ

15. Which numbers are in order
from greatest to least?
Ⓐ 782, 528, 309, 112
Ⓑ 202, 247 278, 293
Ⓒ 967, 723, 856, 321

Continued

Name _____

16. Add. Regroup if you need to.

$$527$$
$$+\ \ 31$$

468   516   518   558
Ⓐ   Ⓑ   Ⓒ   Ⓓ

17. Subtract. Regroup if you need to

$$618$$
$$-\ 457$$

151   161   251   261
Ⓐ   Ⓑ   Ⓒ   Ⓓ

18. Measure the length with a centimeter ruler.

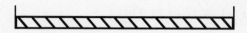

Ⓐ About 11 centimeters

Ⓑ About 6 centimeters

Ⓒ About 1 centimeter

19. Is the heavier or lighter than 1 pound?

Heavier   Lighter
Ⓐ   Ⓑ

20. Is a truck heavier or lighter than 1 kilogram?

Heavier   Lighter
Ⓐ   Ⓑ

22. How many faces does this solid have?

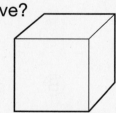

6 faces   4 faces   2 faces
Ⓐ   Ⓑ   Ⓒ

23. How was this shape moved?

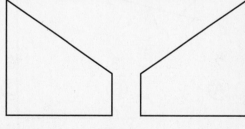

Slide   Flip   Turn
Ⓐ   Ⓑ   Ⓒ

23. Solve the riddle. Which shape am I?

I have more than 1 line of symmetry.

I have no corners.

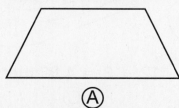   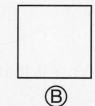   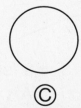

Ⓐ   Ⓑ   Ⓒ

Name _____

Which fraction shows the parts that are shaded?

24.

$\frac{1}{2}$ Ⓐ $\frac{2}{3}$ Ⓑ $\frac{3}{4}$ Ⓒ

25.

$\frac{1}{2}$ Ⓐ $\frac{1}{3}$ Ⓑ $\frac{2}{5}$ Ⓒ

26. How many people are on the seesaws?

2 Ⓐ 3 Ⓑ 6 Ⓒ

27. Find the product.

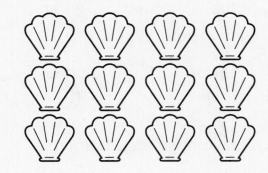

$\begin{array}{r} 4 \\ \times 3 \\ \hline \end{array}$ Ⓐ $\begin{array}{r} 3 \\ \times 2 \\ \hline \end{array}$ Ⓑ $\begin{array}{r} 3 \\ \times 3 \\ \hline \end{array}$ Ⓒ

28. Draw equal groups. Which number sentence shows how many in each group?

9 feathers on 3 hats

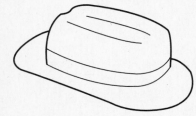 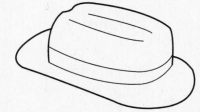 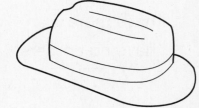

$9 \div 3 = 3$ feathers Ⓐ $8 \div 2 = 4$ feathers Ⓑ $12 \div 3 = 4$ feathers Ⓒ

Vocabulary: In 1–2, match each with its meaning.

1. bar graph **a.** a graph that uses bars to show data   **1.** _____

2. line graph **b.** a graph that connects points to
show how data changes over time   **2.** _____

In 3–4, use the pictograph.

3. How many students like cats?

_____

4. How many more students prefer
fish than birds?

_____

Our Favorite Pets

Bird

Fish

Dog

Cat

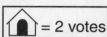 = 2 votes

In 5–6, use the bar graph.

5. Which site has the least votes?

_____

6. Which site has 25 votes?

_____

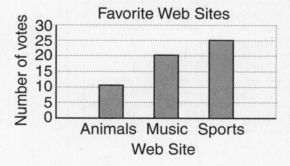

Favorite Web Sites

Number of votes: 30 25 20 15 10 5 0

Animals Music Sports
Web Site

In 7–8, use the line graph.

7. How much did the puppy weigh
by Week 3?

_____

8. How many weeks old was the
puppy when it weighed 50 ounces?

_____

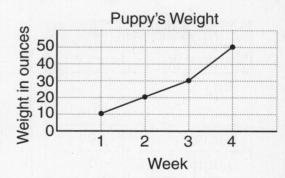

Puppy's Weight

Weight in ounces: 50 40 30 20 10 0

1 2 3 4
Week

9. Write which operation you would use.
Then solve. Jim has 12 apples. He eats
3 apples. How many does he have left? _____

10. Complete the table.
Then write the rule.

In	2	5		11
Out	5	8	11	

_____

Name _____

Date _____ Score _____

1. Which is an example of tally marks?

a. |||| |||| || **b.** |⌐|⌐|⌐|⌐|⌐|⌐|⌐|⌐|⌐⌐|
0 2 4 6 8 10 12 14 16   **c.** ☺ = 5 votes

1. _____

2. Complete the tally table
with the scores shown below.

9, 8, 8, 8, 9, 8, 9, 9, 8, 8

Scores	Tally	Number
8		
9		

3. Use the data in the table. Complete the pictograph.

Favorite Soups	
Soup	Number
Tomato	5
Chili	4
Vegetable	6
Stew	4

Favorite Soups	
Tomato	🥫🥫🥫
Chili	🥫🥫
Vegetable	
Stew	

🥫 = 2 votes

4. Use the data in the table. Complete the bar graph.

Jewelry Display	
Jewelry	Number
Ring	15
Necklace	10
Earring	20
Bracelet	10

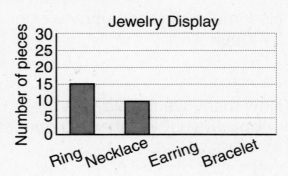

5. Cassandra saves 1 penny this week, 2 pennies the second
week, 3 pennies the third week, and so on. How many pennies
will she have saved by the end of the fourth week?

_____

Name _____

Date _____ Score _____

Vocabulary: In 1–3, match each with its meaning.

1. key

   a. a graph that uses bars to show data

   1. _____

2. pictograph

   b. part of a pictograph that tells what each symbol shows

   2. _____

3. bar graph

   c. a graph that uses pictures, or symbols, to show data

   3. _____

In 4–5, use the pictograph.

4. What is the least popular sport?

   _____

5. How many students chose soccer?

   _____

In 6–7, use the bar graph.

6. What subject has 20 votes?

   _____

7. How many more students prefer math than science?

   _____

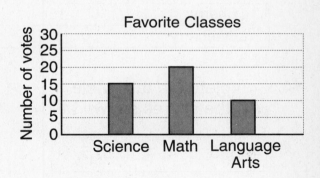

In 8–9, use the line graph.

8. How many books did Joe read in Week 3?

   _____

9. How many more books did Joe read in Week 3 than in Week 1?

   _____

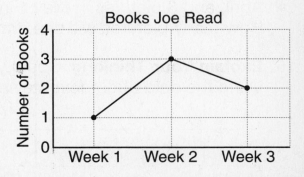

© Scott Foresman Addison Wesley 3

Name _____

10. Write which operation you would use.
Then solve. Kay has 4 oranges. She picks
3 more. How many does she have in all? _____

11. Complete the table.
Then give its rule.

In	5	6	7	8	10
Out	1	2	3		

_____

In 12–13, use the data in the tables. Complete each graph.

12.

Favorite Season	
Season	Number
Spring	6
Summer	4
Fall	8
Winter	5

Favorite Season	
Spring	✳ ✳ ✳
Summer	✳ ✳
Fall	
Winter	

✳ = 2 votes

13.

Favorite Frozen Yogurt	
Flavor	Number
Vanilla	10
Chocolate	20
Cherry	15
Blueberry	5

14. Complete the tally table
with the scores shown below.

4, 5, 5, 5, 4, 4, 4, 5, 5, 5

Scores	Tally	Number
4		
5		

15. Inga drew 2 pictures in March, 5 pictures in
April, and 8 pictures in May. Find a pattern.
How many pictures will she draw in June?

15. _____

16. Explain Your Thinking Could you draw a bar graph
using the data about favorite seasons in Item 12? Explain.

_____

_____

Date _____ Score _____

Vocabulary: In 1–3, match each with its meaning.

1. pictograph

a. a graph that uses bars to show data

1. _____

2. bar graph

b. numbers that show the units used on a bar graph

2. _____

3. scale

c. a graph that uses pictures, or symbols, to show data

3. _____

In 4–5, use the pictograph.

4. What is the most popular fruit?

_____

5. How many students chose oranges?

_____

In 6–7, use the bar graph.

6. What color has 10 votes?

_____

7. How many more students prefer green than red?

_____

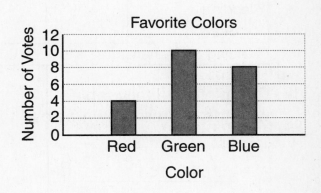

In 8–9, use the line graph.

8. How many games did Don play in Week 3?

_____

9. How many more games did Don play in Week 3 than in Week 1?

_____

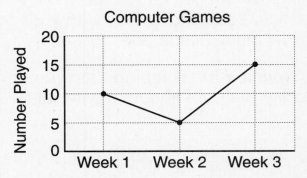

10. Write which operation you would use. Then solve. Que has 5 pennies. She loses 2 pennies. How many pennies does she have left? _____

11. Complete the table. Then give its rule.

In	4	5	6	8	10
Out	1	2			

_____

In 12–13, use the data in the tables. Complete the graphs.

12.

Favorite Summer Activities	
Activity	Number
Swimming	15
Camping	10
Skating	5
Skateboarding	15

Favorite Summer Activities	
Swimming	✹✹✹
Camping	✹✹
Skating	
Skateboarding	

✹ = 5 votes

13.

Favorite Winter Activities	
Activity	Number
Skiing	6
Sledding	8
Ice Skating	4
Building Snowmen	10

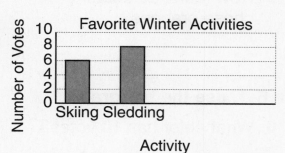

Favorite Winter Activities

14. Complete the tally table with the scores shown below.

7, 7, 7, 7, 7, 8, 8, 7, 7, 8

Scores	Tally	Number
7		
8		

15. Jonathon strings 1 black bead, then 2 blue beads, then 3 red beads, then 1 gold bead. He reverses the pattern beginning with 1 gold bead and ending with 1 black bead. How many beads does he string?

15. _____

16. Explain Your Thinking Can you draw a pictograph using the data about favorite winter activities?

_____

_____

© Scott Foresman Addison Wesley 3

Give the letter of the correct answer.

In 1-4, use the pictograph.

Favorite Fairy Tales	
Snow White	📖 📖 📖 📖 📖
Cinderella	📖 📖 📖 📖 📖 📖
Goldilocks	📖 📖 📖
Sleeping Beauty	📖 📖 📖

📖 = 2 votes

1. Which fairy tale was chosen most often?

   A *Goldilocks*   **B** *Snow White*
   C *Sleeping Beauty* **D** *Cinderella*

2. How many students chose *Goldilocks* as their favorite fairy tale?

   A 4 students   **B** 6 students
   C 7 students   **D** 8 students

3. Which fairy tale was chosen by 5 students?

   A *Goldilocks*   **B** *Snow White*
   C *Sleeping Beauty* **D** *Cinderella*

4. How many more students chose *Cinderella* than *Snow White*?

   A 2 students   **B** 4 students
   C 1 student   **D** Not here

5. What is the rule for this table?

In	5	6	7	8	10
Out	2	3	4	5	7

   A Subtract 3.   **B** Add 3.
   C Subtract 2.   **D** Add 2.

1. _____

2. _____

3. _____

4. _____

5. _____

6. What is the rule for this table?

In	2	4	6	8	10
Out	6	8	10	12	14

6. _____

A Subtract 5.   **B** Add 2.
C Add 7.   **D** Not here

In 7–10, use the bar graph.

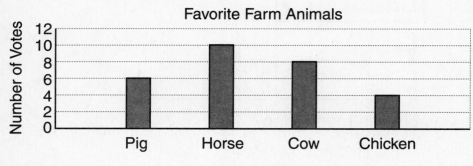

Favorite Farm Animals

7. Which farm animal was the students' favorite?

7. _____

A Pig   **B** Cow   **C** Horse   **D** Chicken

8. How many students chose a chicken as their favorite farm animal?

8. _____

A 7 students   **B** 6 students
C 5 students   **D** 4 students

9. Which animal was chosen by 8 students?

9. _____

A Pig   **B** Cow   **C** Horse   **D** Chicken

10. How many more students chose a cow than a pig?

10. _____

A 2 students   **B** 4 students
C 5 students   **D** 7 students

11. Mr. Chan has 9 tennis balls. Raul has 4 tennis balls. Which operation would you use to find how many more tennis balls Mr. Chan has than Raul?

11. _____

A Addition   **B** Subtraction
C Multiplication   **D** Division

Continued

12. Brittany has 9 red marbles and 4 blue marbles. Which operation would you use to find how many marbles Brittany has in all?

12. _____

A Addition   **B** Subtraction
C Multiplication   **D** Division

In 13–15, use the line graph.

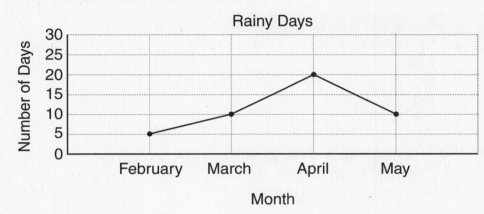

13. How many days did it rain in March?

13. _____

A 5 days   **B** 10 days   **C** 15 days   **D** 20 days

14. Which month had 5 rainy days?

14. _____

A February   **B** March   **C** April   **D** May

15. How many rainy days were there in all four months?

15. _____

A 5 days   **B** 10 days   **C** 20 days   **D** Not here

16. Katie pasted 3 pictures in the first row of her album, 6 pictures in the second row, and 9 pictures in the third row. Find a pattern. How many pictures will she paste in the fourth row?

16. _____

A 9 pictures   **B** 12 pictures
C 18 pictures   **D** Not here

17. Lane is making a border for his watercolor picture. Which shape will come next in the pattern?

17. _____

A Square   **B** Circle   **C** Triangle   **D** Not here

Name _____

18. You need to tally these scores: 1, 3, 3, 4, 3, 2, 1, 3, 3, 7. How many tally marks will you make to show the number of students who score a 3?

18. _____

    A 1 | **B** 2 ||

    C 3 ||| **D** Not here

In 19–22, use the data in the table.

Favorite Pastas		
Pasta	Tally	Number
Noodles	||||	4
Spaghetti	|||| |||| ||	12
Macaroni	|||| ||||	10
Ravioli	|||| |||	8

19. Suppose you make a pictograph. You decide to have each symbol equal 2 votes. How many symbols will you draw to show the votes for spaghetti?

19. _____

    A 2 symbols   **B** 6 symbols

    C 12 symbols   **D** Not here

20. Suppose each symbol in your pictograph equals 2 votes. How many more symbols will you draw to show the votes for macaroni than you draw to show votes for noodles?

20. _____

    A 6 symbols   **B** 5 symbols

    C 3 symbols   **D** Not here

21. Suppose you make a bar graph. Which of these scales would you be most likely to use?

21. _____

    A 10, 20, 30, 40, 50, 60   **B** 25, 50, 75, 100, 125, 150

    C 2, 4, 6, 8, 10, 12   **D** 6, 12, 18, 24, 30, 36

22. Suppose you make a bar graph. Which pasta will the longest bar represent?

22. _____

    A Noodles   **B** Spaghetti   **C** Macaroni   **D** Ravioli

23. What type of marks would you make when counting votes for favorite pasta dishes?

23. _____

    A Stray marks   **B** Key marks

    C Scales   **D** Tally marks

In the fall, leaves turn many different colors.

a. Making Decisions Use four different colors to color all
of the leaves.

b. Recording Data Make a table like the one below. Use
tally marks to complete the table. Then write how many
leaves you have for each color.

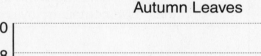

Color	Tally	Number

Complete the bar graph.

Autumn Leaves

Number of Leaves
10
8
6
4
2
0

Color

c. Analyzing Data Use the graph to answer these questions.

What does each bar represent?

How did you decide which color to graph first?

d. Explain Your Thinking

How can you use the bar graph to tell whether two
colors are used on the same number of leaves?

e. Making Decisions Draw and color more leaves. How
will this change the graph? Make another graph to show
the new data.

Teacher Notes

Concepts and Skills This activity requires students to:
- record information in a table.
- make decisions using real-life experiences.
- make a bar graph.
- read and interpret a bar graph.
- compare and order numbers.

Guiding Questions
- What colors do leaves turn in the fall?
- How do you use tally marks?
- On the bar graph, which bar will be tallest? shortest?

Answers
a. Decisions will vary. Check that all leaves are colored.
b. Answers will vary. Check students' work. The total number of leaves should be 20.
c. Each bar represents the number of leaves of one color. Answers will vary. Check students' work.
d. Answers will vary. Two colors are used the same number of times when the bars on the graph are the same height.
e. Answers will vary.

Extension
Have students make a pictograph using the data in the last column of their table.

Evaluation

Level	Standard to be achieved for performance of specified level
4	**Full Achievement** The student records data accurately and is able to complete a bar graph with no errors.
3	**Substantial Achievement** The student may make minor errors in recording data but can complete the bar graph with few errors.
2	**Partial Achievement** The student has some difficulty using tally marks when recording data and makes many errors. He or she needs some help in completing the bar graph.
1	**Little Achievement** The student needs help in using tally marks and recording data. Both the table and the graph contain many errors.

In 1–4, use the pictograph.

Favorite Vegetable	
Peas	(4 symbols)
Corn	(6 symbols)
Spinach	(1½ symbols)
Carrots	(2½ symbols)

= 2 votes

1. How many votes does each symbol represent?   1. _____

2. Which vegetable received the most votes?   2. _____

   A Peas   **B** Corn   **C** Spinach   **D** Carrots

3. Which vegetable did exactly 5 students prefer?   3. _____

   A Peas   **B** Corn   **C** Spinach   **D** Carrots

4. How many more students prefer peas than carrots?   4. _____

   A 5 students   **B** 4 students
   C 3 students   **D** Not here

In 5–6, complete each table. Then give each rule.

5.

In	2	3	4	5	6
Out	6	7	8		

5. _____

6.

In	8	11	14	17	20
Out	3	6	9		

6. _____

7. Jesse has 4 model airplanes and 5 model cars. What   7. _____
operation would you use to find how many models
Jesse has altogether?

   A Addition   **B** Subtraction
   C Multiplication   **D** Division

Name _____

8. Marlene has 5 mystery books and 3 science books. What operation would you use to find how many more mystery books than science books Marlene has?

8. _____

In 9–11, use the bar graph.

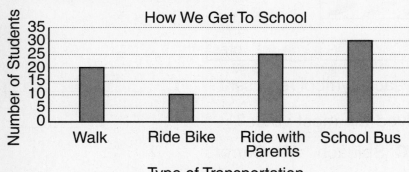

9. What do the numbers on the scale stand for? _____

10. How many students ride the bus to school?

10. _____

11. What transportation did exactly 10 students use?

11. _____

12. How many more students ride to school with their parents than walk to school?

12. _____

    A 10 students   **B** 20 students
    C 30 students   **D** Not here

In 13–14, use the line graph.

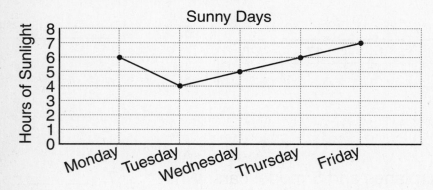

13. How many hours did the sun shine on Monday?

13. _____

14. What was the sunniest day?

14. _____

Continued

Name _____

15. Suppose you want to find how many different kinds of dogs are in your neighborhood. You survey your neighbors. Which of the following would you use to record their answers?

15. _____

A Key   **B** Symbol   **C** Scale   **D** Tally marks

16. Use the data in the table. Complete the pictograph.

Favorite Types of Music	
Music	Number
Country	5
Rock	8
Classical	4
Alternative	7

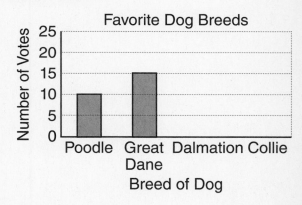

17. Use the data in the table. Complete the bar graph.

Favorite Dog Breeds	
Breed	Number
Poodle	10
Great Dane	15
Dalmation	20
Collie	10

18. Marta plants 1 tomato plant in the first row of her garden. She plants 3 in the second row, and 5 in the third row. Find the pattern. How many will she plant in the fourth row?

18. _____

19. Performance Task Suppose you want to graph your math test scores for the year. Which type of graph would you use? Explain.

_____

_____

_____

— Computation —

Use counting to find the missing numbers.

1. 4, 6, 8, 10, ■, ■, ■

2. 30, 40, 50, 60, ■, ■, ■

1. _____

2. _____

Find each sum or difference.

3. $2 + 4$ **4.** $5 - 3$ **5.** $8 - 5$ **6.** $4 + 5$

_____   _____   _____   _____

7. $5 + 1$ **8.** $7 - 3$ **9.** $1 + 2$ **10.** $5 - 1$

_____   _____   _____   _____

11. $\begin{array}{r} 9 \\ -5 \\ \hline \end{array}$ **12.** $\begin{array}{r} 3 \\ +4 \\ \hline \end{array}$ **13.** $\begin{array}{r} 6 \\ +3 \\ \hline \end{array}$ **14.** $\begin{array}{r} 7 \\ -6 \\ \hline \end{array}$

— Concepts —

Complete each table. Then give each rule.

15.

In	6	7	8	9	10
Out	2	3			

15. _____

16.

In	1	3	4	7	8
Out	3	5			

16. _____

17.

In	5	6	7	8	10
Out	8	9			

17. _____

18.

In	8	9	10	12	14
Out	6	7			

18. _____

Name _____

Use the pictograph for 19-21.

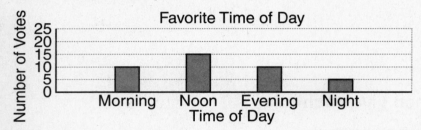

Color of Eyes	
Blue	
Brown	
Black	
Green	

= 2 votes

19. Which eye color do most students have?   **19.** _____

20. How many students have green eyes?   **20.** _____

21. Which operation would you use to find how many
more students have black eyes than blue eyes?   **21.** _____

    A Addition   **B** Subtraction
    C Multiplication   **D** Division

Use the bar graph for 22–25.

Favorite Time of Day

Number of Votes: 25, 20, 15, 10, 5, 0

Time of Day: Morning, Noon, Evening, Night

22. What do the numbers on the scale stand for?   **22.** _____

23. How many students chose morning as their
favorite time of day?   **23.** _____

    A 4 students   **B** 5 students
    C 10 students   **D** 15 students

24. How many students chose evening or night
as their favorite time of day?   **24.** _____

    A 15 students   **B** 10 students
    C 5 students   **D** 0 students

25. Which operation would you use to find how
many students voted?   **25.** _____

    A Addition   **B** Subtraction
    C Multiplication   **D** Division

Name _____

Use the line graph for 26–29.

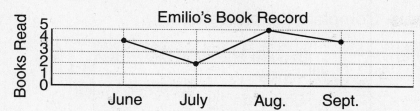

26. How many books did Emilio read during August?

26. _____

27. How many more books did Emilio read in June than in July?

27. _____

28. During which months did Emilio read 4 books?

28. _____

29. Suppose you want to find your friends' favorite movies. How would you record their answers in order to make a graph?

29. _____

   A Bar marks   **B** Scale marks
   C Key marks   **D** Tally marks

Use the data in the table for 30–31.

Favorite Authors		
Author	Tally	Number
Louisa May Alcott	卌 卌	10
Hans Christian Anderson	卌 III	8
Mark Twain	卌 卌 II	12
Laura Ingalls Wilder	IIII	4

30. Suppose you make a pictograph using this data. Which key would be the easiest to use when making the graph?

30. _____

   A 📖 = 2   **B** 📖 = 10

   C = 25   **D** Not here

31. Suppose you make a bar graph using this data. Which scale would you use when making the graph?

31. _____

   A 0, 1, 2, 3, 4, 5, 6   **B** 0, 2, 4, 6, 8, 10, 12
   C 0, 10, 20, 30, 40, 50, 60   **D** 0, 25, 50, 75, 100, 125, 150

Name _____

— Applications —

32. Use the data in the table. Complete the pictograph.

Favorite Milkshake Flavors	
Flavors	Number
Vanilla	4
Chocolate	10
Cherry	8
Strawberry	6

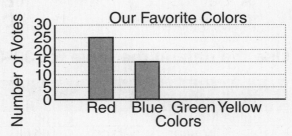

Favorite Milkshake Flavors	
Vanilla	🥤 🥤
Chocolate	🥤 🥤 🥤 🥤 🥤
Cherry	
Strawberry	

🥤 = 2 votes

33. In your pictograph, how many more symbols did you use to show cherry than strawberry?

A 1 symbol **B** 2 symbols
C 6 symbols **D** Not here

33. _____

34. How many more students chose chocolate than chose strawberry?

34. _____

35. Use the data in the table. Complete the bar graph.

Favorite Colors	
Color	Number
Red	25
Blue	15
Green	10
Yellow	20

Our Favorite Colors

Number of Votes: 30 25 20 15 10 5 0

Red Blue Green Yellow
Colors

`36. In your bar graph, which bar is the tallest?

A Red **B** Blue **C** Green **D** Yellow

36. _____

37. How many more students chose yellow than blue?

37. _____

38. Cheng walked 5 blocks to the butcher shop. He then walked 4 blocks to his grandmother's house. How many blocks did Cheng walk in all?

38. _____

39. Belinda is making a necklace. Which bead should she string next on the necklace?

39. ○ _____

△ ◯ ▢ ▢ ◯ △ ◯ ▢ ▢

Vocabulary: In 1–3, match each with its meaning.

1. digit

a. the value given to the place a digit has in a number

1. _____

2. place value

b. group of three digits in a number, separated by a comma

2. _____

3. period

c. 0, 1, 2, 3, 4, 5, 6, 7, 8, and 9

3. _____

In 4–7, write each number in standard form.

4. 400 + 60 + 7

4. _____

5.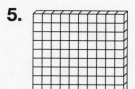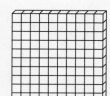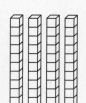

5. _____

6. nine thousand, two hundred ninety-seven

6. _____

7. 5,000 + 400 + 80 + 7

7. _____

In 8–9, write the word name for each number.

8. 348 _____

9. 5,641 _____

In 10–11, write each missing value.

10. 9 hundreds = ■ tens

10. _____

11. ■ ones = 3 hundreds

11. _____

In 12–13, write the value of each underlined digit.

12. 6<u>9</u>7,256

12. _____

13. <u>3</u>14,649

13. _____

14. Tai wants to pack 34 shirts in boxes that hold 10 shirts or 1 shirt. How many ways can he pack the boxes?

14. _____

Vocabulary: in 1–3, match each with its meaning.

1. compare

a. to place numbers from least to greatest or greatest to least

1. _____

2. estimate

b. to decide which of two numbers is greater

2. _____

3. order

c. to find a number that is close to the exact number

3. _____

In 4–7, compare. Use <, >, or =.

4. 712 ● 527

4. _____

5. 1,240 ● 124

5. _____

6. 3,126 ● 4,983

6. _____

7. 4,314 ● 4,314

7. _____

In 8–9, order from least to greatest.

8. 401, 104, 410 _____

9. 5,136, 8,542, 5,734 _____

In 10–11, order from greatest to least.

10. 678, 786, 687 _____

11. 7,162, 7,216, 795 _____

In 12–14, round to the nearest ten.

12. 23

13. $45

14. 213

_____

_____

_____

In 15–17, round to the nearest hundred.

15. 760

16. 148

17. $527

_____

_____

_____

Name _____

Date _____ Score _____

Vocabulary: in 1–3, match each with its meaning.

1. A.M.   **a.** times from noon to midnight   **1.** _____

2. P.M.   **b.** numbers used for ordering   **2.** _____

3. ordinal numbers   **c.** times from midnight to noon   **3.** _____

In 4–5, write each time two ways.

4.    **5.**    **4.** _____

            5. _____

            _____

In 6–7, write each time two ways. Write A.M. or P.M.

6.    **7.**    **6.** _____

            _____

go to school   look at moon   **7.** _____

            _____

8. Marie began reading a book at 5:00 P.M. and read for 1 hour and 20 minutes. What time did she stop reading?   **8.** _____

9. A computer class lasts from 10:00 A.M. until 11:40 A.M. How long is the class?   **9.** _____

10. Use the calendar. What day of the week is the 20th?

_____

JUNE						
Sun	Mon	Tues	Wed	Thu	Fri	Sat
1	2	3	4	5	6	7
8	9	10	11	12	13	14
15	16	17	18	19	20	21
22	23	24	25	26	27	28
29	30					

Date _____ Score _____

Vocabulary: In 1–3, match each with its meaning.

1. place value

a. times between midnight and noon

1. _____

2. estimate

b. the value given to the place a digit has in a number

2. _____

3. A.M.

c. to find a number that is close to the exact number

3. _____

In 4–5, write each number in standard form.

4. 600 + 40 + 9

4. _____

5. six thousand, two hundred forty-six

5. _____

6. Write the word name for 607. _____

7. Write the word name for 5,210 _____

In 8–9, write each missing value.

8. 90 ones = ■ tens

8. _____

9. ■ tens = 5 hundreds

9. _____

In 10–11, write the value of each underlined digit.

10. 379,6<u>2</u>5

10. _____

11. <u>9</u>34,271

11. _____

12. Carmen wants to pack 45 books in boxes that hold 10 books or 1 book. How many ways can she pack the boxes?

12. _____

In 13–14, compare. Use <, >, or =.

13. 435 ● 921

13. _____

14. 3,215 ● 2,513

14. _____

15. Order 413, 431, and 341 from greatest to least.

15. _____

16. Round 87 to the nearest ten.   **16.** _____

17. Round 315 to the nearest ten.   **17.** _____

18. Round 245 to the nearest hundred.   **18.** _____

19. Round 552 to the nearest hundred.   **19.** _____

In 20–21, write each time in two ways.

20.    **21.**    **20.** _____

_____

21. _____

_____

In 22–23, write each time in two ways. Write A.M. or P.M.

22.    **23.**    **22.** _____

_____

23. _____

set dinner table   school starts

_____

24. Chris cleaned for 2 hours and 5 minutes. He   **24.** _____
started at 9:00 A.M. What time did he finish?

25. LaRonda had dance class from 4:00 P.M.   **25.** _____
until 5:05 P.M. How long was the class?

26. What is the eighth month?   **26.** _____

27. Explain Your Thinking Which numbers round to 250
when rounded to the nearest ten? Which of these
numbers round to 200 when rounded to the nearest
hundred? Explain why your answers don't match.

_____

_____

Date _____ Score _____

Vocabulary: In 1–3, match each with its meaning.

1. digit

   a. times between noon and midnight

   1. _____

2. rounding

   b. 0, 1, 2, 3, 4, 5, 6, 7, 8, and 9

   2. _____

3. P.M.

   c. replacing a number with a number that tells about how many or how much

   3. _____

In 4–5, write each number in standard form.

4. five hundred thirty-eight

   4. _____

5. 3,000 + 400 + 70 + 9

   5. _____

6. Write the word name for 649. _____

7. Write the word name for 2,109. _____

In 8–9, write each missing value.

8. 4 hundreds = ■ tens

   8. _____

9. ■ ones = 8 hundreds

   9. _____

In 10–11, write the value of each underlined digit.

10. 237,<u>4</u>95

    10. _____

11. <u>4</u>72,839

    11. _____

12. Tony wants to pack 37 dishes in boxes that hold 10 dishes or 1 dish. How many ways can he pack the boxes?

    12. _____

In 13–14, compare. Use <, >, or =.

13. 589 ● 256

    13. _____

14. 2,134 ● 2,341

    14. _____

15. Order 742, 427, and 472 from least to greatest.

    15. _____

Name _____

16. Round 42 to the nearest ten.

16. _____

17. Round 756 to the nearest ten.

17. _____

18. Round 415 to the nearest hundred.

18. _____

19. Round 675 to the nearest hundred.

19. _____

In 20–21, write each time in two ways.

20.

21.

20. _____

_____

21. _____

_____

In 22–23, write each time in two ways. Write A.M. or P.M.

22.

23.

get dressed

play with friends

22. _____

_____

23. _____

_____

24. Rama read for 1 hour and 40 minutes. She started at 7:00 P.M. What time did she end?

24. _____

25. Lonnie had soccer practice from 3:00 P.M. until 4:15 P.M.. How long was the practice?

25. _____

26. What is the fifth month?

26. _____

27. Extend Your Thinking Which numbers round to 450 when rounded to the nearest ten? Which of these numbers round to 500 when rounded to the nearest hundred? Explain why your answers don't match.

_____

_____

_____

Give the letter of the correct answer.

1. Give 600 + 20 + 7 in standard form.

   A 672   **B** 726   **C** 672   **D** Not here

   1. _____

2. Give five hundred thirty-eight in standard form.

   A 538   **B** 583   **C** 835   **D** 38

   2. _____

3. Give the word name for 740.

   A Seven hundred forty   **B** Seventy-four
   C Seven hundred four   **D** Not here

   3. _____

4. Give the missing value. 70 ones = ■ tens

   A 700   **B** 7,000   **C** 70   **D** 7

   4. _____

5. Give the missing value. ■ ones = 6 hundreds

   A 6   **B** 60   **C** 600   **D** 6,000

   5. _____

6. Give 2,000 + 600 + 30 + 9 in standard form.

   A 9,362   **B** 2,693   **C** 2,639   **D** Not here

   6. _____

7. Give four thousand, two hundred sixty in standard form.

   A 4,206   **B** 4,260   **C** 4,026   **D** Not here

   7. _____

8. Give the word name for 9,050.

   A Nine thousand five   **B** Ninety thousand fifty
   C Ninety thousand five   **D** Nine thousand fifty

   8. _____

9. Give the value of the underlined digit in 3̲97,246.

   A 300,000   **B** 30,000   **C** 3,000   **D** 300

   9. _____

10. Give the value of the underlined digit in 846̲,213.

    A 600,000   **B** 60,000   **C** 6,000   **D** 600

    10. _____

11. Give two hundred forty-five thousand in standard form.

    A 200,000   **B** 245,000   **C** 245   **D** 200

    11. _____

12. Tito wants to pack 38 hats into boxes that hold 10 hats or 1 hat. How many ways can he pack the boxes?

12. _____

A 1 way   **B** 2 ways   **C** 4 ways   **D** 38 ways

13. Julia wants to pack 24 volleyballs into boxes that hold 10 balls or 1 ball. How many ways can she pack the boxes?

13. _____

A 24 ways   **B** 1 way   **C** 2 ways   **D** 3 ways

14. Compare 736 ● 637. Use <, >, or =.

14. _____

A <   **B** >   **C** =

15. Compare 7,234 ● 7,432. Use <, >, or =.

15. _____

A <   **B** >   **C** =

16. Compare 6,002 ● 6,002. Use <, >, or =.

16. _____

A <   **B** >   **C** =

17. Order 245, 452, and 254 from greatest to least.

17. _____

A 245, 254, 452   **B** 452, 254, 245
C 452, 245, 254   **D** 254, 245, 452

18. Order 769, 976, and 967 from least to greatest.

18. _____

A 976, 967, 769   **B** 769, 976, 967
C 967, 769, 976   **D** 769, 967, 976

19. Order 2,109, 2,019, 2,091 from least to greatest.

19. _____

A 2,109, 2,019, 2,091   **B** 2,091, 2,019, 2,109
C 2,019, 2,091, 2,109   **D** 2,019, 2,109, 2,091

20. Round 34 to the nearest ten.

20. _____

A 30   **B** 40   **C** 35   **D** Not here

21. Round 746 to the nearest ten.

21. _____

A 740   **B** 750   **C** 700   **D** Not here

22. Round 455 to the nearest ten.

22. _____

A 450   **B** 500   **C** 460   **D** 400

Continued

23. Round 289 to the nearest hundred.

    A 200   **B** 300   **C** 290   **D** 280

23. _____

24. Round 750 to the nearest hundred.

    A 700   **B** 750   **C** 760   **D** Not here

24. _____

25. Round 432 to the nearest hundred.

    A 400   **B** 430   **C** 440   **D** 500

25. _____

In 26–31, tell what time is shown on each clock.

26. A 7:25
    B 7:05
    C eight thirty-five
    D seven thirty

26. _____

27. A 8 minutes before 6
    B 8 minutes past 7
    C 40 minutes past 6
    D 40 minutes before 6

27. _____

28. A Three sixty-three
    B Three twenty-five
    C Four twenty-five
    D Three thirty-three

28. _____

29. A 6:19
    B 6:11
    C 6:49
    D Not here

29. _____

30. A 12:30 A.M.
    B 12:30 P.M.
    C 12:06 A.M.
    D 12:06 P.M.

play tag

30. _____

31. **A** 3:15 A.M.
B 3:30 P.M.
C 3:15 P.M.
D 3:15 A.M.

31. _____

leave school

32. Trent began studying at 5:00 P.M. and finished 1 hour and 22 minutes later. What time did he finish?

A 6:22 A.M.   **B** 5:22 P.M.   **C** 6:10 P.M.   **D** 6:22 P.M.

32. _____

33. Maura began basketball practice at 3:00 P.M. and finished 50 minutes later. What time did she finish?

A 3:50 P.M.   **B** 3:05 A.M.   **C** 4:05 P.M.   **D** 4:50 A.M.

33. _____

34. Lance fished from 6:00 A.M. to 9:45 A.M. How long did he fish?

A 3 hours
C 3 hours and 45 minutes
B 3 hours and 15 minutes
D 4 hours and 45 minutes

34. _____

Use the calendar for 35–37.

SEPTEMBER

Sun	Mon	Tues	Wed	Thu	Fri	Sat
					1	2
3	4	5	6	7	8	9
10	11	12	13	14	15	16
17	18	19	20	21	22	23
24	25	26	27	28	29	30

35. What day of the week is the 12th?

A Monday   **B** Tuesday   **C** Thursday   **D** Friday

35. _____

36. How many Fridays are there in this September?

A 3 Fridays   **B** 4 Fridays   **C** 5 Fridays   **D** Not here

36. _____

37. Which date is 6 days after September 14?

A September 8
C September 30
B September 20
D Not here

37. _____

How do you spend your time in school? These are the things that some third graders do in school.

study language arts, math, science, spelling, social studies
play ball games   eat lunch   recess
color or paint   talk with friends   watch a movie

a. Making Decisions Make a list of the things you would like to do during one school day. Be sure to include all the subjects you are studying in class. Then write how long you would like to spend on each activity to fill one school day.

b. Recording Data Make a table like the one below. List times starting with the time your school starts. Continue writing times by every fifteen minutes until the time school ends. Then make a schedule showing an ideal school day. List all your subjects and other activities in the order you would like to have your day arranged.

Time	Activity

c. Analyzing Data Use the table to answer these questions.

Which subject do you study first?

Which subject takes the least time in your day?

d. Analyzing Data List the times you spend on the activities from least to greatest.

What is the total time you spend on all the activities in your table? How do you know your answer is correct?

e. Making Decisions Are there any activities on which you are planning to spend less time or more time than you would spend in your actual class? Explain why.

Teacher Notes

Concepts and Skills This activity requires students to:
- record information in a table.
- make decisions using real-life experiences.
- estimate amounts of time.
- determine elapsed time.
- compare and order numbers.
- evaluate personal scheduling of time.

Guiding Questions
- Suppose you paint for 30 minutes each day. How many lines will you need in the table?
- How will you decide how long you will spend on an activity?
- How will you decide which activities in your schedule take more time than the same activity in your regular class?

Answers
a. Decisions will vary.
b. Check students' schedules. Times should be listed in 15-minute increments for the school day.
c. Check students' answers.
d. Check students' answers.
e. Answers will vary.

Extension
Have students write problems about elapsed time that can be answered using their schedules.

Evaluation

Level	Standard to be achieved for performance of specified level
4	**Full Achievement** The student can write a schedule using 15-minute increments of time and is able to schedule activities to fill the time. All comparisons are correct, and the explanation of any changes from the regular daily class is well written.
3	**Substantial Achievement** The student can write a schedule using 15-minute increments of time and is able to schedule activities to fill the time. Some errors may occur in writing segments in the schedule. The ordering of the activities may contain some minor errors, and the explanation of any changes the student might make is basically well written and logical.
2	**Partial Achievement** The student has some difficulty deciding on the activities to list and needs help listing the times. The ordering of activities contains major errors. The explanation of any changes the student might make is not well written.
1	**Little Achievement** The student needs help identifying activities he or she would like to do and the times in which to do them. The computations contain many errors and the concepts of comparing and ordering are not grasped. The student makes very little attempt to decide on changes in schedule and offers no explanation.

In 1–4, write the number in standard form.

1. 700 + 20 + 4

2. Three hundred fifty-eight

3. Eight thousand, four hundred six

4. 4,000 + 900 + 30 + 1

1. _____

2. _____

3. _____

4. _____

In 5–6, write the word name for each number.

5. 2,129 _____

6. 83,094 _____

In 7–8, choose the missing number.

7. 300 ones = ■ hundreds

    A 300   **B** 30   **C** 3   **D** Not here

7. _____

8. 4 tens = ■ ones

    A 40   **B** 400   **C** 4   **D** Not here

8. _____

9. Write the value of the underlined digit in 4̲72,391.

9. _____

10. Alison wants to pack 54 movie tapes into boxes that hold 10 movie tapes or 1 movie tape. How many ways can she pack the boxes?

    A 5 ways   **B** 6 ways   **C** 9 ways   **D** 10 ways

10. _____

In 11–12, compare. Use <, >, or =.

11. 713 ● 317

12. 2,413 ● 3,314

11. _____

12. _____

In 13–14, order from least to greatest.

13. 325, 532, 523 _____

14. 4,174, 4,471, 4,147 _____

15. Round 74 to the nearest ten.

    A 70   **B** 75   **C** 80   **D** 100

15. _____

16. Round 589 to the nearest ten.

    A 500   **B** 580   **C** 690   **D** Not here

16. _____

17. Round 434 to the nearest hundred.

17. _____

18. Round 250 to the nearest hundred.

18. _____

In 19–20, write each time two ways.

19.

20.

19. _____

_____

20. _____

_____

21. What time is shown on the clock below?

    A 11:00 A.M.
    B 11:30 P.M.
    C 11:00 P.M.
    D Not here

21. _____

eating lunch

22. The Saturday troop meeting started at 10:00 A.M. and was over at 11:45 A.M. How long was the meeting?

22. _____

23. What day is the 25th?

    A Monday
    B Tuesday
    C Thursday
    D Not here

23. _____

NOVEMBER						
Sun	Mon	Tues	Wed	Thu	Fri	Sat
	1	2	3	4	5	6
7	8	9	10	11	12	13
14	15	16	17	18	19	20
21	22	23	24	25	26	27
28	29	30				

24. Performance task Describe how to order these numbers: 6,718, 6,781, 6,871.

_____

_____

Date _____   Score _____

— Computation —

Find each sum or difference.

1. 3 + 4

_____

2. 9 + 5

_____

3. 7 − 4

_____

4. 6 + 9

_____

5. 8 − 3

_____

6. 9 − 4

_____

7.   3
      + 2

8.   6
      − 4

9.   4
      − 3

— Concepts —

10. Write six hundred forty-eight in standard form.

10. _____

11. Write 2,000 + 300 + 90 + 2 in standard form.

11. _____

12. Give the missing number. 80 ones = ■ tens

A 8   **B** 80   **C** 800   **D** 8,000

12. _____

13. Give the value of the underlined digit. 2<u>9</u>4,312

A 9   **B** 90   **C** 9,000   **D** 90,000

13. _____

14. Pãolo wants to pack 32 baseballs into boxes that hold 10 balls or 1 ball. How many ways can he pack the boxes?

14. _____

In 15–16, compare. Use <, >, or =.

15. 492 ● 429

15. _____

16. 9,346 ● 9,463

16. _____

17. Order 536, 356, and 365 from least to greatest.

A 536, 356, 365   **B** 365, 356, 536
C 356, 365, 536   **D** Not here

17. _____

18. Round 51 to the nearest ten.

19. Round 450 to the nearest hundred.

20. Round 214 to the nearest hundred.

In 21–22, write the time two ways.

21.

22.

18. _____

19. _____

20. _____

21. _____

_____

22. _____

_____

23. What time is shown on the clock below?

A 3:30 A.M.
B 3:30 P.M.
C 3:06 A.M.
D 3:06 P.M.

go to the movies

23. _____

24. Andy walked for 1 hour and 10 minutes. He started at 4:00 P.M. What time did he finish?

24. _____

— Applications —

25. Martin Luther King Jr.'s birthday is the 15th day of January. What day is his birthday this year?

A Saturday
B Thursday
C Tuesday
D Monday

JANUARY						
Sun	Mon	Tues	Wed	Thu	Fri	Sat
				1	2	3
4	5	6	7	8	9	10
11	12	13	14	15	16	17
18	19	20	21	22	23	24
25	26	27	28	29	30	31

25. _____

26. There were 452 students at the Spring Concert. The headline of the school paper will round that number to the nearest ten. What number will be in the headline?

26. _____

Vocabulary: In 1–3, match each with its meaning.

1. sum

a. a number that is added to find a sum

1. _____

2. addend

b. to find a number that is close to an exact number

2. _____

3. estimate

c. the number obtained when adding numbers

3. _____

In 4–5, complete the number sentences.

4. $3 + 5 = \blacksquare$

4. _____

   $30 + \blacksquare = 80$

_____

   $\blacksquare + 500 = 800$

_____

5. $\$4 + \$5 = \blacksquare$

5. _____

   $\$40 + \blacksquare = \$90$

_____

   $\$\blacksquare + \$500 = \$900$

_____

In 6–7, find each sum. You may use a hundred chart to help.

6. $35 + 40$

6. _____

7. $67 + 15$

7. _____

In 8–9, find each missing number.
You may use color cubes to help.

8. $17 + \blacksquare = 22$

8. _____

9. $\blacksquare + 19 = 26$

9. _____

10. Estimate the sum of 42 and 26.

10. _____

11. Estimate the sum of 476 and 315.

11. _____

12. Estimate the sum of 527 and 168.

12. _____

Vocabulary: in 1–3, match each with its meaning.

1. regroup	**a.** a number that is added to find a sum	**1.** _____
2. sum	**b.** to name a number in a different way	**2.** _____
3. addend	**c.** the number obtained when adding numbers	**3.** _____

In 4–5, find each sum. You may use place-value blocks to help.

4. $65 + 19$ **4.** _____

5. $48 + 49$ **5.** _____

In 6–9, add. Estimate to check.

6. $16 + 42$ **6.** _____

7. $28 + 53$ **7.** _____

8. $426 + 231$ **8.** _____

9. $134 + 657$ **9.** _____

In 10–14, add.

10. $3,624 + 245$ **10.** _____

11. $4,135 + 562$ **11.** _____

12. $9 + 63 + 21$ **12.** _____

13.
$$
\begin{array}{r}
7\,6 \\
1\,9 \\
+\,2\,4 \\
\hline
\end{array}
$$

14.
$$
\begin{array}{r}
3\,2 \\
4 \\
+\,9\,1 \\
\hline
\end{array}
$$

13. _____

14. _____

15. Guess and check to solve. The sum of two numbers is 45. The numbers are 3 apart. What are they?

15. _____

Vocabulary: in 1–3, match each with its meaning.

1. cent   a. using the digits in the greatest   1. _____
               place value to estimate

2. dollar   b. unit of money   2. _____

3. front-end   c. a bill or coin worth 100 cents   3. _____
   estimation

In 4–5, use mental math to find each sum.

4. 36 + 9   4. _____

5. 29 + 42   5. _____

In 6–7, write the total value.

6.   6. _____

7.   7. _____

8. Marcello buys an apple that costs $0.35. He pays with
   $1.00. List which coins and bills you would use to make
   change. Then write the change in dollars and cents.

   _____

9. Find the sum of $3.72 and $2.26   9. _____

10. Use front-end estimation to estimate the   10. _____
    sum of 309, 146, and 432.

11. Write if you need an exact answer or an estimate. Then
    solve. Jose has $4.00. Does he have enough money to
    buy two notebooks costing $2.75 each?

    _____

Vocabulary: In 1–3, match each with its example.

1. sum

a. a number that is added to find a sum

2. regroup

b. the number obtained when adding numbers

3. addend

c. to name a number in a different way

1. _____

2. _____

3. _____

In 4, complete the number sentences.

4. 4 + 3 = ■

40 + ■ = 70

■ + 300 = 700

4. _____

_____

_____

In 5–6, find each sum. You may use a hundred chart to help.

5. 27 + 30

6. 46 + 15

5. _____

6. _____

In 7–8, find each missing number. You may use color cubes to help.

7. 14 + ■ = 21

8. ■ + 16 = 24

7. _____

8. _____

In 9–12, find each sum. Estimate to check.

9.   5 7
       + 2 5

10.   3 1 4
        + 4 5 4

11.   3,5 1 8
        +   3 4 1

12.   1 7
          2 3
        + 4 5

9. _____

10. _____

11. _____

12. _____

13. Guess and check to solve. Jan has 3 more red bows than green bows. She has 15 bows in all. How many green bows does she have?

13. _____

In 14–15, use mental math to find each sum.

14. 23 + 9

14. _____

15. 48 + 12

15. _____

In 16–17, write the total value.

16.

16. _____

17.

17. _____

18. Basil buys a fruit juice that costs $0.85. He pays with $5.00. Write the change in dollars and cents.

18. _____

In 19–20, add.

19. $3.71 + $1.25

19. _____

20. $1.37 + $2.61

20. _____

In 21–22, use rounding to estimate each sum.

21. 38 + 53

21. _____

22. 523 + 172

22. _____

In 23–24, use front-end estimation to estimate each sum.

23. 428 + 219

23. _____

24. 374 + 425

24. _____

25. Explain Your Thinking How much would it cost to buy 1 red pencil for $0.95, 1 black pen for $0.89, and 1 blue pen for $0.79? Explain whether you need an exact answer or an estimate.

Vocabulary: In 1–3, match each with its example.

1. regroup   **a.** a number that is added to find a sum   1. _____

2. addend   **b.** the number obtained when adding numbers   2. _____

3. sum   **c.** to name a number in a different way   3. _____

In 4, complete the number sentences.

4. 2 + 6 = ■   4. _____

   20 + ■ = 80   _____

   ■ + 600 = 800   _____

In 5–6, find each sum. You may use a hundred chart to help.

5. 29 + 8   5. _____

6. 47 + 23   6. _____

In 7–8, find each missing number. You may use color cubes to help

7. 19 + ■ = 27   7. _____

8. ■ + 17 = 23   8. _____

In 9–12, find each sum. Estimate to check.

9.   4 6
    + 3 8

10.   2 5 1
    + 3 2 8

9. _____

10. _____

11.   2,1 7 3
  +   5 2 4

12.   1 2
    4 6
    + 3 1

11. _____

12. _____

Name _____

13. Guess and check to solve. Carly has 4 fewer marbles than Neka. They have 12 marbles in all. How many marbles does Neka have?

13. _____

In 14–15, use mental math to find each sum.

14. 21 + 5

14. _____

15. 61 + 43

15. _____

In 16–17, write the total value.

16.

16. _____

17.

17. _____

18. Arne buys a book that costs $2.45. He pays with $5.00. Write the change in dollars and cents.

18. _____

In 19–20, add.

19. $2.31 + $2.14

19. _____

20. $1.56 + $2.27

20. _____

In 21–22, use rounding to estimate each sum.

21. 26 + 31

21. _____

22. 213 + 478

22. _____

In 23–24, use front-end estimation to estimate each sum.

23. 521 + 318

23. _____

24. 492 + 258

24. _____

25. Explain Your Thinking Suppose you have $4.00. Is this enough money to buy a hamburger for $2.25 and a drink for $0.98? Explain whether you need an exact answer or an estimate.

Name _____

Date _____ Score _____

Give the letter of the correct answer.

1. If 4 + 3 = 7, then 40 + ■ = 70.

   A 3   **B** 30   **C** 300   **D** Not here

   1. _____

2. If 2 + 5 = 7, then 200 + ■ = 700.

   A 4   **B** 50   **C** 500   **D** Not here

   2. _____

3. Find 27 + 30. You may use a hundred chart to help.

   A 30   **B** 40   **C** 47   **D** 57

   3. _____

4. Find 18 + 47. You may use a hundred chart to help.

   A 65   **B** 200   **C** 55   **D** 63

   4. _____

5. Find 15 + 38. You may use a hundred chart to help.

   A 15   **B** 53   **C** 43   **D** 54

   5. _____

6. Find the missing number in 16 + ■ = 21. You may use color cubes to help.

   A 15   **B** 37   **C** 10   **D** 5

   6. _____

7. Find the missing number in 17 + ■ = 25. You may use color cubes to help.

   A 15   **B** 42   **C** 8   **D** 2

   7. _____

8. Estimate the sum of 38 and 53 by rounding.

   A 90   **B** 80   **C** 70   **D** Not here

   8. _____

9. Estimate the sum of 23 and 45 by rounding.

   A 60   **B** 50   **C** 40   **D** Not here

   9. _____

10. Estimate the sum of 32 and 27 by rounding.

    A 55   **B** 50   **C** 10   **D** Not here

    10. _____

Continued **81**

Name _____

11. Estimate the sum of 34 and 68 by rounding.

    A 110   **B** 100   **C** 120   **D** Not here

11. _____

In 12–18, add.

12. 437 + 261

    A 496   **B** 690   **C** 698   **D** Not here

12. _____

13. 284 + 314

    A 598   **B** 599   **C** 588   **D** 589

13. _____

14.   6 2 7
    + 2 5 1

    A 978   **B** 977   **C** 887   **D** 878

14. _____

15. 2,734 + 142

    A 876   **B** 2,875   **C** 2,876   **D** Not here

15. _____

16.   6,4 3 3
    + 1,2 5 6

    A 689   **B** 7,689   **C** 7,698   **D** Not here

16. _____

17. 14 + 32 + 21

    A 67   **B** 68   **C** 57   **D** 58

17. _____

18. 13 + 38 + 42

    A 83   **B** 80   **C** 90   **D** 93

18. _____

19. Guess and check to solve. The sum of two numbers is 34. The numbers are 4 apart. What are they?

    A 18, 14   **B** 19, 15   **C** 20, 14   **D** Not here

19. _____

20. Guess and check to solve. Jay sold 4 more tickets to the school play than Sara. They sold 16 tickets in all. How many tickets did Jay sell?

    A 6 tickets   **B** 8 tickets
    C 10 tickets   **D** 12 tickets

20. _____

Continued

21. Use mental math to add 19 and 7.

    A 26   **B** 8   **C** 27   **D** Not here

21. _____

22. Use mental math to add 24 and 16.

    A 30   **B** 40   **C** 42   **D** 44

22. _____

23. Use mental math to add 34 and 11.

    A 44   **B** 45   **C** 24   **D** 25

23. _____

In 24–27, write the total value.

24.

24. _____

    A $0.47   **B** $0.48   **C** $0.52   **D** $0.57

25.

25. _____

    A $0.63   **B** $0.68   **C** $0.78   **D** $0.73

26.

26. _____

    A $1.35   **B** $1.37   **C** $1.47   **D** $1.45

27.

27. _____

    A $2.35   **B** $2.25   **C** $3.25   **D** $3.35

28. Powa buys a book that costs $0.47. He pays with $1.00. What is his change in dollars and cents?

    A $53   **B** $0.47   **C** $0.53   **D** $1.47

28. _____

29. Andrea buys a card that costs $1.35. She pays with $5.00. What is her change in dollars and cents?

    A $0.76   **B** $3.65   **C** $4.65   **D** $1.65

29. _____

30. Bo buys a can of paint that costs $2.45. He pays with $5. What coins and bills would you give him for change?

    A Four dollars, two quarters, and one nickel
    B Four dollars, one quarter, and two dimes
    C Two dollars, one quarter, and two dimes
    D Two dollars, two quarters, and one nickel

30. _____

In 31-33, add.

31. $1.35 + $3.25

    A $4.60   **B** $4.55   **C** $4.50   **D** $4.45

31. _____

32. $2.43 + $2.16

    A $4.27   **B** $4.59   **C** $2.59   **D** Not here

32. _____

33. $3.14 + $1.67

    A $4.71   **B** $4.51   **C** $4.77   **D** Not here

33. _____

34. Use front-end estimation to estimate 119 + 678.

    A 500   **B** 600   **C** 700   **D** 800

34. _____

35. Use front-end estimation to estimate 342 + 510.

    A 800   **B** 700   **C** 600   **D** 500

35. _____

36. You have $4.00. Is this enough money to buy a package of carrots for $1.19 and a bag of potatoes for $3.79? Do you need to find an exact answer or make an estimate?

    A Find exact answer.   **B** Make an estimate.

36. _____

A	B	C	D	E	F	G	H	I	J
1	2	3	4	5	6	7	8	9	0
K	L	M	N	O	P	Q	R	S	T
1	2	3	4	5	6	7	8	9	0
U	V	W	X	Y	Z				
1	2	3	4	5	6				

Word Addition is played by choosing two words and adding to find the total value. For example, find the sum of *SEE* and *SAW*.

S	E	E
9	5	5
S	A	W
9	1	3

$$\begin{array}{r} 955 \\ +\ 913 \\ \hline 1{,}868 \end{array}$$

a. Recording Data Write five pairs of two- or three-letter words. Write the value of the letters to make an addition problem. Find the sum of each pair of words.

b. Analyzing Data

Which pair of words had the greatest sum?

Which pair of words had the least sum?

c. Explain Your Thinking How can you estimate to check whether your sums are reasonable?

d. Making Decisions You are playing a game. You want the greatest sum. What letters will you choose? Why?

You are playing a game. You want the least sum. What letters will you choose? Why?

Teacher Notes

Concepts and Skills This activity requires students to:
- read a chart.
- make decisions using real-life experiences.
- find sums.
- compare numbers.
- evaluate game strategies.

Guiding Questions
- Look at the game pieces. What is the value of the word *CAT*?
- How do you find the sum of two numbers?
- What does *greatest* mean?
- What does *least* mean?

Answers
a. Choices will vary.
b. Answers will vary. Check students' answers.
c. Check students' answers.
d. For the greatest scores, choose words with letters *H, I, R,* and *S.* For the least scores, choose words with *A, J, K, T,* and *U.*

Extension
Have students try to get a specific sum, such as 500.

Evaluation

Level	Standard to be achieved for performance of specified level
4	**Full Achievement** The student adds two- and three-digit numbers, with and without renaming, correctly. All comparisons are correct, and the explanation of estimation is well written. A logical strategy is used when deciding which letters to choose for the greatest or least sum.
3	**Substantial Achievement** The student adds two- and three-digit numbers, with and without renaming, with only minor recording or computation errors. All comparisons are correct, and the explanation of estimation is basically well written. A logical strategy is used when deciding which letters to choose for the greatest or least sum.
2	**Partial Achievement** The student has some difficulty with addition of two- and three-digit numbers with and without renaming, making several recording or computation errors. Some comparisons are incorrect, and the explanation of estimation is not well written. Little thought is given to the strategy to be used when deciding which letters to choose for the greatest or least sum.
1	**Little Achievement** The student has much difficulty with addition of two- and three-digit numbers with and without renaming. The computation contains many errors, and the concepts of comparing and ordering are not grasped. The student makes little attempt to describe the use of estimation or find a strategy to be used when deciding which letters to choose for the greatest or least sum.

Date _____ Score _____

In 1–10, add to find each sum.

1. $32 + 40$

2. $37 + 28$

3. $\begin{array}{r} 1\,5 \\ +\,1\,9 \\ \hline \end{array}$

4. $\begin{array}{r} 4\,2 \\ +\,3\,9 \\ \hline \end{array}$

5. $\begin{array}{r} 2\,1\,5 \\ +\,6\,5\,4 \\ \hline \end{array}$

6. $\begin{array}{r} 5\,2\,3 \\ +\,2\,7\,2 \\ \hline \end{array}$

7. $4{,}124 + 672$

8. $214 + 6{,}571$

9. $24 + 13 + 41$

10. $37 + 24 + 12$

1. _____

2. _____

3. _____

4. _____

5. _____

6. _____

7. _____

8. _____

9. _____

10. _____

In 11–14, find the missing number.
You may use color cubes for 13 and 14.

11. If $3 + 6 = 9$, then $30 + \blacksquare = 90$

12. If $4 + 2 = 6$, then $\blacksquare + 200 = 600$

13. $14 + \blacksquare = 22$

14. $\blacksquare + 18 = 25$

11. _____

12. _____

13. _____

14. _____

In 15–16, use rounding to estimate each answer.

15. $342 + 589$

   A 931 **B** 800 **C** 700 **D** 900

16. $24 + 59$

   A 80 **B** 90 **C** 70 **D** Not here

17. Guess and check to solve. The sum of two numbers is 21. The numbers are 3 apart. What are they?

15. _____

16. _____

17. _____

Name _____

In 18–20, use mental math to find the answer.

18. 18 + 7

    A 27   **B** 11   **C** 25   **D** Not here

18. _____

19. 36 + 14

    A 50   **B** 40   **C** 30   **D** 12

19. _____

20. 43 + 12

    A 45   **B** 55   **C** 65   **D** Not here

20. _____

In 21–23, write the total value.

21.

21. _____

22.

22. _____

23. Jackie buys a notebook for $0.79. She pays with $5.00. How much change will she get in dollars and cents?

    A $4.79   **B** $4.21   **C** $5.79   **D** $1.21

23. _____

24. Find $2.46 + $2.38.

24. _____

25. Use front-end estimation to estimate: 321 + 415.

25. _____

26. Write if you need an exact answer or an estimate. Then solve. Tyrell has $5.00. Does he have enough money to buy a sandwich costing $2.15 and a drink costing $1.10?

27. Performance Task Scott bought a sticker for $0.56. He paid with a one-dollar bill. As change, he received the fewest number of coins possible. What coins did he receive?

— Computation —

1. 17
      +29

2. 65
      +38

3. 314
      +561

4. 526
      +322

5. 5,235 + 513

6. 2,427 + 358

7. 52 + 15 + 21

8. 63 + 59 + 78

9. $1.43 + $2.35

10. $2.37 + $2.48

1. _____

2. _____

3. _____

4. _____

5. _____

6. _____

7. _____

8. _____

9. _____

10. _____

In 11–12, write the total value.

11.

A $0.20 **B** $0.35 **C** $0.60 **D** Not here

11. _____

12.

12. _____

13. Write the elapsed time from 3:25 P.M. to 4:30 P.M.

13. _____

— Concepts —

14. Do you eat breakfast at 7:00 A.M. or 7:00 P.M.?

14. _____

15. Round 270 to the nearest hundred.

15. _____

16. Write four hundred twenty-six in standard form.

16. _____

17. Compare 345 ● 624. Use <, >, or =.

17. _____

In 18–22, write the missing number.

18. 20 ones = ■ tens

18. _____

19. ■ + 40 = 90

19. _____

20. 300 + ■ = 800

20. _____

21. 18 + ■ = 25

21. _____

22. ■ + 8 = 21

22. _____

23. Round to estimate the sum of 79 + 14.

23. _____

24. Use front-end estimation to estimate the sum of 431, 228, and 198.

24. _____

In 25–26, use mental math to choose the correct answer.

25. 17 + 6

A 20   **B** 27   **C** 13   **D** Not here

25. _____

26. 39 + 41

A 18   **B** 70   **C** 80   **D** Not here

26. _____

—— Applications ——

27. Arturo has 4 more model cars than Jeff. Together they have 20 models. How many model cars does Arturo have?

27. _____

28. Josie buys a granola bar for $0.45. She pays with $5.00. What is her change in dollars and cents?

A $4.55   **B** $5.45   **C** $5.55   **D** Not here

28. _____

29. How much will it cost to buy a sandwich for $2.99, a salad for $1.99, and a drink for $1.19? Write if you need an exact answer or an estimate. Then solve.

Give the letter of the correct answer.

In 1–3, use the line graph.

1. How much rain fell in May?

   A 6 inches
   B 4 inches
   C 3 inches
   D 2 inches

1. _____

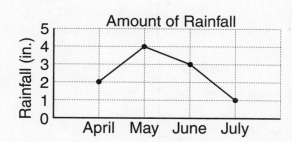

2. In what month did 2 inches of rain fall?

   A April   **B** May   **C** June   **D** July

2. _____

3. How much more rain fell in May than July?

   A 1 inch   **B** 2 inches   **C** 3 inches   **D** 4 inches

3. _____

4. Pedro had 5 tickets to the movies. He used 3 tickets. Which number sentence would you use to find how many tickets he has left?

   A $5 + 3 = 8$ **B** $5 - 3 = 2$
   C $8 - 3 = 5$ **D** Not here

4. _____

5. Minnie put 10 books on the first shelf of her book case, 8 books on the second shelf, and 6 books on the third shelf. Find a pattern. How many books will she put on the fourth shelf?

   A 6 books   **B** 5 books   **C** 4 books   **D** 3 books

5. _____

6. Give two thousand, six hundred seventy-three in standard form.

   A 2,637   **B** 2,763   **C** 2,370   **D** Not here

6. _____

7. Give the value of the underlined digit in 4<u>9</u>5,312.

   A 900,000   **B** 90,000   **C** 9,000   **D** 90

7. _____

8. Compare: 743 ● 734. Use <, >, or =.

    A <   **B** >   **C** =

8. _____

9. Order 314, 341, and 134 from greatest to least.

    A 314, 341, 134   **B** 341, 134, 314
    C 134, 341, 314   **D** 341, 314, 134

9. _____

10. Round 654 to the nearest ten.

    A 650   **B** 660   **C** 700   **D** Not here

10. _____

11. Round 873 to the nearest hundred.

    A 800   **B** 870   **C** 890   **D** 900

11. _____

Tell the time that is shown on the clock.

12. A 3:50
    B 3:10
    C three fifty-five
    D four ten

12. _____

13. The hockey game began at 7:15 P.M. and finished 1 hour and 15 minutes later. What time did it end?

    A 8:15 P.M.   **B** 9:15 P.M.   **C** 8:30 P.M.   **D** 8:30 A.M.

13. _____

In 14–15, use the calendar.

DECEMBER						
Sun	Mon	Tues	Wed	Thu	Fri	Sat
	1	2	3	4	5	6
7	8	9	10	11	12	13
14	15	16	17	18	19	20
21	22	23	24	25	26	27
28	29	30	31			

14. What day of the week is the 12th?

    A Monday   **B** Tuesday   **C** Thursday   **D** Friday

14. _____

15. Which date is 9 days after December 15?

    A December 26   **B** December 25
    C December 24   **D** December 23

15. _____

In 16–18, estimate each sum by rounding.

16. 47 + 34

    A 70   **B** 80   **C** 90   **D** Not here

16. _____

17. 26 + 29

    A 60   **B** 70   **C** 80   **D** Not here

17. _____

18. 12 + 74

    A 80   **B** 90   **C** 100   **D** Not here

18. _____

In 19–25, find the sum. Estimate to check.

19.   25
    + 36

    A 51   **B** 52   **C** 61   **D** 70

19. _____

20. 48 + 24

    A 62   **B** 63   **C** 73   **D** Not here

20. _____

21. 59 + 34

    A 83   **B** 84   **C** 93   **D** 94

21. _____

22.   743
    + 381

    A 1,124   **B** 1,024   **C** 1,034   **D** Not here

22. _____

23.   568
    + 213

    A 773   **B** 783   **C** 771   **D** 781

23. _____

24. 368 + 529

    A 887   **B** 897   **C** 1,007   **D** Not here

24. _____

25. Find 15 + 38 + 25.

    A 68   **B** 78   **C** 88   **D** Not here

25. _____

26. Find 31 + 67 + 25.

    A 112   **B** 118   **C** 123   **D** Not here

26. _____

27. Jamie drew two more pictures than Marlon. They drew 28 pictures in all. How many pictures did Marlon draw?

    A 30 pictures   **B** 13 pictures
    C 15 pictures   **D** Not here

27. _____

28. Use mental math to add 38 and 12.

    A 40   **B** 50   **C** 60   **D** Not here

28. _____

29. Give the total value in dollars and cents.

29. _____

    A $2.75   **B** $2.60   **C** $2.85   **D** Not here

30. Find $3.94 + $2.15.

    A $5.09   **B** $5.81   **C** $6.09   **D** Not here

30. _____

31. Find $2.75 + $4.21.

    A $6.96   **B** $6.54   **C** $7.94   **D** Not here

31. _____

32. Use front-end estimation to estimate 337 + 144.

    A 600   **B** 500   **C** 400   **D** Not here

32. _____

33. Use front-end estimation to estimate 248 + 353.

    A 500   **B** 600   **C** 700   **D** Not here

33. _____

34. You have $5.00 and need to know if this is enough money to buy a notebook for $2.59 and a pen for $0.89. Do you need to find an exact answer or make an estimate?

    A Find exact answer.   **B** Make an estimate.

34. _____

Name _____

Date _____ Score _____

In 1–2, write a number sentence for each. Then solve.

1. Sally bought 4 shirts in one store and bought 2 pairs of pants in another store. How many more shirts did she buy than pants?

1. _____

_____

2. Majel planted 5 trees in her backyard and 4 in her front yard. How many more trees did she plant in her backyard than in her front yard?

2. _____

_____

In 3–4, look for a pattern. Write each missing number.

3. $7 - 2 = \blacksquare$

$70 - \blacksquare = 50$

$700 - 200 = \blacksquare$

3. _____

_____

4. $9 - 5 = \blacksquare$

$90 - \blacksquare = 40$

$900 - 500 = \blacksquare$

4. _____

_____

_____

In 5–8, subtract. You may use a hundred chart to help.

5. $37 - 7 = \blacksquare$

5. _____

6. $45 - 21 = \blacksquare$

6. _____

7. $55 - 18 = \blacksquare$

7. _____

8. $74 - 32 = \blacksquare$

8. _____

9. Estimate the difference: $825 - 536$.

9. _____

10. Estimate the difference: $\$3.19 - \$1.76$.

10. _____

11. Regroup 1 ten for 10 ones:
$84 = 7$ tens $\blacksquare$ ones.
Write the missing number.

11. _____

Name _____

Date _____ Score _____

In 1–8, subtract. Check each answer.

1. 56
    − 38

2. 74
    − 27

3. 43
    − 18

4. 65
    − 48

5. 472
    − 19

6. 593
    − 67

7. 682 − 437

8. 754 − 328

In 9–14, subtract.

9. 623
    − 358

10. 735
    − 297

11. 942
    − 567

12. 702
    − 35

13. 408 − 146

14. 600 − 382

15. Find the difference of 458 and 187.

16. Find the difference of 725 and 348.

17. Jenny weighs 45 pounds. Her dog, Buster, weighs 94 pounds. How much more does Buster weigh than Jenny?

18. A weak category 3 hurricane can have wind speeds of 111 miles per hour. A strong category 3 hurricane can have wind speeds of 130 miles per hour. How much faster is the wind speed of the strong hurricane?

1. _____

2. _____

3. _____

4. _____

5. _____

6. _____

7. _____

8. _____

9. _____

10. _____

11. _____

12. _____

13. _____

14. _____

15. _____

16. _____

17. _____

18. _____

In 1–4, solve. Check each answer.

1. 4,857 − 2,325

2. 5,738 − 1,527

3. 8,624 − 5,218

4. 4,803 − 1,627

5. A juice drink costs $1, and a sandwich costs $2. Kara bought two sandwiches and three juice drinks. How much did she pay?

6. A notebook costs $2, and a box of pencils costs $3. Doug bought two boxes of pencils and two notebooks. How much more did Doug spend on pencils than on notebooks?

In 7–9, write what number you would add to each in order to subtract mentally. Then subtract.

7. 24 − 9

8. 87 − 26

9. 245 − 19

In 10–11, subtract. Check each answer.

10. $4.85
    − 2.31

11. $5.00
    − 3.68

12. $6.50 − 2.15

13. Donna has 3 library books. She brought 1 book back and checked out 3 more. The next day, she returned 2 books. How many library books does she have checked out now?

1. _____

2. _____

3. _____

4. _____

5. _____

6. _____

7. _____

8. _____

9. _____

10. _____

11. _____

12. _____

13. _____

Name _____

Date _____ Score _____

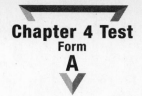
In 1–2, write a number sentence for each. Then solve.

1. Carlos owns 5 baseballs and 2 mitts. How
many more baseballs does Carlos own
than mitts?

1. _____

2. Sue made 4 soccer goals in her first game
and 6 soccer goals in her second game.
How many more goals did she make in her
second game?

2. _____

In 3–4, find each difference using mental math.

3. If $5 - 2 = 3$, then $50 - 20 = \blacksquare$.

3. _____

4. If $9 - 4 = 5$, then $900 - \blacksquare = 500$.

4. _____

In 5–12, subtract. Check each answer.

5. $\begin{array}{r} 4\,8 \\ -\,2\,1 \\ \hline \end{array}$ **6.** $\begin{array}{r} 3\,4 \\ -\,1\,8 \\ \hline \end{array}$

5. _____

6. _____

7. $52 - 27$

7. _____

8. $68 - 47$

8. _____

9. $\begin{array}{r} 3\,5\,7 \\ -\,\ \ 2\,3 \\ \hline \end{array}$ **10.** $\begin{array}{r} 2\,1\,9 \\ -\,1\,3\,8 \\ \hline \end{array}$

9. _____

10. _____

11. $483 - 298$

11. _____

12. $725 - 367$

12. _____

In 13–15, estimate each difference.

13. $35 - 21$

13. _____

14. $562 - 221$

14. _____

15. $\$4.89 - \$1.76$

15. _____

16. Regroup 1 ten for 10 ones: $78 = 6$ tens $\blacksquare$ ones.
Write the missing number.

16. _____

17. Regroup 1 hundred for 10 tens:
356 = ■ hundreds ■ tens 6 ones.
Write the missing numbers.

17. _____

_____

In 18–19, subtract. Check each answer.

18. 207 − 64

18. _____

19. 404 − 38

19. _____

In 20–21, solve. Check each answer.

20. 3,786 − 1,252

20. _____

21. 5,703 − 1,538

21. _____

22. A paint brush costs $3. A set of paints
costs $4. Elle bought two brushes and
two sets of paints. How much more did
she spend on paints than on brushes?

22. _____

**In 23–24, write what number you would add to
each in order to subtract mentally. Then subtract.**

23. 37 − 19

23. _____

24. 64 − 27

24. _____

In 25–26, subtract.

25. $3.58 − $1.27

25. _____

26. $6.28 − $2.57

26. _____

27. Charon uses 3 drops of yellow paint for
every 2 drops of blue paint. If she uses
9 drops of yellow, how many drops of
blue will she use?

27. _____

28. Explain Your Thinking Use the digits 0, 2, 4, 5, 6, and
8 to write two money amounts that you can subtract by
trading 1 dime for 10 pennies. Then solve.

Name _____

Date _____ Score _____

In 1–2, write a number sentence for each. Then solve.

1. Mara owns 5 baseballs and 2 bats.
How many more baseballs does Mara
own than bats?

1.

_____

2. Brad baked 3 apples and 7 potatoes.
How many more potatoes did he bake
than apples?

2.

_____

In 3–4, find each difference using mental math.

3. If $6 - 2 = 4$, then $60 - 20 = $ ■.

3. _____

4. If $8 - 5 = 3$, then $800 - $ ■ $ = 300$.

4. _____

In 5–12, subtract. Check each answer.

5. $37 - 24$

5. _____

6. $56 - 29$

6. _____

7. $71 - 48$

7. _____

8. $46 - 35$

8. _____

9. $286 - 75$

9. _____

10. $395 - 246$

10. _____

11. $635 - 287$

11. _____

12. $421 - 178$

12. _____

In 13–15, estimate each difference.

13. $78 - 35$

13. _____

14. $312 - 178$

14. _____

15. $\$5.74 - \$2.41$

15. _____

16. Regroup 1 ten for 10 ones:
$85 = 7$ tens ■ ones.
Write the missing number.

16. _____

Name _____

17. Regroup 1 hundred for 10 tens:
438 = ■ hundreds ■ tens 8 ones.
Write the missing numbers.

17. _____

_____

In 18–19, subtract. Check each answer.

18. 109 − 58

18. _____

19. 306 − 127

19. _____

In 20–21, solve. Check each answer.

20. 4,857 − 1,653

20. _____

21. 5,705 − 2,549

21. _____

22. Movie tickets cost $6 for adults and $3
for students. How much more does it cost
for 2 adults to see a movie than it costs for
2 students?

22. _____

**In 23–24, write what number you would add to
each in order to subtract mentally. Then subtract.**

23. 42 − 28

23. _____

24. 65 − 36

24. _____

In 25–26, subtract.

25. $2.67 − $1.35

25. _____

26. $5.24 − $2.67

26. _____

27. Michelle's mother gives her 2 pennies for
every 3 dollars she saves. Michelle has
saved $15. How many pennies has her
mother given her?

27. _____

28. Explain Your Thinking Use the digits 1, 3, 4, 5, 7, and
9 to write two money amounts that you can subtract by
trading 1 dollar for 10 dimes. Then solve.

_____

Give the letter of the correct answer.

1. Kevin bought 5 pencils and 3 erasers. Give the number sentence that shows how many more pencils he bought than erasers.

   A $5 - 3 = 2$ **B** $5 + 3 = 8$
   C $5 - 3 = 8$ **C** $8 - 5 = 3$

1. _____

2. Eric has 4 model cars and 6 model planes. Give the number sentence that shows how many more planes than cars he has.

   A $4 + 6 = 10$ **B** $6 - 4 = 2$
   C $4 - 6 = 2$ **D** $10 - 6 = 4$

2. _____

3. If $5 - 2 = 3$, then $50 - 20 = \blacksquare$.

   A 3   **B** 7   **C** 30   **D** 70

3. _____

4. If $8 - 5 = 3$, then $80 - \blacksquare = 30$.

   A 11   **B** 5   **C** 40   **D** 50

4. _____

In 5–10, subtract.

5. $\begin{array}{r} 9\,8 \\ -\,5\,2 \\ \hline \end{array}$

   A 64   **B** 36   **C** 46   **D** 150

5. _____

6. $\begin{array}{r} 8\,7 \\ -\,3\,4 \\ \hline \end{array}$

   A 83   **B** 53   **C** 121   **D** Not here

6. _____

7. $53 - 26$

   A 27   **B** 37   **C** 33   **D** Not here

7. _____

8. $43 - 28$

   A 25   **B** 71   **C** 35   **D** Not here

8. _____

Name _____

9. 75 − 36

   A 49   **B** 39   **C** 29   **D** Not here

9. _____

10. 64 − 29

   A 55   **B** 45   **C** 35   **D** Not here

10. _____

In 11–14, estimate the difference by rounding.

11. 834 − 325

   A 400   **B** 500   **C** 1,100   **D** 300

11. _____

12. 526 − 283

   A 800   **B** 400   **C** 200   **D** 100

12. _____

13. 451 − 150

   A 100   **B** 200   **C** 300   **D** 400

13. _____

14. 795 − 321

   A 500   **B** 400   **C** 300   **D** Not here

14. _____

15. Regroup 1 ten for 10 ones:
35 = ■ tens ■ ones.

   A 1 ten and 10 ones   **B** 2 tens and 15 ones
   C 3 tens and 15 ones   **D** 4 tens and 15 ones

15. _____

16. Regroup 1 hundred for 10 tens:
427 = ■ hundreds ■ tens 7 ones.

   A 3 tens and 12 ones
   B 1 hundred and 10 tens
   C 4 hundreds and 12 ones
   D 3 hundreds and 12 tens

16. _____

In 17–29, subtract.

17.   4 8 6
   −   3 8
   ‾‾‾‾‾‾‾

   A 442   **B** 452   **C** 448   **D** 458

17. _____

Continued

Name _____

18.   3 7 4
        − 1 3 9

A 235   **B** 245   **C** 145   **D** Not here

19. 483 − 267

A 226   **B** 216   **C** 116   **D** Not here

20. 735 − 358

A 367   **B** 387   **C** 487   **D** Not here

21. 842 − 469

A 373   **B** 473   **C** 383   **D** 483

22.   2 0 9
        −   7 8

A 131   **B** 231   **C** 287   **D** Not here

23.   3 0 7
        − 1 3 5

A 272   **B** 342   **C** 72   **D** 172

24. 504 − 237

A 367   **B** 267   **C** 377   **D** 277

25.   2,4 7 8
        − 1,2 6 4

A 1,214   **B** 3,214   **C** 1,204   **D** Not here

26. 7,843 − 2,375

A 5,568   **B** 5,468   **C** 5,478   **D** Not here

27. $4.68
        − 2.45

A $2.23   **B** $2.25   **C** $6.23   **D** Not here

Name _____

28. $5.28 − $1.76

    A $3.62   **B** $3.52   **C** $4.62   **D** $4.52

28. _____

29. $7.00 − $5.26

    A $2.74   **B** $2.84   **C** $1.84   **D** $1.74

29. _____

30. Subtract 19 from 43 mentally. Tell what number you would add to each number. Then give the answer.

    A 2, 24   **B** 2, 22   **C** 1, 24   **D** 1, 22

30. _____

31. Subtract 27 from 68 mentally. Tell what number you would add to each number. Then give the answer.

    A 3, 41   **B** 1, 41   **C** 3, 39   **D** 1, 39

31. _____

32. An afternoon movie ticket costs $3. A bag of popcorn costs $2. Marshall bought a ticket and two bags of popcorn. How much did he spend?

    A $1   **B** $2   **C** $7   **D** $8

32. _____

33. A balloon costs $1. A rubber ball costs $2. Sanjit bought two balloons and two rubber balls. How much more did he spend for the rubber balls than he spent for the balloons?

    A $6   **B** $4   **C** $3   **D** $2

33. _____

34. Annie receives 2 free movie passes for every 5 movie tickets she buys. She now has 6 free passes. How many tickets has she bought?

    A 15 tickets   **B** 10 tickets
    C 6 tickets   **D** Not here

34. _____

35. Brian went on a 7-hour train ride. He read a book for 2 hours. He slept for 3 hours. Then he listened to music for 1 hour. How many more hours did Brian have left to ride on the train?

    A 6 hours   **B** 2 hours   **C** 1 hour   **D** Not here

35. _____

Name _____

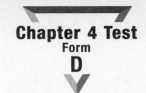

Date _____ Score _____

Suppose you and your sister collected these sports cards.

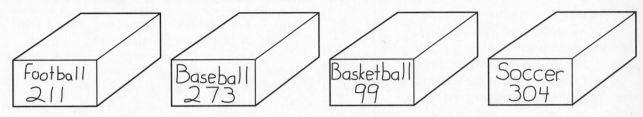

Football 211   Baseball 273   Basketball 99   Soccer 304

a. Making Decisions Your sister says that at least 400 of the cards are hers. She wants at least 70 of each kind of card, but not more than 150 of any one kind. Think about how many of each kind of card you will give to your sister.

b. Recording Data Make a table like the one below. Show how many of each kind of card you will give to your sister.

	Number in stack	Number given to sister	Number left
Football Cards			
Baseball Cards			
Basketball Cards			
Soccer Cards			

c. Analyzing Data

How many cards did you give to your sister in all?

How many cards do you have left?

d. Critical Thinking How can you check your answer?

e. Making Decisions You have $3.00 to spend. You can buy one pack of cards. Which pack will you buy? How much money will you have left?

BASEBALL $1.89   Basketball $1.57   Football $2.08

Teacher Notes

Concepts and Skills This activity requires students to:
- record information in a table.
- make decisions using real-life experiences.
- find sums using whole numbers.
- find differences using whole numbers.
- find differences using money.

Guiding Questions
- Suppose you had 200 sports cards and gave me 123. How many cards would you have left?
- How can you find the number of cards in all of the boxes?
- How will you know whether you have given your sister enough cards?

Answers
a. Decisions will vary.
b. Answers will vary. Check that the number left plus the number given to sister is equal to the number in the stack.
c. Possible answer: If 400 cards are given to the sister, there are 487 cards left.
d. Check students' answers. Estimation of 900 − 500 = 400 is one possible answer.
e. Answers will vary depending upon pack chosen. Possible answer: Baseball, $1.11; Basketball, $1.43; Football, $0.92.

Extension
Tell students that they have $5. They are to buy two packs of cards. Which packs will they buy? How much money will they have left?

Evaluation

Level	Standard to be achieved for performance of specified level
4	**Full Achievement** The student can subtract whole numbers and money and complete the table correctly. He or she understands that the total number of cards given to the sister is 400 or more.
3	**Substantial Achievement** The student can subtract whole numbers and money and complete the table with minor computational errors. He or she may need some help in clarifying how many cards to give the sister.
2	**Partial Achievement** The student has difficulty subtracting whole numbers and money and completing the table. He or she has little understanding of either estimation or the relationship between addition and subtraction.
1	**Little Achievement** The student demonstrates little if any understanding of the task at hand and needs considerable help completing the table. The computation contains many errors, and subtraction concepts are not grasped.

In 1–2, find each missing number using mental math.

1. If $5 - 1 = 4$, then $500 - 100 = $ ■.

2. If $9 - 6 = 3$, then $900 - $ ■ $= 300$.

1. _____

2. _____

In 3–5, subtract. Check each answer.

3. $57 - 16$

4. $91 - 56$

5. $76 - 39$

3. _____

4. _____

5. _____

In 6–7, write a number sentence for each. Then solve.

6. Johnny bought 6 shirts and 3 pairs of jeans. How many more shirts did he buy than jeans?

6.

_____

7. Van gave 5 roses to Natalie and 7 roses to Candace. How many more roses did he give to Candace than to Natalie?

7.

_____

In 8–9, estimate each difference.

8. $347 - 198$

   A 300   **B** 200   **C** 100   **D** Not here

8. _____

9. $550 - 389$

   A 100   **B** 200   **C** 300   **D** 400

9. _____

10. Regroup 1 ten for 10 ones:
    $63 = $ ■ tens ■ ones.

    A 1 tens and 10 ones   **B** 6 tens and 13 ones
    C 5 tens and 3 ones   **D** 5 tens and 13 ones

10. _____

11. Regroup 1 hundred for 10 tens:
    $387 = $ ■ hundreds ■ tens 7 ones.

    A 2 hundreds and 18 tens
    B 3 hundreds and 18 tens
    C 2 hundreds and 8 tens
    D 1 hundred and 18 tens

11. _____

Name _____

In 12–17, subtract. Check each answer.

12. 487 − 256

13. 532 − 283

14. 308 − 184

15. 704 − 326

16. 3,835 − 1,482

17. 4,824 − 2,575

18. A notebook costs $2, and a pen costs $1. Stephanie bought two notebooks and three pens. How much did she spend?

In 19–20, write what number you would add to each in order to subtract mentally. Then subtract.

19. 35 − 17

20. 56 − 29

In 21–22, subtract to find the answer.

21. $3.78 − $1.26

   A $1.52   **B** $1.42   **C** $2.52   **D** $2.42

22. $4.83 − $1.48

   A $3.45   **B** $3.35   **C** $2.35   **D** Not here

23. Performance Task There are 31 students on a field trip. Of these, 18 are boys. To find the number of girls, subtract 18 from 31. Explain how you would regroup to solve this problem. You can use place-value blocks to help explain. Then give the number of girls.

_____

_____

_____

12. _____

13. _____

14. _____

15. _____

16. _____

17. _____

18. _____

19. _____

20. _____

21. _____

22. _____

Date _____ Score _____

— Computation —

In 1–12, add or subtract.

1. $\begin{array}{r} 53 \\ +235 \\ \hline \end{array}$ 2. $\begin{array}{r} 348 \\ +293 \\ \hline \end{array}$

3. 46 − 25

4. 63 − 38

5. 83 − 49

6. $\begin{array}{r} 387 \\ -68 \\ \hline \end{array}$ 7. $\begin{array}{r} 523 \\ +198 \\ \hline \end{array}$

8. 408 − 124

9. 603 − 238

10. $\begin{array}{r} 4,849 \\ -2,184 \\ \hline \end{array}$ 11. $\begin{array}{r} 3,724 \\ -2,476 \\ \hline \end{array}$

12. $3.27 − $1.84

1. _____

2. _____

3. _____

4. _____

5. _____

6. _____

7. _____

8. _____

9. _____

10. _____

11. _____

12. _____

— Concepts —

In 13–14, choose the missing number.

13. If 8 − 6 = 2, then 80 − ■ = 20

    A 6   **B** 60   **C** 100   **D** 600

14. If 7 − 4 = 3, 700 − ■ = 300

    A 100   **B** 4   **C** 40   **D** 400

15. Emily carried 8 boxes and 5 bags to the basement. Choose the number sentence that shows how many more boxes she carried than bags.

    A 5 + 3 = 8   **B** 8 − 3 = 5   **C** 8 − 5 = 3   **D** Not here

13. _____

14. _____

15. _____

Name _____

16. Chuck brought 6 sandwiches and 3 pieces
of fruit to a picnic. Write a number sentence
to show how many more sandwiches he
brought than pieces of fruit.

16. _____

17. Estimate the difference of 827 − 398 by rounding.

17. _____

    A 400   **B** 300   **C** 500   **D** Not here

18. Regroup 1 ten for 10 ones:
54 = ■ tens ■ ones.

18. _____

    A 1 tens and 54 ones   **B** 4 tens and 14 ones
    C 5 tens and 14 ones   **D** 4 tens and 4 ones

19. What number would you add to each number in
58 − 17 in order to use mental math to subtract?

19. _____

    A 3   **B** 1   **C** 13   **D** Not here

▬ Applications ▬

Aluminum Cans Collected for Recycling	
Suke	🥫 🥫 🥫 🥫
Joy	🥫 🥫 🥫
Mary	🥫 🥫 🥫 🥫 🥫 🥫 🥫 🥫

🥫 = 10 cans

20. Which girl collected the most cans?

20. _____

21. How many cans did Suke and Joy collect
in all?

21. _____

    A 30 cans   **B** 40 cans   **C** 70 cans   **D** Not here

22. How many more cans did Mary collect than
both Suke and Joy altogether?

22. _____

23. Alex has 2 shirts and 2 pairs of pants. Use
objects to find how many different outfits he
can wear.

23. _____

Name _____

Date _____ Score _____

Vocabulary: use 2 × 5 = 10 to answer 1–3.

1. Write the factors.　　　　　　　　　　1. _____

2. Write the product.　　　　　　　　　　2. _____

3. Show the multiplication sentence with an array.　3. _____

In 4–5, copy and complete.

4. ● ●　　● ●　　● ●

■ + ■ + ■ = ■　　　　_____

■ groups of ■ equals ■.　　_____

■ × ■ = ■　　　　　　_____

5. ● ●　● ●　　● ●　　● ●
　● 　● 　　● 　　● ●
● ●　● ●　　● ●　　● ●

■ + ■ + ■ + ■ = ■　　_____

■ groups of ■ equals ■.　　_____

■ × ■ = ■　　　　　　_____

In 6–9, you may use counters to solve.

6. There were 4 sacks of oranges. Each sack held 7 oranges. How many oranges were there in all?　　6. _____

7. There were 4 hockey teams. Each team had 6 players. How many players were there?　　7. _____

8. A spider has 8 legs. How many legs do 3 spiders have?　　8. _____

9. There were 6 butterflies. Each butterfly had 2 wings. How many wings were there in all?　　9. _____

Vocabulary: In 1, choose the best word for the sentence.

Word List
factor   multiple
product   array

1. 20 is a _____ of 5.

In 2–21, find each product.

2. $\begin{array}{r} 6 \\ \times 2 \\ \hline \end{array}$

3. $\begin{array}{r} 3 \\ \times 5 \\ \hline \end{array}$

4. $\begin{array}{r} 4 \\ \times 9 \\ \hline \end{array}$

5. $\begin{array}{r} 8 \\ \times 1 \\ \hline \end{array}$

6. $\begin{array}{r} 4 \\ \times 1 \\ \hline \end{array}$

7. $\begin{array}{r} 3 \\ \times 9 \\ \hline \end{array}$

8. $\begin{array}{r} 3 \\ \times 2 \\ \hline \end{array}$

9. $\begin{array}{r} 4 \\ \times 5 \\ \hline \end{array}$

10. $\begin{array}{r} 2 \\ \times 8 \\ \hline \end{array}$

11. $\begin{array}{r} 0 \\ \times 2 \\ \hline \end{array}$

12. $\begin{array}{r} 9 \\ \times 8 \\ \hline \end{array}$

13. $\begin{array}{r} 5 \\ \times 7 \\ \hline \end{array}$

14. 2×5

15. 5×7

16. 9×6

17. 0×5

18. 0×6

19. 9×7

20. 5×6

21. 2×8

22. Lance bought an apple for $0.75, a sandwich for $2.50, and a T-shirt for $9.95. How much did Lance spend on food?

22. _____

23. Carrie is sitting on a park bench in the middle of a group of students. John and Betty are sitting on her right. How many students are sitting on the bench? Draw a picture to help.

23. _____

Vocabulary: use 2 × 4 = 8 to answer 1–3.

1. Write the product.

2. Write the factors.

3. 8 is a multiple of ■.

1. _____

2. _____

3. _____

In 4–5, copy and complete.

4.

■ + ■ + ■ = ■   _____

■ groups of ■ equals ■.   _____

■ × ■ = ■   _____

5.

■ + ■ + ■ + ■ = ■   _____

■ groups of ■ equals ■.   _____

■ × ■ = ■   _____

6. Some camels have 2 humps. How many humps would 5 of these camels have? Write the multiplication sentence and give the answer.

6. _____
_____

7. A fly has 6 legs. How many legs would 3 flies have? You may use counters to solve.

7. _____

8. Some spiders have 4 eyes. How many eyes would 5 spiders have? You may use counters to help.

8. _____

Name _____

In 9–32, find each product.

9.
$$\begin{array}{r} 2 \\ \times\,2 \\ \hline \end{array}$$

10.
$$\begin{array}{r} 2 \\ \times\,3 \\ \hline \end{array}$$

11.
$$\begin{array}{r} 4 \\ \times\,2 \\ \hline \end{array}$$

12.
$$\begin{array}{r} 2 \\ \times\,7 \\ \hline \end{array}$$

13.
$$\begin{array}{r} 5 \\ \times\,3 \\ \hline \end{array}$$

14.
$$\begin{array}{r} 4 \\ \times\,5 \\ \hline \end{array}$$

15.
$$\begin{array}{r} 7 \\ \times\,5 \\ \hline \end{array}$$

16.
$$\begin{array}{r} 5 \\ \times\,8 \\ \hline \end{array}$$

17.
$$\begin{array}{r} 4 \\ \times\,9 \\ \hline \end{array}$$

18.
$$\begin{array}{r} 9 \\ \times\,6 \\ \hline \end{array}$$

19.
$$\begin{array}{r} 7 \\ \times\,9 \\ \hline \end{array}$$

20.
$$\begin{array}{r} 9 \\ \times\,9 \\ \hline \end{array}$$

21.
$$\begin{array}{r} 8 \\ \times\,1 \\ \hline \end{array}$$

22.
$$\begin{array}{r} 1 \\ \times\,6 \\ \hline \end{array}$$

23.
$$\begin{array}{r} 0 \\ \times\,4 \\ \hline \end{array}$$

24.
$$\begin{array}{r} 3 \\ \times\,0 \\ \hline \end{array}$$

25. 2×8 _____

26. 5×6 _____

27. 9×3 _____

28. 1×2 _____

29. 0×4 _____

30. 2×6 _____

31. 1×7 _____

32. 9×7 _____

33. There are 5 sticks of gum in a package. Each package costs $0.50. How many sticks of gum are in 3 packages?

33. _____

34. **Explain Your Thinking** Manford is making a necklace that will have 9 beads. Beads 1 and 9 will have the same color, beads 2 and 8 will have the same color, and so on. Explain what strategy you might use to find the number of different colors needed. Then give the answer.

_____

_____

_____

_____

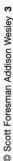

Vocabulary: use 2 × 3 = 6 to answer 1–3.

1. Write the factors.

2. Write the product.

3. 6 is a multiple of ■.

1. _____

2. _____

3. _____

In 4–5, copy and complete.

4.

■ + ■ + ■ = ■

■ groups of ■ equals ■.

■ × ■ = ■

_____

_____

_____

5.

■ + ■ + ■ + ■ = ■

■ groups of ■ equals ■.

■ × ■ = ■

_____

_____

_____

6. A dog has 4 legs. How many legs would 2 dogs have? Write the multiplication sentence and give the answer.

6. _____

_____

7. Camp Feelgood puts 2 paddles in each canoe. How many paddles do they need to put in 7 canoes? You may use counters to solve.

7. _____

8. You want to put 3 flags on each car in a parade. There are 6 cars in the parade. How many flags will you need? You may use counters to solve.

8. _____

Name _____

In 9–32, find each product.

9. $\begin{array}{r} 3 \\ \times\ 2 \\ \hline \end{array}$ 10. $\begin{array}{r} 6 \\ \times\ 2 \\ \hline \end{array}$ 11. $\begin{array}{r} 2 \\ \times\ 7 \\ \hline \end{array}$ 12. $\begin{array}{r} 2 \\ \times\ 8 \\ \hline \end{array}$

13. $\begin{array}{r} 4 \\ \times\ 5 \\ \hline \end{array}$ 14. $\begin{array}{r} 6 \\ \times\ 5 \\ \hline \end{array}$ 15. $\begin{array}{r} 8 \\ \times\ 5 \\ \hline \end{array}$ 16. $\begin{array}{r} 9 \\ \times\ 5 \\ \hline \end{array}$

17. $\begin{array}{r} 9 \\ \times\ 3 \\ \hline \end{array}$ 18. $\begin{array}{r} 4 \\ \times\ 9 \\ \hline \end{array}$ 19. $\begin{array}{r} 9 \\ \times\ 6 \\ \hline \end{array}$ 20. $\begin{array}{r} 8 \\ \times\ 9 \\ \hline \end{array}$

21. $\begin{array}{r} 4 \\ \times\ 1 \\ \hline \end{array}$ 22. $\begin{array}{r} 1 \\ \times\ 6 \\ \hline \end{array}$ 23. $\begin{array}{r} 7 \\ \times\ 0 \\ \hline \end{array}$ 24. $\begin{array}{r} 0 \\ \times\ 8 \\ \hline \end{array}$

25. 2×2 26. 5×4 27. 9×3 28. 1×2

_____   _____   _____   _____

29. 0×6 30. 2×4 31. 1×6 32. 9×9

_____   _____   _____   _____

33. There are 2 muffins in a package. Each   33. _____
package costs $0.75. How many muffins
are in 8 packages?

34. **Explain Your Thinking** Celia is making a necklace that
will have 9 beads. Beads 1 and 9 will have the same
color, beads 2 and 8 will have the same color, and so
on. Explain what strategy you might use to find if any
beads of the same color are next to each other. Then
give the answer.

_____

_____

_____

Name _____

Date _____ Score _____

Give the letter of the correct answer.

1. $7 \times 3 = 21$. 7 is a ■ of 21.

   A product   **B** multiple   **C** factor   **D** Not here

   1. _____

2. Which number sentence describes the array?

   • • • • • •
   • • • • • •
   • • • • • •

   A $6 + 6 + 6 = 18$ **B** 3 rows of 6 equals 18
   C $3 \times 6 = 18$ **D** All of them

   2. _____

3. Which number sentence does *not* describe the array?

   • • • • •
   • • • • •
   • • • • •
   • • • • •

   A $4 \times 4 = 16$ **B** 4 rows of 5 equals 20
   C $5 + 5 + 5 + 5 = 20$ **D** $4 \times 5 = 20$

   3. _____

4. There are 2 forks in a formal table setting. How many forks will there be in 8 settings?

   A 10 forks   **B** 6 forks   **C** 16 forks   **D** Not here

   4. _____

5. Fast Food Pizza cuts each pizza into 6 slices. How many slices will there be in 3 pizzas?

   A 3 slices   **B** 6 slices   **C** 9 slices   **D** 18 slices

   5. _____

6. An elephant has 4 legs. How many legs would 3 elephants have? Choose the multiplication sentence that gives the answer.

   A $3 \times 4 = 12$ **B** $4 \times 1 = 4$
   C $3 + 4 = 7$ **D** Not here

   6. _____

7. A bowling ball has 3 holes. How many holes would 2 bowling balls have? Choose the multiplication sentence you would use to find the answer.

   A $2 + 3 = 5$ **B** $2 \times 3 = 5$
   C $2 \times 3 = 6$ **D** Not here

   7. _____

Name _____

In 8–29, multiply.

8. 1
   $\times\,2$

   A 3   **B** 2   **C** 1   **D** Not here

8. _____

9. 7
   $\times\,2$

   A 14   **B** 9   **C** 5   **D** Not here

9. _____

10. 2 × 4

   A 6   **B** 2   **C** 4   **D** Not here

10. _____

11. 2 × 9

   A 7   **B** 11   **C** 18   **D** Not here

11. _____

12. 3
   $\times\,5$

   A 8   **B** 2   **C** 1   **D** 15

12. _____

13. 7
   $\times\,5$

   A 35   **B** 12   **C** 5   **D** 15

13. _____

14. 5 × 6

   A 11   **B** 35   **C** 30   **D** 40

14. _____

15. 9
   $\times\,5$

   A 4   **B** 45   **C** 14   **D** 50

15. _____

16. 4
   $\times\,9$

   A 36   **B** 5   **C** 13   **D** 32

16. _____

Continued

17. 8
$\times\,9$

A 17 **B** 1 **C** 72 **D** 68

17. _____

18. 9 × 6

A 36 **B** 54 **C** 15 **D** Not here

18. _____

19. 9 × 3

A 12 **B** 6 **C** 18 **D** Not here

19. _____

20. 0
$\times\,4$

A 4 **B** 1 **C** 0 **D** Not here

20. _____

21. 6
$\times\,1$

A 1 **B** 6 **C** 5 **D** Not here

21. _____

22. 0 × 7

A 0 **B** 7 **C** 1 **D** Not here

22. _____

23. 1 × 8

A 1 **B** 9 **C** 18 **D** Not here

23. _____

24. 2 × 3

A 2 **B** 5 **C** 6 **D** 1

24. _____

25. 8
$\times\,5$

A 13 **B** 3 **C** 35 **D** 40

25. _____

26. 9 × 7

A 16 **B** 36 **C** 63 **D** 64

26. _____

27. 1 × 7

A 1 **B** 8 **C** 7 **D** 6

27. _____

28. 0×8

    A 0   **B** 1   **C** 8   **D** Not here

28. _____

29. 9×2

    A 11   **B** 16   **C** 19   **D** Not here

29. _____

30. Anita bought 3 packages of socks. There are 5 pairs of socks in each package. The socks cost $9.95 per package. How many pairs of socks did Anita buy?

    A $9.95   **B** 8 socks   **C** 15 socks   **D** Not here

30. _____

31. Audrey buys 2 boxes of chalk. Each box holds 8 pieces of chalk. The chalk will be shared with 3 other students. How many pieces of chalk are there?

    A 10 pieces   **B** 16 pieces
    C 3 pieces   **D** 11pieces

31. _____

32. In a row of four desks, Bill is sitting in front of Monte. Monte is sitting in front of Wilma. Jane is sitting in front of Bill. Who is at the front of the row?

    A Bill   **B** Monte   **C** Wilma   **D** Jane

32. _____

33. Caren uses this pattern to string beads for a necklace. She begins by stringing 2 red beads, then 3 blue beads, then 2 red beads, then 3 blue beads and so on. She put 17 beads on the string. How many blue beads are on the bracelet?

    A 6 beads   **B** 8 beads   **C** 9 beads   **D** 17 beads

33. _____

34. Pang is standing in line between Dionne and Carol. Ian is standing in front of Dionne. Who is first in line?

    A Carol   **B** Pang   **C** Dionne   **D** Ian

34. _____

35. Which numbers are multiples of 2?

    A 10, 11, 12   **B** 2, 5, 8   **C** 8, 7, 6   **D** Not here

35. _____

For your birthday party, you invite four friends to go with you to the carnival. You buy a roll of ride tickets for you and your friends to use. Everybody will ride the merry-go-round. Then each of you can go on four more rides. You will need 2 or 5 tickets for each ride.

a. Making Decisions Decide which rides each person will go on.

b. Recording Data Make a table like the one shown below.

Write your name and the names of your friends in the table.

Put an X in the column beside each person's name to show which five rides he or she will go on.

Name	Merry-Go-Round	Ferris Wheel	Train	Tilt-A-Whirl	Mini Cars	Air-planes	Roller Coaster
		2 Tickets each			5 Tickets each		
Your Name	X						
Friend's Name	X						
Number of Riders	5						
Number of Tickets	10						

c. Analyzing Data

Find the total number of riders for each different ride.

Find the total number of tickets needed for each ride.

d. Critical Thinking Does each person plan to use the same number of tickets for all of their rides? Explain your answer.

e. Making Decisions At the end of your party, you have some tickets left. What will you do with them?

Teacher Notes

Concepts and Skills This activity requires students to:

- record information in a table.
- make decisions using real-life experiences.
- find products for basic multiplication facts.
- find sums.

Guiding Questions

- Suppose you go on the Ferris Wheel and the Mini Cars. How many tickets will you need?
- How will you find the number of riders?
- How will you find the number of tickets?

Answers

a. Decisions will vary.
b. Check that students' tables have 5 names and that 5 rides are chosen for each name.
c. Check students' answers. Help students understand that they can find the number of tickets needed by multiplying the number of riders by 2 in the first four columns and by 5 in the last three columns. Then they can count the X's to find how many tickets will be used altogether.
d. Answers may vary. However, students should recognize whether or not the same number of tickets was used by each of the riders.
e. Answers will vary.

Extension

Suppose each rider is given 15 tickets. What is the greatest number of rides they could take? [7 rides] The least? [3 rides]

Evaluation

Level	Standard to be achieved for performance of specified level
4	**Full Achievement** The student completes the table correctly, making no errors. The explanation of whether or not all riders used the same number of tickets and what to do with left-over tickets is well written.
3	**Substantial Achievement** The student completes the table correctly, making few errors. He or she understands whether or not all riders used the same number of tickets and can decide what to do with left-over tickets.
2	**Partial Achievement** The student needs help in completing the table and makes several errors in finding the number of riders and number of tickets needed for each ride. He or she has difficulty explaining whether or not all riders used the same number of tickets and cannot decide what to do with the left-over tickets.
1	**Little Achievement** The student needs help in order to complete the table and find the total number of tickets needed. He or she makes many errors and cannot multiply by 2 and 5. The student cannot decide whether or not each rider used the same number of tickets and little thought is given in answering the last question.

Name _____

Date _____ Score _____

In 1–2, copy and complete.

1. ● ●   ● ●   ● ●   ● ●   ● ●
     ●   ●   ●   ●   ●

■ + ■ + ■ + ■ + ■ = ■ _____

■ groups of ■ equals ■. _____

■ × ■ = ■ _____

2. ● ●   ● ●   ● ●   ● ●

■ + ■ + ■ + ■ = ■ _____

■ groups of ■ equals ■. _____

■ × ■ = ■ _____

3. Lupe has 3 board games. Each game has 4 counters. How many counters does she have? Choose the number sentence that gives the correct answer. You may use counters.

3. _____

A $3 + 4 = 7$ **B** $3 \times 4 = 12$
C $4 - 3 = 1$ **D** Not here

4. Carl has 8 bags of marbles. There are 5 marbles in each bag. Choose the multiplication sentence that gives the correct answer.

4. _____

A $8 + 5 = 13$ **B** $8 \times 5 = 13$
C $8 \times 5 = 40$ **D** Not here

5. Cleo has 3 groups of bears in her collection. There are 6 bears in each group. How many bears does she have in all? You may use counters.

5. _____

A 3 bears   **B** 9 bears
C 18 bears   **D** Not here

6. Jo has 3 blankets in each of 2 boxes. How many blankets does Jo have all together?

6. _____

A 1 blanket   **B** 5 blankets
C 9 blankets   **D** Not here

In 8–18, find each product.

7. $\begin{array}{r} 4 \\ \times\, 2 \\ \hline \end{array}$ **8.** $\begin{array}{r} 8 \\ \times\, 2 \\ \hline \end{array}$ **9.** $\begin{array}{r} 7 \\ \times\, 5 \\ \hline \end{array}$ **10.** $\begin{array}{r} 3 \\ \times\, 5 \\ \hline \end{array}$

11. 0×6 **12.** 1×8 **13.** 1×3 **14.** 0×4

_____   _____   _____   _____

15. 9×6 **16.** 9×3 **17.** 3×2 **18.** 5×8

_____   _____   _____   _____

19. Juan buys 3 packages of granola bars. There are 2 bars in each package. The packages cost $1 each. How many granola bars did Juan buy?

19. _____

A 6 bars   **B** 5 bars   **C** $3   **D** Not here

20. Luke buys 2 boxes of pencils. Each box costs $2. Each box holds 10 pencils. How many pencils did Luke buy?

20. _____

A $4   **B** 12 pencils   **C** 20 pencils   **D** $20

21. Bobby is standing to the left of Conrad. Brooke is standing to the right of Conrad. Are Bobby and Brooke standing next to each other? Explain.

_____

_____

22. Performance Task Explain how you can find the product of 9×9 if you know the product of 9×8 is 72.

_____

_____

_____

Name _____

Date _____ Score _____

— Computation —

1. Copy and complete.

■ + ■ = ■　　　　_____

■ groups of ■ equals ■.　　_____

In 2–13, find each product.

2. 2×3　　　　**3.** 5×8　　　　**4.** 0×4　　　　**5.** 9×4

_____　　　　_____　　　　_____　　　　_____

6. 1×7　　　　**7.** 2×8　　　　**8.** 9×6　　　　**9.** 5×6

_____　　　　_____　　　　_____　　　　_____

10. $\begin{array}{r} 6 \\ \times 2 \\ \hline \end{array}$　　**11.** $\begin{array}{r} 3 \\ \times 5 \\ \hline \end{array}$　　**12.** $\begin{array}{r} 7 \\ \times 9 \\ \hline \end{array}$　　**13.** $\begin{array}{r} 7 \\ \times 1 \\ \hline \end{array}$

In 14–17, add or subtract.

14. Find $485 + 239$.

　　A 614　　**B** 624　　**C** 714　　**D** 724

15. Find $723 - 248$.

　　A 475　　**B** 485　　**C** 525　　**D** 585

16. Find $\$7.16 - \$2.24$.

　　A $4.12　　**B** $4.92　　**C** $5.25　　**D** $5.85

17. Find $\$2.36 + \$3.27$.

　　A $5.82　　**B** $5.92　　**C** $6.82　　**D** Not here

14. _____

15. _____

16. _____

17. _____

Name _____

— Concepts —

18. What time is shown on the clock?

A 7:45 A.M.
B 7:50 P.M.
C 7:55 P.M.
D Not here

watch a sunset

19. Choose the number sentence that uses multiplication to show the same thing as
$3 + 3 + 3 + 3 + 3 = 15$.

A $3 \times 15 = 15$ **B** $5 \times 3 = 15$
C $3 \times 3 = 9$ **D** Not here

— Applications —

20. Denise has 3 boxes of pens. Each box has 9 pens. How many pens does Denise have?

21. Sam found 5 bags of marbles. Each bag had 7 marbles in it. Sam needs 10 marbles to play a game. How many marbles does he have?

A 12 marbles **B** 35 marbles
C 10 marbles **D** Not here

22. Joan is making a necklace that will spell her name in letter beads. Between each letter, she will put 4 gold beads. She will put 3 gold beads at each end of the name. How many gold beads will she need for the necklace?

23. Jeremy has 10 model cars and 7 model airplanes. Which operation would you use to find how many more model cars he has than model airplanes?

A Addition **B** Subtraction
C Multiplication **D** Division

In 1–24, find each product.

1. 3
$\times$ 6

2. 4
$\times$ 3

3. 5
$\times$ 3

4. 3
$\times$ 8

5. 4
$\times$ 4

6. 4
$\times$ 8

7. 7
$\times$ 4

8. 4
$\times$ 9

9. 6
$\times$ 9

10. 5
$\times$ 6

11. 4
$\times$ 6

12. 6
$\times$ 7

13. 3
$\times$ 7

14. 5
$\times$ 8

15. 8
$\times$ 7

16. 8
$\times$ 9

17. 7×7

18. 9×7

19. 5×7

20. 7×2

_____ _____ _____ _____

21. 8×2

22. 8×6

23. 8×8

24. 5×8

_____ _____ _____ _____

25. Megan buys 4 cartons of eggs. Each carton holds 6 eggs. How many eggs does she buy?

25. _____

26. Cora plants 7 marigolds in each of 9 rows in her flower garden. How many marigolds does she plant all together?

26. _____

27. Elvin has 8 model cars. Each car has 4 wheels. How many wheels are there in all?

27. _____

28. Nara buys 8 cartons of soda. Each carton holds 6 bottles. How many bottles does she buy?

28. _____

Vocabulary: In 1–2, match each with its meaning.

1. multiple

    a. the product of a given whole number and any other whole number

1. _____

2. grouping

    b. when you multiply, you can group factors in any order and the product will be the same

2. _____

In 3–5, write *true* or *false*. You may use a hundred chart to help.

3. 14 is a multiple of 3.

3. _____

4. 24 is a multiple of 6.

4. _____

5. 56 is a multiple of 6.

5. _____

In 6–8, continue each pattern.

6. 33, 44, 55, ■, ■, ■

6. _____

7. 90, 80, 70, ■, ■, ■

7. _____

8. 24, 36, 48, ■, ■, ■

8. _____

In 9–11, find each product.

9. $3 \times 4 \times 2$

9. _____

10. $(2 \times 3) \times 7$

10. _____

11. $1 \times (6 \times 0)$

11. _____

12. Wesley is having a party for 38 friends. Each cake will serve 9 guests. How many cakes will Wesley need to bake?

12. _____

13. Three people can sit in a roller coaster car seat. How many seats are needed for you and 10 of your friends?

13. _____

Vocabulary: In 1–3, match each with its meaning.

1. square number

2. grouping

3. multiple

a. the product of a given whole number and any other whole number

b. the product when both factors are the same

c. when you multiply, you can group factors in any order and the product will be the same

1. _____

2. _____

3. _____

In 4–19, find each product.

4. 3
$\times\,5$

5. 6
$\times\,3$

6. 4
$\times\,2$

7. 9
$\times\,4$

8. 6
$\times\,5$

9. 9
$\times\,6$

10. 7
$\times\,3$

11. 5
$\times\,7$

12. 4×8

13. 3×8

14. 7×6

15. 6×2

_____

_____

_____

_____

16. 9×7

17. 7×8

18. 6×8

19. 8×8

_____

_____

_____

_____

20. Nina bought 6 packages of butter. Each package contains 4 sticks. How many sticks of butter did Nina buy?

20. _____

21. A group of students were taking a field trip. They traveled in 7 vans with 5 students riding in each van. How many students were going on the trip?

21. _____

Name _____

In 22–24, write *true* or *false*. You may use a hundred chart to help.

22. 21 is a multiple of 3.   **22.** _____

23. 35 is a multiple of 3.   **23.** _____

24. 36 is a multiple of 6.   **24.** _____

In 25–27, continue each pattern.

25. 40, 50, 60, ■, ■, ■   **25.** _____

26. 77, 66, 55, ■, ■, ■   **26.** _____

27. 36, 48, 60, ■, ■, ■   **27.** _____

In 28–31, find each product.

28. 2 × 3 × 4   **28.** _____

29. (3 × 2) × 8   **29.** _____

30. 1 × (4 × 7)   **30.** _____

31. 3 × (1 × 6)   **31.** _____

32. Tim has 4 board games. Each game can have 4 players. Will Tim have enough games so that he and 23 friends can play at one time? Explain.

_____

33. Juanita is mixing pitchers of lemonade for the 29 students in her class. One pitcher will serve 4 students. How many pitchers does she need to make?

33.

34. Explain Your Thinking Explain how you can use the product of 4 × 3 to find 8 × 3. Then give the product.

_____

_____

Vocabulary: In 1–3, match each with its meaning.

1. multiple

a. when you multiply, you can group factors in any order and the product will be the same

2. grouping property

b. the product when both factors are the same

3. square number

c. the product of a given whole number and any other whole number

1. _____

2. _____

3. _____

In 4–19, find each product.

4. $\begin{array}{r} 3 \\ \times\ 4 \\ \hline \end{array}$ **5.** $\begin{array}{r} 9 \\ \times\ 3 \\ \hline \end{array}$ **6.** $\begin{array}{r} 5 \\ \times\ 4 \\ \hline \end{array}$ **7.** $\begin{array}{r} 4 \\ \times\ 2 \\ \hline \end{array}$

8. $\begin{array}{r} 7 \\ \times\ 6 \\ \hline \end{array}$ **9.** $\begin{array}{r} 6 \\ \times\ 3 \\ \hline \end{array}$ **10.** $\begin{array}{r} 7 \\ \times\ 5 \\ \hline \end{array}$ **11.** $\begin{array}{r} 3 \\ \times\ 7 \\ \hline \end{array}$

12. 9×8 **13.** 5×8 **14.** 8×8 **15.** 7×8

_____   _____   _____   _____

16. 2×7 **17.** 6×8 **18.** 5×6 **19.** 4×6

_____   _____   _____   _____

20. Robin bought 3 bags of potatoes. Each bag weighs 8 pounds. How many pounds of potatoes did Robin buy?

20. _____

21. A group of students were playing in the gym. There were 4 teams with 7 players on each team. How many students were playing in the gym?

21. _____

Name _____

In 22–24, write *true* or *false*. You may use a hundred chart to help.

22. 35 is a multiple of 6.

23. 24 is a multiple of 3.

24. 56 is a multiple of 6.

22. _____

23. _____

24. _____

In 25–27, continue each pattern.

25. 44, 55, 66, ■, ■, ■

26. 36, 48, 60, ■, ■, ■

27. 80, 70, 60, ■, ■, ■

25. _____

26. _____

27. _____

In 28–31, find each product.

28. $1 \times 3 \times 2$

29. $(2 \times 4) \times 6$

30. $7 \times (4 \times 2)$

31. $6 \times (2 \times 3)$

28. _____

29. _____

30. _____

31. _____

32. Avril brought 7 packages of balloons to a school party. Each package had 5 balloons. There were 32 students at the party. Did Avril bring enough balloons for everyone? Explain.

_____

33. Horace is making cookies for 49 friends. Each batch makes 8 very large cookies. How many batches will Horace need to make if each friend gets one cookie?

33. _____

34. Explain Your Thinking Explain how you can use the product of 2×6 to find 4×6. Then give the product.

_____

_____

Date _____ Score _____

Give the letter of the correct answer.

Find each product.

1. 3×4

   A 12   **B** 7   **C** 8   **D** 14

2. 3×7

   A 10   **B** 21   **C** 4   **D** 2

3. 3×5

   A 8   **B** 10   **C** 15   **D** 20

4. 4×4

   A 4   **B** 8   **C** 16   **D** 20

5. 4×7

   A 3   **B** 11   **C** 24   **D** 28

6. 2×4

   A 8   **B** 2   **C** 6   **D** 9

7. 6×8

   A 4   **B** 8   **C** 48   **D** 20

8. 5×6

   A 11   **B** 1   **C** 35   **D** Not here

9.   6
   $\times 6$

   A 12   **B** 32   **C** 36   **D** Not here

10.   2
   $\times 7$

   A 9   **B** 14   **C** 5   **D** 16

11. 7×5

   A 35   **B** 12   **C** 2   **D** 45

1. _____
2. _____
3. _____
4. _____
5. _____
6. _____
7. _____
8. _____
9. _____
10. _____
11. _____

12. 7×9

    A 54   **B** 16   **C** 2   **D** Not here

12. _____

13. 8×4

    A 12   **B** 32   **C** 4   **D** 36

13. _____

14. 9×8

    A 1   **B** 17   **C** 72   **D** 64

14. _____

15. 5×8

    A 13   **B** 30   **C** 3   **D** 40

15. _____

16. 3×6

    A 18   **B** 9   **C** 24   **D** Not here

16. _____

17. 4×9

    A 13   **B** 36   **C** 32   **D** 5

17. _____

18. $\begin{array}{r} 9 \\ \times 6 \end{array}$

    A 15   **B** 56   **C** 54   **D** Not here

18. _____

19. $\begin{array}{r} 7 \\ \times 6 \end{array}$

    A 49   **B** 54   **C** 36   **D** 42

19. _____

20. $\begin{array}{r} 6 \\ \times 4 \end{array}$

    A 54   **B** 36   **C** 18   **D** 24

20. _____

21. $\begin{array}{r} 3 \\ \times 9 \end{array}$

    A 24   **B** 27   **C** 36   **D** 32

21. _____

22. $\begin{array}{r} 4 \\ \times 5 \end{array}$

    A 10   **B** 20   **C** 9   **D** Not here

22. _____

23.   0
   × 4

A 0   **B** 4   **C** 1   **D** Not here

23. _____

24.   8
   × 2

A 18   **B** 6   **C** 16   **D** 10

24. _____

25.   1
   × 4

A 0   **B** 5   **C** 3   **D** 4

25. _____

26.   2
   × 6

A 14   **B** 12   **C** 24   **D** 8

26. _____

27.   7
   × 7

A 56   **B** 42   **C** 49   **D** 36

27. _____

In 28–31, choose *True* or *False*. You may use a hundred chart to help.

28. 18 is a multiple of 3.

   A True   **B** False

28. _____

29. 32 is a multiple of 6.

   A True   **B** False

29. _____

30. 48 is a multiple of 6.

   A True   **B** False

30. _____

31. 20 is a multiple of 3.

   A True   **B** False

31. _____

32. Complete the pattern: 90, 80, 70, ■, ■, ■

   A 60, 50, 40   **B** 40, 50, 60
   C 6, 5, 4   **D** 80, 90, 100

32. _____

33. Complete the pattern: 33, 44, 55, ■, ■, ■

    A 6, 7, 8   **B** 60, 70, 80
    C 66, 77, 88   **D** Not here

33. _____

34. Complete the pattern: 12, 24, 36, ■, ■, ■

    A 37, 38, 39   **B** 48, 60, 72
    C 24, 12, 1   **D** 40, 50, 60

34. _____

In 35–38, find each product.

35. $2 \times 1 \times 3$

    A 9   **B** 5   **C** 3   **D** Not here

35. _____

36. $(2 \times 4) \times 3$

    A 9   **B** 18   **C** 24   **D** 36

36. _____

37. $3 \times (4 \times 1)$

    A 7   **B** 12   **C** 15   **D** Not here

37. _____

38. $4 \times (3 \times 3)$

    A 10   **B** 12   **C** 24   **D** 36

38. _____

39. Jefferson School has 5 groups of students entered in the Sports Mania Relay Race. There are 4 students in each group. How many students will be running in the race?

    A 9 students   **B** 1 student
    C 20 students   **D** Not here

39. _____

40. Caroline serves popcorn to 21 friends at a slumber party. Each bag serves 4 people. How many bags does she need?

    A 6 bags   **B** 5 bags   **C** 4 bags   **D** 25 bags

40. _____

41. Derrick plans to serve pizza to 14 friends at a pre-game party. Each pizza serves 6 people. How many pizzas should he order?

    A 7 pizzas   **B** 6 pizzas
    C 3 pizzas   **D** 1 pizza

41. _____

Name _____

Date _____ Score _____

Your parent is taking you and your friends on a two-day
camping trip. Your group will need these items.

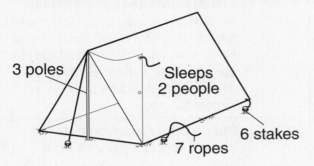

3 poles

Sleeps
2 people

6 stakes

7 ropes

4 bottles
per day
per person

1 can
per person

a. Making Decisions How many people, including
yourself, are going camping? Choose 6, 7, 8, or 9.

b. Recording Data Complete the table.

Item	Number of items per person	Number of items per group	Total number of items
Tents			
Stakes			
Poles			
Ropes			
Water			
Repellent			

Make a list showing what food you will bring.

c. Analyzing Data Use the table. Suppose it takes you
and your friends 9 minutes to put up one tent. How long
will it take you to set up all the tents?

d. Making Decisions When you get to the campsite,
what will you need to do before you go fishing, hiking,
swimming, and so on? List each chore in the order it
will be done.

Would it make any difference if you arrive at the
campsite at noon, at 5 P.M., or at 7 P.M.? Explain.

Teacher Notes

Concepts and Skills This activity requires students to:
- make decisions using real-life experiences.
- use basic multiplication facts to complete a table.
- make scheduling decisions.

Guiding Questions
- How can you decide how many tents you need?
- Why is it important to make a list of the food and other items you are taking?

Answers
a. Decisions will vary.
b. Answers will vary depending upon how many people go camping. Check students' answers.
c. Answers will vary depending upon how many people go camping.
d. Answers will vary. If the group arrives at the campsite at noon, they may want to eat first. If they arrive at 7 P.M., they probably should set up the tents first.

Extension
Have students find how many ounces of water will be needed for each person during the trip. Then encourage them to use a calculator to find how many ounces of water are needed for the entire group during the two-day camping trip.

Evaluation

Level	Standard to be achieved for performance of specified level
4	**Full Achievement** The student records data accurately and makes logical lists of needed food items. He or she determines what chores are necessary upon reaching the campsite and orders them in a logical fashion.
3	**Substantial Achievement** The student records data accurately but may make some careless errors. The lists of needed items are logical. The list of chores to be done upon reaching the campsite is logical but may not be ordered well.
2	**Partial Achievement** The student has some trouble recording data and may make errors in computation. He or she makes an incomplete list of food needs, and the listing and ordering of chores to be performed upon reaching the campsite are incomplete and illogical.
1	**Little Achievement** The student needs help in completing the table and makes many errors in computation. His or her decisions about what food to take on the hike are incomplete and/or illogical. The description of chores involved in setting up a campsite is incomplete and disorganized.

In 1–20, find each product.

1.   3
   $\times\,3$

2.   5
   $\times\,3$

3.   3
   $\times\,8$

4.   7
   $\times\,4$

5.   4
   $\times\,9$

6.   4
   $\times\,6$

7.   6
   $\times\,7$

8.   6
   $\times\,9$

9.   3
   $\times\,6$

10.   3
   $\times\,7$

11.   7
   $\times\,5$

12.   7
   $\times\,9$

13.   2
   $\times\,8$

14.   8
   $\times\,6$

15.   8
   $\times\,4$

16.   8
   $\times\,7$

17. 4×4
_____

18. 6×6
_____

19. 7×7
_____

20. 8×8
_____

21. The art room has 9 tables. Four students can work at each table. How many students can work in the art room at one time?

21. _____

22. Maxine brought 6 boxes to school. Each box held 8 friendship pins. How many friendship pins did Maxine have?

22. _____

   A 14 pins   **B** 48 pins   **C** 36 pins   **D** 24 pins

In 23–24, write *true* or *false*. You may use a hundred chart to help.

23. 24 is a multiple of 6.

23. _____

24. 10 is a multiple of 3.

24. _____

Name _____

In 25–27, complete each pattern.

25. 40, 50, 60, ■, ■, ■

26. 77, 66, 55, ■, ■, ■

27. 72, 60, 48, ■, ■, ■

25. _____

26. _____

27. _____

In 28–32, find each product.

28. $3 \times 1 \times 2$

    A 2   **B** 3   **C** 6   **D** 7

29. $4 \times (3 \times 2)$

    A 12   **B** 24   **C** 36   **D** Not here

30. $(2 \times 4) \times 6$

    A 36   **B** 24   **C** 48   **D** 12

31. $3 \times (3 \times 2)$

    A 3   **B** 9   **C** 12   **D** 18

32. $2 \times (4 \times 2)$

    A 8   **B** 16   **C** 10   **D** 24

28. _____

29. _____

30. _____

31. _____

32. _____

33. Gary's father has 43 chickens on his farm. Each coop holds 9 chickens. How many coops does Gary's father need to hold all the chickens?

33. _____

34. Mitch has 58 CDs. One CD wallet holds 8 CDs. How many CD wallets does Mitch need to hold all his CDs?

34. _____

35. Performance Task If you know 4×5, what other multiplication fact do you know? Explain. Draw a picture to support your answer.

_____

_____

_____

━ Computation ━

In 1–18, find each product.

1.   3
    $\times$ 7

2.   4
    $\times$ 9

3.   6
    $\times$ 2

4.   5
    $\times$ 8

5.   7
    $\times$ 9

6.   4
    $\times$ 5

7.   8
    $\times$ 3

8.   2
    $\times$ 9

9.   3
    $\times$ 6

10.   8
     $\times$ 9

11.   4
     $\times$ 6

12.   3
     $\times$ 3

13. 4×7

14. 8×7

15. 8×4

16. 5×4

_____   _____   _____   _____

17. $3 \times (4 \times 2)$

    A 12   **B** 6   **C** 18   **D** 24

17. _____

18. $(2 \times 4) \times 7$

    A 42   **B** 56   **C** 28   **D** 13

18. _____

In 19–23, find each sum or difference.

19.   3 4 9
     + 2 6 7

20.   5 4 8
     − 2 7 5

19. _____

20. _____

21. $1.3 6
     + 0.8 5

22. $5.0 0
     − 3.2 6

21. _____

22. _____

23. $5 + 42 + 31$

23. _____

Name _____

— Concepts —

24. Complete the pattern: 20, 30, 40, ■, ■, ■.　　　　　**24.** _____

    A 70, 60, 50　　　　　　**B** 10, 20, 30
    C 50, 60, 70　　　　　　**D** 60, 70, 80

In 25–26, write *true* or *false*. You may use a hundred chart to help.

25. 28 is a multiple of 6.　　　　　　　　　　　**25.** _____

26. 15 is a multiple of 3.　　　　　　　　　　　**26.** _____

27. Compare: 748 ● 835. Use <, >, or =.　　　　**27.** _____

    A <　　**B** >　　**C** =

28. Order 351, 531, and 135 from greatest to least.　　**28.** _____

    A 351, 135, 531　　　　**B** 135, 351, 531
    C 531, 351, 135　　　　**D** 531, 135, 351

29. Write the time
in two ways.
Write A.M. or P.M.

go to a movie

29. _____

_____

— Applications —

30. Chester is having a party for 22 friends.
Party favors come in packages of 8.
How many packages should he buy?

30. _____

31. Joaquin has baseball practice from
4:15 P.M. to 5:10 P.M. How long is Joaquin's
baseball practice?

31. _____

32. Kesi made 4 trips to the library to return
overdue books. The fine for overdue books
is 25 cents per book. On each trip, she
returned 3 books. How many books did
Kesi return?

32. _____

Give the letter of the correct answer.

In 1–2, use the pictograph.

1. How many students chose dress shoes?

Favorite Shoes	
Dress Shoes	👞👞👞
Sandles	👞👞
Sneakers	👞👞👞👞👞

👞 = 2 votes

   A 2 students
   B 3 students
   C 5 students
   D 6 students

   1. _____

2. How many more chose sneakers than chose sandals?

   A 2 students   **B** 3 students
   C 4 students   **D** 6 students

   2. _____

3. Noah put 2 pictures in the first row on the bulletin board, 5 in the second row, and 8 in the third row. Find a pattern. How many will he put in the fourth row?

   A 7 pictures   **B** 13 pictures
   C 10 pictures   **D** 11 pictures

   3. _____

4. Give the value of the underlined digit in 3̲46,298

   A 300,000   **B** 30,000   **C** 3,000   **D** 30

   4. _____

5. Compare: 413 ● 431. Use <, >, or =.

   A <   **B** >   **C** =

   5. _____

6. Order 415, 541, and 145 from least to greatest.

   A 415, 145, 541   **B** 541, 415, 145
   C 145, 415, 541   **D** 145, 541, 415

   6. _____

7. The school play began at 7:30 P.M. and finished 1 hour and 20 minutes later. What time did it end?

   A 8:30 P.M.   **B** 8:20 P.M.   **C** 9:20 P.M.   **D** 8:50 P.M.

   7. _____

8. Estimate the sum by rounding: 64 + 25.

   A 90   **B** 80   **C** 85   **D** Not here

   8. _____

Name _____

In 9–14, add. Estimate to check.

9. 18 + 24

   A 30   **B** 32   **C** 40   **D** Not here

9. _____

10. 265
    + 326

   A 581   **B** 591   **C** 593   **D** 867

10. _____

11. 397
    + 475

   A 862   **B** 863   **C** 871   **D** 872

11. _____

12. 4,700
    + 1,200

   A 3,500   **B** 4,900   **C** 5,900   **D** Not here

12. _____

13. 12 + 34 + 16

   A 52   **B** 62   **C** 72   **D** Not here

13. _____

14. $1.38 + $3.29

   A $1.91   **B** $4.57   **C** $4.67   **D** Not here

14. _____

15. Estimate the difference by rounding: 47 − 35.

   A 10   **B** 20   **C** 30   **D** Not here

15. _____

In 16–21, subtract. Estimate to check.

16. 47 − 38

   A 5   **B** 11   **C** 15   **D** Not here

16. _____

17. 358 − 149

   A 507   **B** 211   **C** 209   **D** 201

17. _____

18. 762
    − 283

   A 461   **B** 479   **C** 521   **D** 1,045

18. _____

Continued

19. 601
　－ 293

　　A 408　　**B** 418　　**C** 492　　**D** 308

19. _____

20. 4,300
　－ 1,400

　　A 2,900　　**B** 5,700　　**C** 3,900　　**D** 2,100

20. _____

21. $4.19 − 2.38

　　A $2.81　　**B** $2.21　　**C** $1.81　　**D** Not here

21. _____

22. Claude had 5 bushels of apples. He gave 2 bushels to Clara and then picked 4 more bushels. How many bushels does he have?

　　A 11 bushels　　**B** 3 bushels　　**C** 7 bushels　　**D** 1 bushel

22. _____

23. Which picture shows 2×5?

A • • • •
　• • • •

B • • • • •
　• • • • •

C • • •
　• • •

D • • • •
　• • • •

23. _____

24. Julie's craft club has 5 members. Each member brought 3 milk cartons to their first meeting. How many cartons were brought to the meeting?

　　A 6 cartons　　**B** 12 cartons　　**C** 24 cartons　　**D** 15 cartons

24. _____

In 25–27, multiply.

25. 9×8

　　A 42　　**B** 54　　**C** 72　　**D** 81

25. _____

26. 5×7

　　A 35　　**B** 12　　**C** 42　　**D** Not here

26. _____

27. 0×3

　　A 3　　**B** 30　　**C** 0　　**D** Not here

27. _____

28. Marissa buys a birthday card for $1.19 and a holiday card for $0.75. She also buys a stuffed animal for $7.59. How much will she spend for the cards?

    A $1.84   **B** $1.94   **C** $9.43   **D** $9.53

28. _____

In 29–35, multiply.

29. 3×8

    A 21   **B** 24   **C** 25   **D** 27

29. _____

30. 7×4

    A 21   **B** 24   **C** 27   **D** 28

30. _____

31. 8×6

    A 42   **B** 48   **C** 49   **D** 54

31. _____

32. $\begin{array}{r} 3 \\ \times 7 \\ \hline \end{array}$

    A 18   **B** 21   **C** 24   **D** 28

32. _____

33. $\begin{array}{r} 6 \\ \times 4 \\ \hline \end{array}$

    A 12   **B** 15   **C** 18   **D** 24

33. _____

34. $(2 \times 4) \times 8$

    A 48   **B** 24   **C** 64   **D** Not here

34. _____

35. $(3 \times 3) \times 9$

    A 81   **B** 27   **C** 54   **D** Not here

35. _____

36. Continue the pattern: 30, 40, 50, ■, ■, ■.

    A 50, 40, 30   **B** 70, 80, 90
    C 60, 70, 80   **D** 60, 50, 40

36. _____

37. May, Lila, Jack, and Mel are waiting in line for lunch. Jack is third in line. Mel is between Lila and Jack. Who is first in line?

    A May   **B** Lila   **C** Jack   **D** Mel

37. _____

In 1–2, complete each division sentence.

1.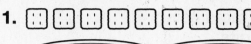

$10 \div 2 = \blacksquare$

_____

2.

Pencils   Pencils   Pencils

$9 \div 3 = \blacksquare$

_____

In 3–4, solve. You may use counters or draw pictures.

3.

8 oranges
2 in each group
How many groups?

_____

4.

12 shutters
2 on each window
How many windows?

_____

5. Becky gave 10 index cards to 5 friends. She gave each friend the same number of cards. How many cards did she give to each friend?

5. _____

6. Miguel put 20 photographs in an album. He put 4 photographs on each page. How many pages did he fill?

6. _____

7. Amanda gave 18 apples to her aunts. Each aunt received 6 apples. How many aunts does Amanda have?

7. _____

8. Darlene gave 12 stickers to Glenn, Angie, and Sierra. She gave each person the same number of stickers. How many stickers did each person get?

8. _____

9. Roger ran 15 miles. If he ran 5 miles each day, how many days did he run?

9. _____

Vocabulary: in 1–4, match each with its meaning.

1. quotient

a. a group of related facts using the same set of digits

1. _____

2. fact family

b. the number by which a dividend is divided

2. _____

3. dividend

c. the answer to a division problem

3. _____

d. the number to be divided in a division number sentence

4. divisor

4. _____

5. What multiplication fact can you use to find 28 ÷ 4?

5. _____

6. Complete the fact family using 5, 6, and 30.

$5 \times 6 = \boxed{}$

$30 \div 5 = \boxed{}$

$6 \times \boxed{} = 30$

$\boxed{} \div 6 = 5$

In 7–18, find each quotient.

7. 16 ÷ 2

8. 27 ÷ 3

9. 18 ÷ 2

10. 35 ÷ 5

_____

_____

_____

_____

11. $5\overline{)40}$

12. $4\overline{)36}$

13. $2\overline{)10}$

14. $4\overline{)24}$

15. 15 ÷ 5

16. 0 ÷ 3

17. 4 ÷ 1

18. 2 ÷ 2

_____

_____

_____

_____

In 19–20, write which operation you would use to solve the problem. Then solve.

19. Alisha has 16 beads. She uses 4 beads to make a necklace. How many necklaces can she make? _____

20. Marco bought 2 red balloons and 5 blue balloons. How many balloons did he buy in all? _____

Name _____

Date _____ Score _____

Vocabulary: in 1–2, match each with its meaning.

1. even number

a. a whole number that has 1, 3, 5, 7, or 9 in the ones place

1. _____

2. odd number

b. a whole number that has 0, 2, 4, 6, or 8 in the ones place

2. _____

3. What multiplication fact can help you find 63 ÷ 7?

3. _____

In 4–11, find each quotient.

4. 6)̄42   **5.** 7)̄56   **6.** 9)̄72   **7.** 6)̄24

8. 35 ÷ 7   **9.** 64 ÷ 8   **10.** 45 ÷ 9   **11.** 32 ÷ 8

_____   _____   _____   _____

In 12–14, write even or odd. You may use color cubes to help.

12. 22   **12.** _____

13. 17   **13.** _____

14. 41   **14.** _____

15. Ben has 12 sports pictures to put on his wall. He wants to put the pictures into equal rows. What are all the ways to arrange the pictures?

_____

_____

16. Box A has 12 marbles inside. Each box B has an equal number of marbles inside. How many marbles are in each box B?

16. _____

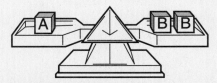

Name _____

Date _____ Score _____

Vocabulary: In 1–4, match each with its meaning.

1. divisor

a. a whole number that has 0, 2, 4, 6 or 8 in the ones place

1. _____

2. quotient

b. the number by which a dividend is divided

2. _____

3. odd number

c. the answer to a division problem

3. _____

4. even number

d. a whole number that has 1, 3, 5, 7, or 9 in the ones place

4. _____

5. Complete the division sentence.

5. _____

$6 \div 2 = \blacksquare$

6. 8 dogs
2 in each pen
How many pens?

6. _____

In 7–9, complete.

7. $8 \times \boxed{} = 24$

$24 \div \boxed{} = 8$

8. $7 \times \boxed{} = 56$

$56 \div 7 = \boxed{}$

9. $\boxed{} \times 7 = 35$

$35 \div \boxed{} = 7$

In 10–21, find each quotient.

10. $12 \div 2$ **11.** $25 \div 5$ **12.** $5 \div 1$ **13.** $28 \div 4$

_____ _____ _____ _____

14. $2\overline{)16}$ **15.** $3\overline{)21}$ **16.** $6\overline{)0}$ **17.** $5\overline{)40}$

18. $54 \div 6$ **19.** $64 \div 8$ **20.** $49 \div 7$ **21.** $72 \div 9$

_____ _____ _____ _____

22. Ruby has 42 dollar bills. She gave 7 dollar bills to each of her nieces. How many nieces does she have?

22. _____

23. Victor shared 28 stickers equally with 3 friends. How many stickers did each person get? (Remember that Victor will have the same number of stickers as each of his friends.)

23. _____

In 24–25, write which operation you would use to solve the problem. Then solve.

24. A loaf of nut bread has 18 slices. If a serving is 3 slices, how many servings are there?

_____

25. Arimoto bought 9 tickets to the choir recital. Each ticket cost $5. How much money did he spend?

_____

26. The band has 20 members that will march in a parade. They will march in equal rows. What are all the ways the leader can arrange them?

_____

_____

27. Box A has 10 cubes inside. Box B has 4 cubes inside. How many cubes are inside Box C?

27. _____

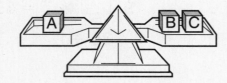

28. Write the next 4 odd numbers after 25.

28. _____

29. Write the next 4 even numbers after 10.

29. _____

30. Explain Your Thinking Arthur has 3 groups of 5 plants. Which operations could you use to find how many plants he has in all? Explain.

_____

_____

Name _____

Date _____ Score _____

Vocabulary: In 1–4, match each with its meaning

1. quotient   **a.** the answer to a division problem   **1.** _____

2. dividend   **b.** a whole number that has 1, 3, 5, 7, or 9 in the ones place   **2.** _____

3. even number   **c.** the number to be divided in a division number sentence   **3.** _____

4. odd number   **d.** a whole number that has 0, 2, 4, 6, or 8 in the ones place   **4.** _____

5. Complete the division sentence.   **5.** _____

$6 \div 3 = \blacksquare$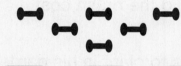

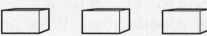

6. 10 students
5 in each row
How many rows?      **6.** _____

In 7–9, complete.

7. $7 \times \boxed{} = 42$ **8.** $\boxed{} \times 6 = 54$ **9.** $8 \times \boxed{} = 40$

$42 \div 7 = \boxed{}$ $54 \div \boxed{} = 6$ $40 \div \boxed{} = 8$

In 10–21, find each quotient.

10. $8 \div 2$ **11.** $20 \div 5$ **12.** $7 \div 1$ **13.** $36 \div 4$

_____   _____   _____   _____

14. $2\overline{)12}$ **15.** $3\overline{)27}$ **16.** $1\overline{)0}$ **17.** $5\overline{)15}$

18. $30 \div 6$ **19.** $48 \div 8$ **20.** $56 \div 7$ **21.** $81 \div 9$

_____   _____   _____   _____

22. A principal presents 45 awards to students each year. If he gives the awards equally among 9 classes, how many awards does he give to each class?

22. _____

23. A group of 6 friends shared equally 36 stamps. How many stamps did each person get?

23. _____

In 24–25, write which operation you would use to solve the problem. Then solve.

24. There are 3 tennis balls in a can. How many tennis balls are in 7 cans?

24. _____

_____

25. Edith bought a scrunchie for $3 and a brush for $6. How much more did the brush cost than the scrunchie?

25. _____

26. Jamie has 18 rose bushes to plant in his garden. He wants to put the bushes in equal rows. What are all the ways he could arrange the rose bushes?

_____

_____

27. Box A has 6 cubes inside. Box B has 1 cube inside. How many cubes are inside Box C?

27. _____

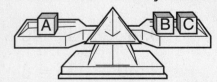

28. Write the next 4 even numbers after 30.

28. _____

29. Write the next 4 odd numbers after 15.

29. _____

30. **Explain Your Thinking** Iona made 12 masks. She wants to give 2 masks to each of her friends. Which operations could you use to find how many friends she will give masks to? Explain.

_____

_____

Give the letter of the correct answer.

1. Give the number that would complete this division sentence: $6 \div 2 = \blacksquare$.

   A 3
   B 4
   C 8
   D Not here

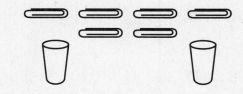

1. _____

2. Give the number that would complete this division sentence: $8 \div 4 = \blacksquare$.

   A 12
   B 2
   C 4
   D 8

2. _____

3. 15 magazines
   3 on each stack
   How many stacks?

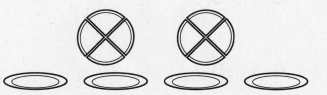

   A 18 stacks   **B** 12 stacks   **C** 5 stacks   **D** 3 stacks

3. _____

4. 9 hats
   3 on each rack
   How many racks?

   A 27 racks   **B** 12 racks   **C** 6 racks   **D** Not here

4. _____

5. Terry, Tracy, and Cindy want to equally share a pack of 24 crayons. How many crayons will each person get?

   A 6 crayons   **B** 8 crayons   **C** 12 crayons   **D** 3 crayons

5. _____

6. A group of golfers had 20 balls. Each golfer used 5 golf balls. How many golfers were in the group?

   A 5 golfers   **B** 4 golfers   **C** 20 golfers   **D** 9 golfers

6. _____

7. If $7 \times 6 = 42$, then $42 \div 7 = \blacksquare$.

   A 7   **B** 5   **C** 6   **D** Not here

7. _____

Name _____

8. Which number sentence belongs with this fact family?
   $7 \times 8 = 56$, $8 \times 7 = 56$, and $56 \div 7 = 8$

   A $58 \div 7 = 6$ **B** $56 \div 7 = 7$
   C $8 \times 8 = 64$ **D** $56 \div 8 = 7$

8. _____

In 9–18, find the quotients.

9. $18 \div 2$

   A 7   **B** 9   **C** 8   **D** 36

9. _____

10. $35 \div 5$

    A 6   **B** 7   **C** 5   **D** 9

10. _____

11. $3\overline{)18}$

    A 6   **B** 9   **C** 5   **D** 7

11. _____

12. $2\overline{)14}$

    A 6   **B** 8   **C** 7   **D** Not here

12. _____

13. $32 \div 4$

    A 8   **B** 6   **C** 7   **D** 9

13. _____

14. $7\overline{)0}$

    A 7   **B** 1   **C** 0   **D** Not here

14. _____

15. $1\overline{)9}$

    A 1   **B** 9   **C** 10   **D** 8

15. _____

16. $36 \div 6$

    A 9   **B** 4   **C** 6   **D** 8

16. _____

17. $7\overline{)63}$

    A 7   **B** 8   **C** 5   **D** Not here

17. _____

18. $81 \div 9$

    A 8   **B** 18   **C** 10   **D** 9

18 _____

Continued

19. Divide. $8\overline{)48}$

    A 8   **B** 7   **C** 4   **D** Not here

19. _____

20. 6 is the divisor. 54 is the dividend. What is the quotient?

    A 9   **B** 8   **C** 7   **D** 6

20. _____

21. Which multiplication fact could you use to find $40 \div 5$?

    A $40 \times 5 = 200$ **B** $5 \times 8 = 40$
    C $5 \times 5 = 25$ **D** $8 \times 8 = 64$

21. _____

In 22–23, choose the number sentence you would use to solve each problem.

22. Mario collected 15 rocks. He gave 5 rocks to his friend Clay. How many rocks does Mario have left?

    A $15 \div 5 = 3$ **B** $15 \times 5 = 75$
    C $15 - 5 = 10$ **D** $15 + 5 = 20$

22. _____

23. Keisha and Brandon have 12 Frisbees. They want to share them equally. How many Frisbees does each friend get?

    A $12 \times 1 = 12$ **B** $2 + 12 = 14$
    C $12 - 2 = 10$ **D** $12 \div 2 = 6$

23. _____

24. If you start with 11, what are the next 5 odd numbers?

    A 12, 13, 14, 15, 16
    B 1, 3, 5, 7, 9
    C 13, 15, 17, 19, 21
    D 12, 14, 16, 18, 20

24. _____

25. If you start with 30, what are the next 5 even numbers?

    A 32, 34, 36, 38, 40
    B 1, 3, 5, 7, 9
    C 31, 32, 33, 34, 35
    D Not here

25. _____

26. Joyce is placing photographs in an album. She has 18 photographs, and wants to put the same number on each page. The number of pages in the album would depend upon how many photos Joyce places on a page. Use these different arrangements to find how many pages could be in the album.

26. _____

A 1 or 2 pages
B 2, 4, 6, or 8 pages
C 1, 2, 3, 6, 9, or 18 pages
D Only 5 pages

27. Shaquille wants to put 24 photographs in a scrapbook that has 8 pages. He wants to put the same number of photographs on a page. How many photographs will be on each page?

27. _____

A 4 photographs   **B** 3 photographs
C 9 photographs   **D** Not here

28. Box A has 8 cubes inside. Each box B has an equal number of cubes. How many cubes are in each box B?

28. _____

A 8 cubes
B 2 cubes
C 16 cubes
D 4 cubes

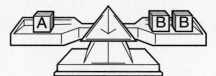

29. Box D has 4 cubes inside. Box E has 8 cubes inside. How many cubes are inside Box C?

29. _____

A 2 cubes
B 4 cubes
C 8 cubes
D Not here

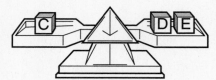

In 30, which operation would you use to solve the problem?

30. Your neighbor promises to give $3 to charity for each mile you walk in a walk-a-thon. If you walk 10 miles, how much will you earn for the charity?

30. _____

A Addition   **B** Subtraction
C Multiplication   **D** Division

© Scott Foresman Addison Wesley 3

Suppose you went to the beach and collected these
sea shells.

a. **Making Decisions** You want to display your shells in
   equal rows. What are all the different ways you can
   arrange the shells? Which of these arrangements would
   you choose?

b. **Recording Data** You can write a division sentence to
   describe each arrangement.

c. **Analyzing Data**

   How many shells are there in all?

   Which arrangements have an odd number of rows?

   Which arrangements have an even number of shells in
   each row?

d. **Explain Your Thinking** How did you decide which way
   you preferred to arrange your shells?

e. **Making Decisions** You give some shells to your best
   friend. How many shells do you give your friend? How
   will you arrange the shells you have left?

Teacher Notes

Concepts and Skills This activity requires students to:
- count given items.
- make decisions using real-life experiences.
- write division sentences to represent real-life situations.
- find quotients for basic division facts.
- make an organized list or draw a picture to decide how to arrange items.

Guiding Questions
- I have 20 shells. I put 5 shells in each row. How many rows do I have?
- Which operation did you use to find how many rows I have?

Answers
a. 1 row of 36 shells, 2 rows of 18 shells each, 3 rows of 12 shells each, 4 rows of 9 shells each, 6 rows of 6 shells each, 9 rows of 4 shells each, 12 rows of 3 shells each, 18 rows of 2 shells each, 36 rows of 1 shell. Answers will vary as to favorite arrangements.
b. $36 \div 1 = 36$, $36 \div 2 = 18$, $36 \div 3 = 12$, $36 \div 4 = 9$, $36 \div 6 = 6$, $36 \div 9 = 4$, $36 \div 12 = 3$, $36 \div 18 = 2$, $36 \div 36 = 1$
c. 36 shells; odd number of rows: 1 row, 3 rows, 9 rows; even number in row: 36 shells, 18 shells, 12 shells, 6 shells, 4 shells, 2 shells
d. Check students' answers.
e. Answers will vary.

Extension
Have students write their own word problems or picture problems involving basic division facts.

Evaluation

Level	Standard to be achieved for performance of specified level
4	**Full Achievement** The student demonstrates a clear understanding of division and can use problem-solving skills to describe possible arrangements. Each division sentence is correctly written.
3	**Substantial Achievement** The student demonstrates a clear understanding of division and can use problem-solving skills to describe possible arrangements. Most arrangements and division sentences are correctly written.
2	**Partial Achievement** The student has some difficulty using division and problem-solving skills to determine arrangements. The student may need help in writing division sentences.
1	**Little Achievement** The student demonstrates little if any understanding of the task at hand and needs considerable help in determining arrangements and in writing division sentences. The computation contains many errors, and the concept of division is not grasped.

1. Give the number that would complete this
   division sentence: $16 \div 4 = \blacksquare$.

   1. _____

   A 4
   B 12
   C 20
   D Not here

2. 10 batteries
   2 in each flashlight
   How many flashlights?

   2. _____

3. Stan sold 15 oranges. If each sack holds
   5 oranges, how many sacks did he sell?

   3. _____

4. Meg made a 64-ounce pitcher of lemonade
   for her party. She and her friends each drank
   8 ounces. How many people are at the party?

   4. _____

5. Which number sentence does not belong
   in a fact family with 3, 8, 24?

   5. _____

   A $3 \times 8 = 24$ **B** $24 \div 3 = 8$
   C $3 \times 3 = 9$ **D** $24 \div 8 = 3$

6. Complete the fact family using 3, 1, and 3.

   $3 \times 1 = \boxed{}$ $3 \div 1 = \boxed{}$

   $1 \times 3 = \boxed{}$ $3 \div 3 = \boxed{}$

In 7–18, find the quotient.

7. $6 \div 2$ 8. $45 \div 5$ 9. $27 \div 3$ 10. $24 \div 4$

_____   _____   _____   _____

11. $8\overline{)0}$ 12. $1\overline{)6}$ 13. $6\overline{)54}$ 14. $2\overline{)16}$

15. $49 \div 7$ 16. $36 \div 9$ 17. $32 \div 8$ 18. $30 \div 5$

_____   _____   _____   _____

Name _____

**In 19–20, write which operation you would use.
Then solve.**

19. Abraham brought in 12 worms for science
class. Tyler gave him 2 more worms. How
many worms did Abraham have then?   _____

20. Myra and 5 friends ate 12 equal-size
servings. Each person ate the same
amount. How many servings did each eat?   _____

21. Which number is an even number?   **21.** _____

  A 47   **B** 63   **C** 34   **D** 21

22. Which number is an odd number?

  A 43   **B** 52   **C** 16   **D** 74   **22.** _____

23. Al has a red shirt and a green shirt. He has black pants
and tan pants. List all the different outfits he can make.

_____

24. Ada May has 8 crystal animals on top of her dresser.
She wants to arrange them in equal rows. What are all
the ways to arrange the crystal figures?

_____

25. Three boxes are on a scale. Box A has 15 plastic   **25.** _____
cubes inside. Box B has 8 plastic cubes inside.
How many cubes are inside Box C?

  A 8 cubes
  B 7 cubes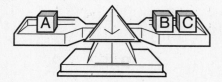
  C 23 cubes
  D 2 cubes

26. Performance Task Rose displays 18 dolls on 2 shelves.
Each shelf has the same number of dolls. Is there an
odd or an even number of dolls on each shelf? Explain.

_____

_____

— Computation —

1. Add: 3,476 + 598 + 2,994

    A 6,068   **B** 7,068   **C** 5,988   **D** 7,168

1. _____

2. Multiply: $9 \times 3 \times 2$

2. _____

In 3–10, find the quotient.

3. $18 \div 2$ **4.** $0 \div 9$ **5.** $16 \div 4$ **6.** $20 \div 5$

_____   _____   _____   _____

7. $6\overline{)54}$ **8.** $7\overline{)49}$ **9.** $8\overline{)64}$ **10.** $3\overline{)21}$

— Concepts —

11. Give the number that would complete this division sentence: $6 \div 3 = \blacksquare$.

    A 2
    B 3
    C 9
    D Not here

11. _____

12. 8 shells
    2 in each bucket
    How many buckets?

12. _____

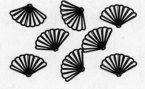

13. Use <, >, or = to compare these numbers.
    2,318 $\blacksquare$ 2,183

13. _____

14. Round 57 to the nearest ten.

    A 60   **B** 50   **C** 55   **D** 100

14. _____

15. Complete the fact family.

    $9 \times \boxed{} = 45$ $5 \times \boxed{} = 45$

    $\boxed{} \div 9 = 5$ $45 \div 5 = \boxed{}$

16. What are the next four odd numbers after 21? **16.** _____

17. What are the next four even numbers after 9? **17.** _____

In 18, write which operation you would use to solve the problem. Then solve.

18. A yo-yo costs $3.95. A top costs $0.99. How much more does the yo-yo cost than the top? _____

19. Block A has 25 cubes inside. Box C has 5 cubes inside. How many cubes are inside Box B? **19.** _____

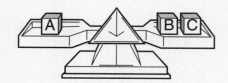

   A 5 cubes
   B 20 cubes
   C 30 cubes
   D Not here

— Applications —

20. Alayne has 40 counters to pass out to 5 students. She wants to give the same number of counters to each student. How many counters will each student get? **20.** _____

   A 200 counters   **B** 35 counters
   C 8 counters   **D** Not here

21. George has 10 stickers. He wants to arrange them in equal rows on the cover of his notebook. What are all the ways to arrange the stickers in rows?

_____

22. Wanda buys a book for $6.95. She gives the clerk a $20 bill. How much change will she receive? **22.** _____

   A $14.05   **B** $16.95   **C** $26.95   **D** $13.05

23. Which elementary school has the most students? **23.** _____

   A Oakridge
   B Maple Lake
   C Mulberry Hill
   D Cedar Crest

Elementary Schools

Number of Students: 500 400 300 200 100 0

Oakridge   Maple Lake   Mulberry Hill   Cedar Crest

School

Vocabulary: In 1–4, match each with its meaning.

1. polygon   a. an angle that forms a square corner   1. _____

2. congruent   b. part of a line   2. _____

3. right angle   c. a closed figure with three or more sides made up of line segments   3. _____

4. line segment   d. having the same size and shape   4. _____

In 5–7, name the solid figure that each object looks like.

5.   6.   7.

_____   _____   _____

In 8–10, write the number of sides that each shape has.

8.   9.   10.

_____   _____   _____

11. Are these lines parallel or intersecting?   11. _____

12. Write slide, flip, or turn.   12. _____

13. Does this drawing show a line of symmetry? Write *yes* or *no*.   13. _____

14. Is this a right angle, less than a right angle, or greater than a right angle?   14. _____

15. How many squares are in this drawing?   15. _____

Vocabulary: In 1–4, match each word with its meaning.

1. perimeter

    a. quantity used as a standard of measurement

1. _____

2. area

    b. the distance around a figure

2. _____

3. volume

    c. the number of cubic units in a solid figure

3. _____

4. unit

    d. the number of square units needed to cover the surface of a figure

4. _____

In 5–6, find the area and perimeter of each shape.

5.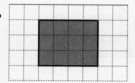

    Perimeter _____

    Area _____

6.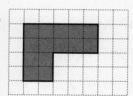

    Perimeter _____

    Area _____

In 7–9, find the volume of each shape.

7.

8.

9.

_____   _____   _____

In 10–11, write the ordered pair that locates each letter.

10. A _____

11. B _____

12. Which letter is located at (5, 4)? ____

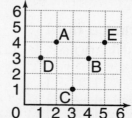

Vocabulary: In 1–4, match each with its example.

1. _____

2. _____

3. _____

4. _____

| **a.** line of symmetry | **b.** line |
| **c.** cylinder | **d.** right angle |

In 5–7, name the solid figure or shape that each object looks like.

5. _____

6. _____

7. _____

8. Are these lines parallel or intersecting? _____

9. Is this angle a right angle, less than a right angle, or greater than a right angle? _____

In 10–12, write congruent or not congruent for each.

10. _____

11.  _____

12. _____

In 13–15, write slide, flip, or turn.

13. _____

14. 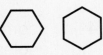 _____

15. _____

Continued **169**

Name _____

In 16–18, is each a line of symmetry? Write *yes* or *no*.

16.

17.

18.

_____   _____   _____

19. How many squares
are in this design?

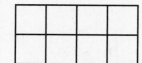

19. _____

In 20–21, find the perimeter and the area of each figure.

20.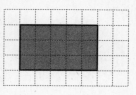

Perimeter _____

Area _____

21.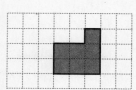

Perimeter _____

Area _____

In 22–24, find the volume of each.

22.

23.

24.

_____   _____   _____

In 25–26, write the ordered pair that locates each letter.

25. A _____

26. B _____

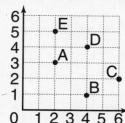

27. Which letter is
located at (2, 5)? ____

28. **Explain Your Thinking** Use 4 line segments
to draw a polygon that has 4 right angles.

Name _____

Date _____   Score _____

Chapter 8 Test
Form
B

Vocabulary: In 1–4, match each with its example.

1.

2.

3.

4.

____   ____   ____   ____

a. line segment	**b.** sphere
c. polygon	**d.** line of symmetry

In 5–7, name the solid figure or shape that each object looks like.

5.

6.   Tomato Soup

7.

_____   _____   _____

8. Are these lines parallel or intersecting?

_____

9. Is this angle a right angle, less than a right angle, or greater than a right angle?

_____

In 10–12, write congruent or not congruent for each.

10.

11.

12.

_____   _____   _____

In 13–15, write slide, flip, or turn.

13.

14.

15.

_____   _____   _____

© Scott Foresman Addison Wesley 3

Chapter 8 Test Form B

Continued **171**

Name _____

In 16–18, is each a line of symmetry? Write *yes* or *no*.

16.

17.

18.

_____   _____   _____

19. How many squares are in this design?

19. _____

In 20–21, find the perimeter and the area of each figure.

20.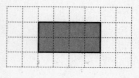

Perimeter _____

Area _____

21.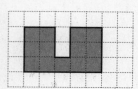

Perimeter _____

Area _____

In 22–24, find the volume of each.

22.

23.

24.

_____   _____   _____

In 25–26, write the ordered pair that locates each letter.

25. A _____

26. B _____

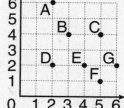

27. Which letter is located at (6, 2)? _____

28. Explain Your Thinking Use 4 line segments to draw a polygon that has 2 right angles and is not a rectangle.

Name _____

Date _____ Score _____

Give the letter of the correct answer.

1. Name the solid figure that this object looks like.   1. _____

   A Sphere
   B Cylinder
   C Rectangular Prism
   D Cone

2. Name the solid figure that this object looks like.   2. _____

   A Pyramid
   B Rectangle
   C Cube
   D Rectangular Prism

3. How many sides does this shape have?   3. _____

   A 4 sides
   B 3 sides
   C 2 sides
   D Not here

4. How many sides does this shape have?   4. _____

   A 2 sides
   B 3 sides
   C 4 sides
   D Not here

5. Give the name for these lines.   5. _____

   A Parallel lines
   B Line segments
   C Intersecting lines
   D Not here

6. Give the name for these lines.   6. _____

   A Parallel lines
   B Line segments
   C Intersecting lines
   D Not here

7. Give the name.

    A Ray
    B Line
    C Line Segment
    D Not here

7. _____

8. Give the name of the angle.

    A Right angle
    B Greater than a right angle
    C Less than a right angle

8. _____

9. Give the number of right angles in the figure.

    A 4 right angles
    B 3 right angles
    C 2 right angles
    D Not here

9. _____

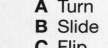

10. How has the figure has been moved?

    A Turn
    B Slide
    C Flip
    D Congruent

10. _____

11. How has the figure has been moved?

    A Turn
    B Slide
    C Flip
    D Congruent

11. _____

12. Which pair of figures is congruent?

12. _____

    A

    B

    C

    D

13. Which is a line of symmetry?

13. _____

A

B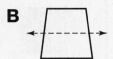

C

D

14. How many triangles are in this figure?

14. _____

A 13 triangles
B 9 triangles
C 10 triangles
D Not here

15. How many rectangles are in this figure?

15. _____

A 6 rectangles
B 9 rectangles
C 12 rectangles
D Not here

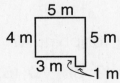

16. What is the perimeter?

16. _____

A 16 in.
B 15 in.
C 5 in.
D Not here

5 in.
3 in.   3 in.
5 in.

17. What is the perimeter?

17. _____

A 18 m
B 19 m
C 20 m
D Not here

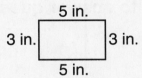
5 m
4 m   5 m
3 m   1 m

18. The perimeter of a square is 36 units.
How long is each side?

18. _____

A 4 units   **B** 6 units
C 18 units   **D** Not here

Name _____

19. What is the area?

    A 9 square units
    B 12 square units
    C 15 square units
    D Not here

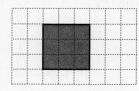

19. _____

20. What is the area?

    A 16 units
    B 7 square units
    C 9 square units
    D 16 square units

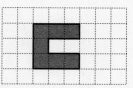

20. _____

21. Give the volume.

    A 22 cubic units
    B 6 cubic units
    C 4 cubic units
    D 1 cubic unit

21. _____

22. Give the volume

    A 6 cubic units
    B 16 cubic units
    C 18 cubic units
    D Not here

22. _____

Use the coordinate grid to answer questions 23–25.

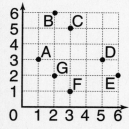

23. What is the ordered pair for point A?

    A (3, 1)   **B** (1, 3)   **C** (2, 3)   **D** (6, 3)

23. _____

24. What is the ordered pair for point C?

    A (4, 4)   **B** (5, 3)   **C** (3, 5)   **D** (5, 1)

24. _____

25. Which letter is located at (4, 3)?

    A A   **B** B   **C** D   **D** Not here

25. _____

You are to design a book cover for your math book.
The cover will wrap all the way around your book.

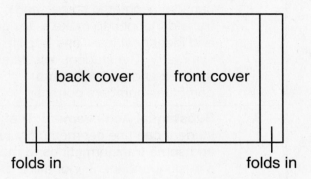

a. **Making Decisions** Put your math book on a piece of grid paper and trace around it. Decide on a design for the front book cover. The design should show slides, flips, and turns, and at least one line of symmetry. Think about which colors you will use to complete the design.

b. **Recording Data** Draw your design for the front cover on the grid paper and color it. Find the perimeter and the area of the front cover. Write these measurements on the front cover.

c. **Analyzing Data**

Which shapes did you use your design?

Where is the line of symmetry?

Which is greater, the number of units in the perimeter of the front cover or the number of square units in its area?

Describe the flips, turns, and slides in your design.

d. **Explain Your Thinking** How did you decide where the line of symmetry would be in your design?

e. **Making Decisions** Are you pleased with your design? Why might you change the design? How would you change it? Use these ideas, and repeat the activity for the back book cover.

Teacher Notes

Concepts and Skills This activity requires students to:
- draw geometric figures.
- identify and draw a line of symmetry.
- create a design using slides, flips, and turns.
- find the perimeter and area of a rectangle drawn on grid paper.
- compare numbers.

Guiding Questions
- What is a line of symmetry?
- How do you find the perimeter of a figure drawn on grid paper?
- How do you find the area of a figure drawn on grid paper?

Answers
a. Decisions will vary.
b. Designs will vary. Check that students' designs include a line of symmetry, slides, flips, and turns.
c. Answers will vary.
d. Explanations will vary.
e. Answers will vary.

Extension
Have students make a design to go on the spine of the book. The design should include the word MATH.

Evaluation

Level	Standard to be achieved for performance of specified level
4	**Full Achievement** The student can use geometric figures and transformations to make a design, and identify at least one line of symmetry. The student calculates the area and perimeter and compares numbers correctly.
3	**Substantial Achievement** The student can use geometric figures and some transformations to make a design, and identify one line of symmetry. The student calculates the area and perimeter and compares numbers with few errors.
2	**Partial Achievement** The student has some difficulty using geometric figures and transformations to make a design and identifying a line of symmetry. The student may make errors when calculating the area and perimeter and comparing numbers.
1	**Little Achievement** The student cannot complete the design without help, nor identify the transformations and line of symmetry. There are errors in calculating the area and perimeter.

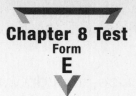

In 1–3, name the solid figure or shape that each object looks like.

1.

2.

3.

_____ _____ 3. _____

4. How many sides does this figure have?

4. _____

5. Give the name.

   A Ray   **B** Line   **C** Segment   **D** Point

5. _____

6. Are these lines parallel or intersecting?

6. _____

In 7–9, write the number of right angles in each polygon.

7.

8.

9.

_____ _____ _____

In 10–13, write slide, flip, or turn.

10.

11.

12.

_____ _____ _____

13. Are these figures congruent or not congruent?

13. _____

14. Does this drawing show a line of symmetry? Write *yes* or *no*.

14. _____

Name _____

15. Does this drawing show a line of symmetry? Write *yes* or *no*.

15. _____

16. How many squares are in this design?

A 7 squares   **B** 9 squares
C 8 squares   **D** 10 squares

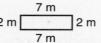

16. _____

17. What is the perimeter?

A 18 inches   **B** 18 square inches
C 9 inches   **D** 9 square inches

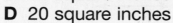

17. _____

18. What is the area?

A 18 inches   **B** 18 square inches
C 20 inches   **D** 20 square inches

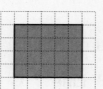

18. _____

19. What is the area?

A 10 inches   **B** 10 square inches
C 18 inches   **D** 20 square inches

19. _____

20. What is the volume?

A 7 inches   **B** 7 square inches
C 7 cubic inches   **D** 14 square inches

20. _____

In 21–22, write the ordered pair that locates each letter.

21. A _____

22. C _____

23. Which letter is located at (2, 4)? ____

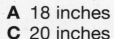

24. Performance Task Explain how you would find the perimeter of this figure. Then solve.

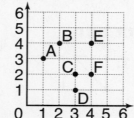

_____

_____

_____

— Computation —

1. Find the sum. $2.46 + $9.78

2. Find the difference. 4,038 − 2,862

3. Find the product. 9 × 5

4. Multiply 5 × 2 × 3.

1. _____

2. _____

3. _____

4. _____

— Concepts —

5. Name the solid figure that
this object looks like.

A Cube   **B** Pyramid
C Sphere   **D** Square

5. _____

6. How many sides does
this figure have?

6. _____

7. Round 26 to the nearest ten.

7. _____

8. Which numbers are even?

A 1, 2, 3   **B** 10, 20, 30
C 1, 3, 5   **D** Not here

8. _____

9. Give the name for these lines.

A Intersecting   **B** Sides
C Parallel   **D** Not here

9. _____

10. Is this a right angle, less
than a right angle, or
greater than a right angle?

_____

11. Are these figures congruent
or not congruent?

11. _____

12. Does this figure show
a line of symmetry?
Write *yes* or *no*.

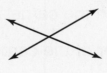

12. _____

13. How many rectangles are in this figure?

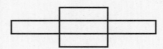

13. _____

14. Which operation would you use to evenly share some models among your friends?

A Addition   **B** Subtraction
C Multiplication   **D** Division

14. _____

15. Find the volume.

15. _____

In 16–17, write the ordered pair that locates each letter.

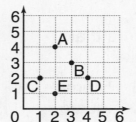

16. A _____

17. C _____

— Applications —

In 18–19, use the carpet.

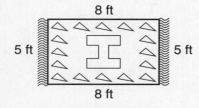

18. Did the artist flip, turn, or slide the triangles to make the design in the carpet?

18. _____

19. What is the perimeter of the carpet?

19. _____

20. What is the area of the tile floor in the playhouse?

A 4 square units   **B** 18 units
C 20 square units   **D** Not here

20. _____

21. Tori wants to fence her garden. How much fencing will she need?

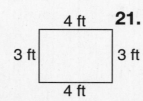

A 14 feet   **B** 12 feet
C 7 feet   **D** Not here

21. _____

In 1–2, complete. You may use place-value blocks.

1. 6×1 ten = ■ tens _____   **2.** 2×8 tens = ■ tens _____

6×10 = ■ . _____ 2×80 = ■ _____

In 3–4, complete.

3. 5×3 = ■ _____   **4.** 4×7 = ■ _____

5×30 = ■ _____ 4×70 = ■ _____

5×300 = ■ _____ 4×700 = ■ _____

In 5–6, find each product using mental math.

5. 8×50 **5.** _____

6. 9×70 **6.** _____

In 7–12, estimate each product.

7. 2×61 **7.** _____

8. 5×72 **8.** _____

9. 7×611 **9.** _____

10. 8×67 **10.** _____

11. 6×58 **11.** _____

12. 8×83 **12.** _____

In 13–14, find each product. You may use place-value blocks to help.

13. 3×13 = ■   **14.** 2×24 = ■   **13.** _____

14. _____

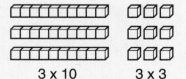

3 x 10   3 x 3

2 x 20   2 x 4

In 1–3, find each product.

1. 38 × 5

2. 24 × 7

3. 47 × 8

In 4–5, find each product. Estimate to check.

4.   1 2
  ×   8

5.   7 5
  ×   4

6.   4 6
  ×   5

In 7–12, find each product.

7.   4 0 5
  ×   6

8.   5 8 2
  ×   5

9.   3 1 3
  ×   7

10. Multiply 9 and 602

11. $1.2 5
  ×   6

12. $3.4 2
  ×   3

In 13–14, find each product using mental math.

13. 26 × 4

14. 65 × 3

In 15, complete the table to solve.

15. At the end of the first week, workers have
painted 6 rooms. After the second week,
12 were painted. If the pattern continues,
how many rooms will they paint in 5 weeks?

Week	1	2	3	4	5
Rooms	6	12			

1. _____

2. _____

3. _____

6.

9.

10. _____

11. _____

12. _____

13. _____

14. _____

15. _____

Name _____

Date _____ Score _____

Vocabulary: write true or false.

1. In 30 ÷ 6 = 5, 6 is the remainder.

1. _____

In 2–3, complete.

2. 18 ÷ 3 = ■ _____   **3.** 24 ÷ 6 = ■ _____

  180 ÷ 3 = ■ _____   240 ÷ 6 = ■ _____

  1,800 ÷ 3 = ■ _____   2,400 ÷ 6 = ■ _____

In 4–5, find each quotient using mental math.

4. 80 ÷ 4

4. _____

5. 480 ÷ 8

5. _____

6. There are 200 students going on a field trip. If they are divided into 5 equal groups, how many students will be in each group?

6. _____

In 7–9, estimate each quotient.

7. 39 ÷ 5

7. _____

8. 55 ÷ 9

8. _____

9. 30 ÷ 7

9. _____

10. Claire poured 62 cups of fruit punch equally into 7 pitchers. About how many cups of punch were in each pitcher?

10. _____

In 11–17, find each quotient and remainder.

11. 3)‾1‾1‾   **12.** 5)‾2‾2‾   **13.** 4)‾3‾4‾

14. _____

14. 13 ÷ 4

15. _____

15. 45 ÷ 7

16. _____

16. 80 ÷ 9

Name _____

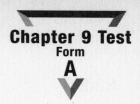
Date _____ Score _____

In 1–2, complete. You may use place-value blocks.

1. 9×1 ten = ■ tens _____

    $9 \times 10 = $ ■   _____

2. 6×7 tens = ■ tens _____

    $6 \times 70 = $ ■   _____

In 3–4, complete.

3. $7 \times 5 = $ ■   _____

    $7 \times 50 = $ ■   _____

    $7 \times 500 = $ ■   _____

4. $3 \times 8 = $ ■   _____

    $3 \times 80 = $ ■   _____

    $3 \times 800 = $ ■ _____

In 5–7, estimate each product.

5. 4×37

6. 6×92

7. 7×523

5. _____

6. _____

7. _____

In 8–9, find each product. You may use place value blocks to help.

8. 3×16

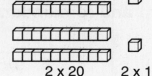

   3 x 10   3 x 6

9. 2×21

   2 x 20   2 x 1

8. _____

9. _____

In 10–17, find each product.

10. 46×5

11. 28×6

12.   1 3
     $\times$ 9

13.   2 8
     $\times$ 7

14.   2 4 7
     $\times$ 5

15.   6 0 2
     $\times$ 7

10. _____

11. _____

12. _____

13. _____

14. _____

15. _____

Name _____

16. $3.2 6
$\times\quad 5$

17. $4.7 8
$\times\quad 4$

In 18–19, find each product using mental math.

18. 37×5

19. 18×7

In 20, complete the table to solve.

20. At the end of the first week, Clyde mowed 9 lawns. After the second week, he had mowed 18 lawns. If the pattern continues, how many weeks will it take him to mow 36 lawns?

Week	1	2	3	4	5
Lawns	9	18			

In 21–23, estimate each quotient.

21. $64 \div 7$

22. $18 \div 5$

23. $50 \div 8$

In 24–30, find each quotient and remainder.

24. $6\overline{)32}$ **25.** $5\overline{)19}$ **26.** $9\overline{)55}$

27. $22 \div 3$

28. $15 \div 4$

29. $74 \div 8$

30. Explain Your Thinking How can you use patterns to find each quotient? Find the quotients.

$27 \div 3 = \blacksquare$
$270 \div 3 = \blacksquare$
$2,700 \div 3 = \blacksquare$

_____

_____

In 1–2, complete. You may use place-value blocks.

1. 4×2 tens = ■ tens _____

$4 \times 20 = $ ■ _____

2. 8×7 tens = ■ tens _____

$8 \times 70 = $ ■ _____

In 3–4, complete.

3. $7 \times 6 = $ ■ _____

$7 \times 60 = $ ■ _____

$7 \times 600 = $ ■ _____

4. $5 \times 6 = $ ■ _____

$5 \times 60 = $ ■ _____

$5 \times 600 = $ ■ _____

In 5–7, estimate each product.

5. 3×42

6. 8×93

7. 9×908

5. _____

6. _____

7. _____

In 8–9, find each product. You may use place value blocks to help.

8. 2×23

9. 4×15

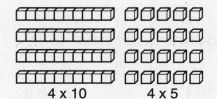

2 x 20   2 x 3   4 x 10   4 x 5

8. _____

9. _____

In 10–17, find each product.

10. 22×8

11. 54×3

12. $\begin{array}{r} 26 \\ \times\ 5 \\ \hline \end{array}$

13. $\begin{array}{r} 89 \\ \times\ 4 \\ \hline \end{array}$

14. $\begin{array}{r} 215 \\ \times\ 7 \\ \hline \end{array}$

15. $\begin{array}{r} 531 \\ \times\ 6 \\ \hline \end{array}$

10. _____

11. _____

12. _____

13. _____

14. _____

15. _____

Continued **189**

Name _____

16. $7.51
    $\times$ 8

17. $5.94
    $\times$ 7

16. _____

17. _____

In 18–19, find each product using mental math.

18. 53 $\times$ 8

19. 59 $\times$ 4

18. _____

19. _____

In 20, complete the table to solve.

20. Cassie wrote 200 words on the first page of her journal. After the second page, she had written 400 words. If the pattern continues, how many pages will it take her to write 1,000 words?

20. _____

Pages	1	2	3	4	5
Words	200	400			

In 21–23, estimate each quotient.

21. 55 $\div$ 6

22. 25 $\div$ 3

23. 37 $\div$ 9

21. _____

22. _____

23. _____

In 24–30, find each quotient and remainder.

24. $6\overline{)40}$ **25.** $3\overline{)17}$ **26.** $9\overline{)82}$

27. 24 $\div$ 5

28. 14 $\div$ 3

29. 50 $\div$ 9

27. _____

28. _____

29. _____

30. Explain Your Thinking How can you use patterns to find each quotient? Find the quotients.

$64 \div 8 = \blacksquare$
$640 \div 8 = \blacksquare$
$6,400 \div 8 = \blacksquare$

_____

_____

Give the letter of the correct answer.

1. If 3×1 ten = 3 tens, then $3 \times 10 =$

    A 3   **B** 30   **C** 31   **D** 300

1. _____

2. Use mental math to find 8×50.

    A 300   **B** 400   **C** 4,000   **D** 40

2. _____

3. Continue this number pattern: $4 \times 8 = 32$
                                           $4 \times 80 = 320$

    A $4 \times 800 = 3,200$ **B** $4 \times 400 = 160$
    C $8 \times 40 = 320$ **D** Not here

3. _____

In 4–5, find each product using mental math.

4. 9×600

    A 540   **B** 630   **C** 4,500   **D** 5,400

4. _____

5. 7×800

    A 4,900   **B** 5,600   **C** 560   **D** 6,300

5. _____

In 6–8 estimate each product.

6. 8×63

    A 240   **B** 480   **C** 4,800   **D** 5,600

6. _____

7. 6×423

    A 3,000   **B** 2,800   **C** 2,400   **D** 240

7. _____

8. 8×28

    A 828   **B** 160   **C** 240   **D** 2,400

8. _____

In 9–10, find each product. You may use place-value blocks to help.

9. 2×13

    A 20   **B** 39
    C 26   **D** Not here

9. _____

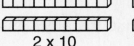

2 x 10   2 x 3

10. 3×18 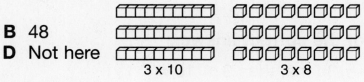   **10.** _____

    A 30   **B** 48

    C 318   **D** Not here 3×10 3×8

In 11–16, find each product.

11. 49×3 **11.** _____

    A 150   **B** 147   **C** 120   **D** 177

12.   7 2   **12.** _____

    $\underline{\times \quad 9}$

    A 638   **B** 729   **C** 6,318   **D** Not here

13.   3 5 1   **13.** _____

    $\underline{\times \quad 5}$

    A 1,755   **B** 1,525   **C** 15,255   **D** 3,515

14.   8 1 4   **14.** _____

    $\underline{\times \quad 8}$

    A 6,484   **B** 64,832   **C** 6,512   **D** 6,432

15. $5.6 3   **15.** _____

    $\underline{\times \quad 8}$

    A $40.48   **B** 4,504   **C** $404.84   **D** $45.04

16. $8.4 7   **16.** _____

    $\underline{\times \quad 5}$

    A $40.25   **B** $42.25   **C** $ 42.35   **D** Not here

17. Eight bits are in a byte. How many bits are in 24 bytes?   **17.** _____

    A 32 bits   **B** 160 bits   **C** 192 bits   **D** Not here

18. A ticket costs $0.75. How much will four tickets cost?   18 _____

    A $3.00   **B** $4.75   **C** $280   **D** $300

In 19–21, find each product using mental math.

19. 36×5 19. _____

    A 200   **B** 180   **C** 150   **D** 365

20. 53×4 20. _____

    A 212   **B** 534   **C** 512   **D** 20,012

21. 41×9 21. _____

    A 419   **B** 369   **C** 360   **D** Not here

In 22–23, complete each table to solve.

22. Lucia's aunt works at an art museum. She made 8 clay   22. _____
pots the first week of her job. By the end of the second
week, she had made 16 pots. If the pattern continues,
how many weeks will it take her to create 32 clay pots?

Week	1	2	3	4	5	6
Pots	8	16				

    A 6 weeks   **B** 5 weeks   **C** 4 weeks   **D** 2 weeks

23. Denzel is saving for a pair of skates. The first week he   23. _____
saves $3.00. By the end of the second week, he has
$6.00. After three weeks, he has $9.00. If the pattern
continues, how much will he have saved after 5 weeks?

Week	1	2	3	4	5	6
Dollars Saved	3	6				

    A $3   **B** $9   **C** $15   **D** Not here

24. Continue this division pattern. $54 \div 9 = 6$ 24. _____
                                        $540 \div 9 = 60$

    A $540 \div 90 = 6$ **B** $5,400 \div 90 = 60$

    C $5,400 \div 9 = 600$ **D** $540 \div 6 = 90$

Name _____

In 25–26, find each quotient using mental math.

25. 630 ÷ 7

    A 900   **B** 90   **C** 9   **D** Not here

25. _____

26. 810 ÷ 9

    A 9   **B** 900   **C** 90   **D** 80

26. _____

In 27–28, estimate each quotient.

27. 50 ÷ 8

    A 2   **B** 4   **C** 10   **D** 6

27. _____

28. 47 ÷ 6

    A 8   **B** 9   **C** 10   **D** 5

28. _____

In 29–32, find each quotient and remainder.

29. $6\overline{)53}$

    A 7 R6   **B** 8 R3   **C** 8 R5   **D** 9 R1

29. _____

30. $4\overline{)25}$

    A 7 R3   **B** 6 R1   **C** 5 R5   **D** 5 R1

30. _____

31. $9\overline{)59}$

    A 6 R8   **B** 6 R5   **C** 7 R4   **D** 10

31. _____

32. $3\overline{)20}$

    A 7 R1   **B** 5 R6   **C** 7 R2   **D** 6 R2

32. _____

You are to make 1 flower arrangement for each table at a class party. Each table seats six people. There will be 30 people at the party.

Flowers for the Party	
Roses	
Red	20
Yellow	40
Tulips	
Red	30
White	50
Daisies	
White	24
Yellow	48

a. Decision Making Use the flowers in the list at the right. All arrangements are to be alike. Use some of each kind and color of flower. (You do not have to use all of the flowers.)

b. Recording Data

Copy and complete a data table like the one below. Fill in the first two columns now.

Kind of Flower	Color	Most that Can Be Used in One Arrangement	Number in One of Your Arrangements	Number in All Arrangements

c. Analyzing Data

Remember, you must use the same flowers and colors in each arrangement. For each type of flower, what is the largest number you could use in each arrangement? Write that in the third column.

How many of each kind/color of flower will you use in each of your arrangements? Write that number in the fourth column in the data table.

d. Critical Thinking How will you find the data needed to complete the last column in the data table? Complete that column now. Do you have enough flowers for each arrangment?

e. Making Decisions Decide what your arrangement will look like. Draw a sketch.

Teacher Notes

Concepts and Skills This activity requires students to:

- record information in a table.
- make decisions using real-life experiences.
- find products.
- find quotients, with and without remainders.
- choose the correct operation needed to solve a problem.
- plan a flower arrangement.

Guiding Questions

- Can flower arrangements have more than one kind of flower? More than one color of flower?
- If you have 28 flowers and need to make 5 arrangements that are all alike, what is the most of that kind of flower that can be used in each arrangement?

Answers

a. Decisions will vary.
b. Check students' tables.
c. At most there could be 4 red roses, 8 yellow roses, 6 red tulips, 10 white tulips, 4 white daisies, and 9 yellow daisies in each arrangement.
d. Answers will vary. The numbers in column five cannot be larger than the corresponding total numbers of flowers of each kind and color of flower given in the list.
e. Check students' sketches.

Extension

Tell students that 12 special guests have been invited to the party at the last minute. Students are to use the flowers not used in the table arrangements to make two more arrangements. These arrangements can be different from those made for original tables. However, the two arrangements must be alike. Have students explain what flowers will be used and draw a sketch.

Evaluation

Level	Standard to be achieved for performance of specified level
4	**Full Achievement** The student is able to choose the correct operation when solving a problem. All columns are correctly completed. The sketch of the arrangement is neatly completed and includes proper flowers and colors.
3	**Substantial Achievement** The student is able to choose the correct operation when solving a problem. All columns are completed with only minor computational errors. The sketch of the arrangement is neatly completed and includes proper flowers and colors.
2	**Partial Achievement** The student may need assistance in choosing the correct operations when solving the problem. Columns are completed with several computational errors. The sketch of the arrangement is complete, but may not be accurate in number, type, or color of flowers.
1	**Little Achievement** The student demonstrates little if any understanding of the task at hand and needs considerable help in choosing the correct operations. The computation contains many errors. The student makes very little attempt to draw an accurate sketch of the arrangement.

In 1–2, complete. You may use place-value blocks.

1. 3×8 tens = ■ tens _____   2. 5×9 tens = ■ ten _____

   $3 \times 80 = $ ■ _____ $5 \times 90 = $ ■ _____

3. Continue this number pattern. $8 \times 9 = 72$ 3. _____
   $$8 \times 90 = 720$$

   A $8 \times 900 = 7,200$ **B** $9 \times 800 = 7,200$
   C $4 \times 900 = 3,600$ **D** Not here

4. Find the product using mental math. 8×600 4. _____

   A 480   **B** 4,200   **C** 4,800   **D** 3,600

In 5–6, estimate each product.

5. 7×53 5. _____

6. 6×92 6. _____

In 7, find the product. You may use place-value blocks to help.

7. 3×14 7. _____

   A 30   **B** 42
   C 39   **D** 45

   3×10 3×4

In 8–14, find each product.

8. 34×6 8. _____

9. $\begin{array}{r} 2\,2 \\ \times\ \ 9 \\ \hline \end{array}$ 10. $\begin{array}{r} 3\,9 \\ \times\ \ 5 \\ \hline \end{array}$ 9. _____

10. _____

11. $\begin{array}{r} 2\,7\,7 \\ \times\ \ \ 6 \\ \hline \end{array}$ 12. $\begin{array}{r} 7\,4\,8 \\ \times\ \ \ 4 \\ \hline \end{array}$ 11. _____

12. _____

13. $\begin{array}{r} \$6.7\,4 \\ \times\ \ \ \ 3 \\ \hline \end{array}$ 14. $\begin{array}{r} \$4.2\,9 \\ \times\ \ \ \ 7 \\ \hline \end{array}$ 13. _____

14. _____

Name _____

15. Find the product using mental math. 46×6 **15.** _____

In 16, complete the table to solve.

16. Ashley started an exercise program. At the end   **16.** _____
of the first week, she had exercised 6 hours. By
the end of the second week, she had exercised
12 hours. If the pattern continues, how many weeks
will it take her to complete 30 hours of exercise?

Week	1	2	3	4	5	6
Hours	6	12				

A 3 weeks   **B** 4 weeks   **C** 5 weeks   **D** Not here

17. Complete. $40 \div 8 = \blacksquare$ **17.** _____

$400 \div 8 = \blacksquare$ _____

$4,000 \div 8 = \blacksquare$ _____

In 18–19, estimate each quotient.

18. $49 \div 8$ **18.** _____

   A 9   **B** 8   **C** 7   **D** 6

19. $69 \div 9$ **19.** _____

   A 9   **B** 8   **C** 7   **D** 6

In 20–22, find each quotient and remainder.

20. $7\overline{)50}$ **21.** $5\overline{)22}$ **22.** $7\overline{)39}$

23. $26 \div 4$ **23.** _____

24. Performance Task Curt has 3 stacks
of 16 newspapers. How many papers
does he have in all? Draw a picture. Then
write a multiplication sentence and solve.

_____

▬ Computation ▬

In 1–4, find each product.

1. 2 × 19

    A 20   **B** 40
    C 35   **D** Not here

2 x 10   2 x 9

1. _____

2. 42 × 9

2. _____

3. 2 2
   × 6

4. 5 4
   × 5

3. _____

4. _____

5. 3 2 9
   ×   6

6. 5 2 6
   ×   9

5. _____

6. _____

7. $8.2 6
   ×   8

8. $6.7 5
   ×   7

7. _____

8. _____

In 9–12, find each quotient and remainder.

9. 6)$\overline{39}$ **10.** 8)$\overline{47}$ **11.** 4)$\overline{27}$

12. 67 ÷ 9

12. _____

▬ Concepts ▬

13. Compare. Use <, >, or =. 4,356 ● 4,625

13. _____

14. Compare. Use <, >, or =. $9.99 ● $15.28

14. _____

In 15–16, estimate each product.

15. 7 × 82

    A 480   **B** 560   **C** 630   **D** 820

15. _____

16. 6 × 58

    A 240   **B** 300   **C** 360   **D** 420

16. _____

Name _____

In 17–18, estimate each quotient.

17. 54 ÷ 7

    A 8   **B** 6   **C** 5   **D** 4

17. _____

18. 41 ÷ 6

    A 4   **B** 5   **C** 7   **D** 8

18. _____

19. Order 623, 326, and 362 from least to greatest. **19.** _____

In 20–21, complete.

20. $8 \times 9 = $ ■   _____

    $8 \times 90 = $ ■   _____

    $8 \times 900 = $ ■ _____

21. $64 \div 8 = $ ■   _____

    $640 \div 8 = $ ■   _____

    $6,400 \div 8 = $ ■ _____

22. If 5×6 tens $= 30$ tens, then $5 \times 60 = $ ■.

    A 300   **B** 30   **C** 3   **D** Not here

22. _____

23. Round 556 to the nearest hundred.

23. _____

24. Write the word name for 5,601. _____

— Applications —

25. Shawn's address is 1493 West Oak Street. Are there more odd or even digits in his address?

25. _____

26. A van carries 14 students. How many students can ride in 3 vans? Use mental math to solve.

26. _____

In 27, complete the table to solve.

27. Tia saved $25 by the end of the first month. After the second month, she had saved $50. If she continues the pattern, how many months will it take her to save $125?

27. _____

Week	1	2	3	4	5	6
Dollars Saved	25	50				

Name _____

Date _____ Score _____

Give the letter of the correct answer.

In 1–2, use the bar graph.

1. How many students chose rye bread?

   A 3 students
   B 4 students
   C 7 students
   D 8 students

1. _____

2. How many more students chose white bread than rye?

   A 2 students   **B** 3 students
   C 4 students   **D** 5 students

2. _____

3. Compare: 354 ● 543. Use $<$, $>$, or $=$.

   A $<$ **B** $>$ **C** $=$

3. _____

4. Choir practice begins at 6:00 P.M. and ends at 7:15 P.M. How long does practice last?

   A 15 minutes   **B** 1 hour
   C 1 hour 15 minutes   **D** Not here

4. _____

In 5–8, add. Estimate to check.

5. 34 + 48

   A 72   **B** 80   **C** 82   **D** Not here

5. _____

6. 439 + 258

   A 686   **B** 687   **C** 696   **D** 697

6. _____

7. 24 + 36 + 15

   A 65   **B** 75   **C** 85   **D** Not here

7. _____

8. Use mental math to add 65 and 75.

   A 10   **B** 130   **C** 140   **D** 150

8. _____

Name _____

In 9–13, subtract. Estimate to check.

9. $84 - 38$

  A 46   **B** 122   **C** 54   **D** Not here

  9. _____

10. $968 - 372$

  A 586   **B** 596   **C** 616   **D** 696

  10. _____

11. $762 - 283$

  A 461   **B** 479   **C** 521   **D** 589

  11. _____

12.   805
    $- 347$

  A 468   **B** 542   **C** 568   **D** 458

  12. _____

13. What number would you add to 61 in order to subtract 28 mentally.

  A 9   **B** 5   **C** 2   **D** Not here

  13. _____

14. Julie took 2 steps for every 3 steps her little sister took. After Julie has walked 12 steps, how many steps has her little sister walked?

  A 6 steps   **B** 9 steps   **C** 12 steps   **D** 18 steps

  14. _____

In 15–18, multiply.

15. 9×2

  A 7   **B** 11   **C** 18   **D** 27

  15. _____

16. 0×9

  A 9   **B** 90   **C** 0   **D** Not here

  16. _____

17. 6×3

  A 21   **B** 24   **C** 25   **D** Not here

  17. _____

18. 4×8

  A 16   **B** 24   **C** 28   **D** 32

  18. _____

Continued

19. Continue the pattern: 44, 55, 66, ■, ■, ■.

    A 76, 86, 96   **B** 67, 68, 69

    C 77, 88, 99   **D** Not here

19. _____

20. Find $(3 \times 2) \times 9$.

    A 45   **B** 63   **C** 64   **D** Not here

20. _____

In 21–24, find each quotient.

21. $45 \div 5$

    A 5   **B** 7   **C** 9   **D** Not here

21. _____

22. $32 \div 4$

    A 6   **B** 7   **C** 9   **D** Not here

22. _____

23. $42 \div 7$

    A 6   **B** 7   **C** 8   **D** 9

23. _____

24. $81 \div 9$

    A 6   **B** 7   **C** 8   **D** 9

24. _____

25. Alonzo and his 3 friends share 8 muffins. Which number sentence would you use to find how many muffins each person got?

    A $8 \div 4 = 2$ **B** $4 \times 8 = 32$

    C $8 - 4 = 4$ **D** $8 + 4 = 12$

25. _____

26. Give the name for these lines.

    A Parallel lines

    B Intersecting lines

    C Line segments

26. _____

27. What is the ordered pair for point L?

    A (1, 2)   **B** (2, 1)

    C (3, 4)   **D** (4, 3)

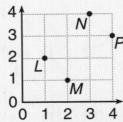

27. _____

Name _____

28. Name the solid figure
that the object looks like.

  A Cone   **B** Cube
  C Cylinder   **D** Sphere

28. _____

29. Find the perimeter
of the rectangle.

  A 13 cm   **B** 16 cm
  C 26 cm   **D** 40 cm

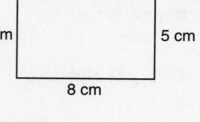

29. _____

30. Estimate the product of 8 and 47.

  A 60   **B** 40   **C** 320   **D** 400

30. _____

In 31–33, find each product. Regroup if needed.

31.   74
   × 3

  A 212   **B** 217   **C** 222   **D** 282

31. _____

32.   312
   × 8

  A 2,496   **B** 2,186   **C** 1,896   **D** Not here

32. _____

33. $2.71
   × 4

  A $1,084   **B** $10.84   **C** $8.84   **D** Not here

33. _____

34. Estimate the quotient: 31 ÷ 8

  A About 3   **B** About 30   **C** About 40   **D** Not here

34. _____

In 35–36, find each quotient and remainder.

35. 74 ÷ 9

  A 6 R8   **B** 7 R1   **C** 8 R2   **D** Not here

35. _____

36. 59 ÷ 6

  A 8 R3   **B** 9 R5   **C** 9 R3   **D** Not here

36. _____

Name _____

Date _____ Score _____

Vocabulary: In 1–4, match each with its meaning.

1. fraction   **a.** top number of a fraction   1. _____

2. numerator   **b.** bottom number of a fraction   2. _____

3. denominator   **c.** fractions that name the same amount   3. _____

4. equivalent   **d.** a comparison of equal parts to a whole number   4. _____

In 5–6, write the equal parts of each whole.

5.   6.   5. _____

6. _____

In 7–8, write the fraction of each figure that is shaded.

7.   8. 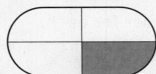   7. _____

8. _____

In 9–10, write if the fractions are equivalent or not equivalent.

9. 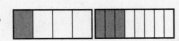   10. 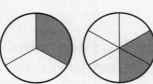   9. _____

10. _____

In 11–12, compare. Write <, >, or =.

11. 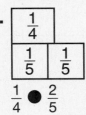   12. 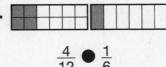   11. _____

$\frac{1}{4} \bullet \frac{2}{5}$ $\frac{4}{12} \bullet \frac{1}{6}$ 12. _____

In 13–14, estimate each amount that is shaded.

13.   14.   13. _____

14. _____

In 1–2, write a fraction that tells what part of each set is circled.

1.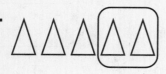

2.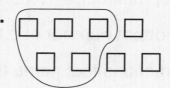

1. _____

2. _____

In 3–6, solve. You may use counters or draw a picture to help.

3. Find $\frac{1}{2}$ of 12.

4. Find $\frac{1}{3}$ of 9.

5. Find $\frac{1}{8}$ of 16.

6. Find $\frac{1}{4}$ of 32.

3. _____

4. _____

5. _____

6. _____

In 7–8, write a mixed number for each.

7.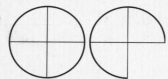

8.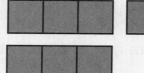

7. _____

8. _____

In 9–14, find each sum or difference. You may use fraction strips or draw a picture to help.

9. $\frac{5}{8} - \frac{2}{8}$

10. $\frac{3}{10} + \frac{4}{10}$

11. $\frac{4}{5} - \frac{1}{5}$

12. $\frac{2}{12} + \frac{7}{12}$

13. $\frac{9}{10} - \frac{3}{10}$

14. $\frac{10}{12} - \frac{3}{12}$

9. _____

10. _____

11. _____

12. _____

13. _____

14. _____

Name _____

Date _____ Score _____

Vocabulary: In 1–3, write *true* or *false*.

1. An inch is a standard unit of measure.

2. One foot is longer than one inch.

3. One yard is longer than one mile.

In 4–5, estimate each length. Then measure to the nearest inch.

4.

5.

6. Measure the french fry to the nearest $\frac{1}{2}$ inch.

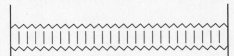

7. Measure the car to the nearest $\frac{1}{4}$ inch.

8. Write 2 feet in inches.

9. Write 5 feet, 4 inches in inches.

In 10–12, compare. Write <, >, or =.

10. 1 yard ● 4 feet

11. 6 feet ● 2 inches

12. 36 inches ● 3 feet

13. Wapy, Mosi, Amber, and Molly are standing in line. Molly is first. Wapy is between Molly and Mosi. Write the order they are in line from first to last.

1. _____

2. _____

3. _____

4. _____

5. _____

6. _____

7. _____

8. _____

9. _____

10. _____

11. _____

12. _____

Vocabulary: In 1–3, match each with its meaning.

1. unit fraction

a. fractions that name the same amount

2. fraction

b. a fraction with a numerator of 1

3. equivalent fractions

c. a comparison of equal parts to a whole number

1. _____

2. _____

3. _____

In 4–5, write the equal parts of each whole.

4.

5.

4. _____

5. _____

In 6–7, write the fraction of each figure that is shaded.

6.

7.

6. _____

7. _____

In 8–9, are the fractions equivalent or not equivalent?

8.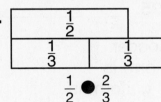

9.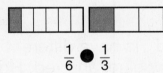

8. _____

9. _____

In 10–11, compare. Write <, >, or =.

10.

$\frac{1}{2} \bullet \frac{2}{3}$

11.

$\frac{1}{6} \bullet \frac{1}{3}$

10. _____

11. _____

In 12–13, estimate the amount that is shaded.

12.

13.

12. _____

13. _____

In 14–15, solve. You may draw a picture to help.

14. Find $\frac{1}{4}$ of 20.

15. Find $\frac{1}{5}$ of 15.

14. _____

15. _____

Name _____

In 16–17, write a mixed number for each picture.

16.    **17.**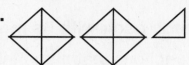

16. _____

17. _____

18. Find the difference. $\frac{5}{8} - \frac{3}{8}$

18. _____

19. Find the sum. $\frac{3}{10} + \frac{4}{10}$

19. _____

20. Measure the glue stick to the nearest inch.

20. _____

21. Measure the binder clip to the nearest $\frac{1}{2}$ inch.

21. _____

22. Measure the pen cap to the nearest $\frac{1}{4}$ inch.

22. _____

23. Write 1 foot 6 inches in inches.

23. _____

In 24–25, compare. Write <, >, or =.

24. 3 yards ● 10 feet

24. _____

25. 72 inches ● 2 yards

25. _____

26. Shane, Jorie, Hoy, and Tia have different color soccer uniforms: white, yellow, blue, and red. Hoy's uniform is white. Jorie's uniform matches her red hair. Tia's uniform is the color of the sky. What color is each person's uniform?

_____

27. Explain Your Thinking Draw 6 flowers. Color some of them. Write a fraction that names how many flowers are colored. Explain what the numerator and denominator mean.

_____

_____

Vocabulary: In 1–3, match each with its meaning.

1. equivalent   **a.** a comparison of equal parts to a   **1.** _____
    fractions   whole number

2. unit fraction **b.** a fraction with a numerator of 1   **2.** _____

3. fraction   **c.** fractions that name the same   **3.** _____
                          amount

In 4–5, write the equal parts of each whole.

4.   **5.**   **4.** _____

                                                           5. _____

In 6–7, write the fraction of each figure that is shaded.

6. 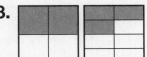   **7.** 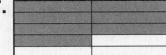   **6.** _____

                                                           7. _____

In 8–9, are the fractions equivalent or not equivalent?

8.   **9.** 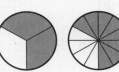   **8.** _____

                                                           9. _____

In 10–11, compare. Write <, >, or =.

10. 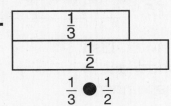   **11.** 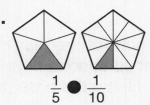   **10.** _____

$\frac{1}{3}$ ● $\frac{1}{2}$ $\frac{1}{5}$ ● $\frac{1}{10}$ **11.** _____

In 12–13, estimate the amount that is shaded.

12.   **13.**    **12.** _____

                                                           13. _____

In 14–15, solve. You may draw a picture to help.

14. Find $\frac{1}{5}$ of 30.   **14.** _____

15. Find $\frac{1}{3}$ of 27.   **15.** _____

Name _____

In 16–17, write a mixed number for each picture.

16.   17.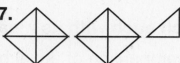

16. _____

17. _____

18. Find the difference. $\frac{4}{5} - \frac{2}{5}$ 18. _____

19. Find the sum. $\frac{1}{12} + \frac{5}{12}$ 19. _____

20. Measure darning needle to the nearest inch.   20. _____

21. Measure yarn to the nearest $\frac{1}{2}$ inch.   21. _____

22. Measure spool of thread to the nearest $\frac{1}{4}$ inch.   22. _____

23. Write 1 foot 10 inches in inches.   23. _____

In 24–25, compare. Write <, >, or =.

24. 2 yards ● 8 feet   24. _____

25. 50 inches ● 3 feet   25. _____

26. The winners of the sack races at the picnic were Max, Lisa,
Ryan, and Kala. Max finished second. Ryan finished last.
Lisa finished before Kala. Name the order that the winners
crossed the finish line.

_____

27. **Explain Your Thinking** Draw 10 flowers. Color some of
them. Write a fraction that names how many flowers are not
colored. Explain what the numerator and denominator mean.

_____

_____

Give the letter of the correct answer.

1. Give the equal parts of the whole.

   A Fourths   **B** Sixths
   C Eighths   **D** Tenths

   1. _____

2. Give the equal parts of the whole.

   A Thirds   **B** Fourths
   C Fifths   **D** Sixths

   2. _____

3. Give the fraction of the figure that is shaded.

   A $\frac{2}{3}$ **B** $\frac{2}{4}$
   C $\frac{2}{5}$ **D** Not here

   3. _____

4. Give the fraction of the figure that is shaded.

   A $\frac{3}{5}$ **B** $\frac{3}{6}$
   C $\frac{3}{8}$ **D** $\frac{3}{10}$

   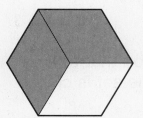

   4. _____

5. Complete. $\frac{2}{3} = \frac{\blacksquare}{9}$

   A $\frac{2}{3} = \frac{2}{9}$ **B** $\frac{2}{3} = \frac{3}{9}$
   C $\frac{2}{3} = \frac{3}{6}$ **D** Not here

   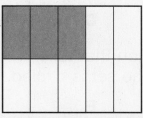

   $\frac{2}{3} = \frac{\blacksquare}{9}$

   5. _____

6. Which shows equivalent fractions?

   A    **B**

   C   **D**

   6. _____

7. Choose the correct comparison.

   A $\frac{2}{4} < \frac{4}{8}$ **B** $\frac{2}{4} > \frac{3}{8}$
   C $\frac{2}{4} = \frac{4}{8}$ **D** Not here

   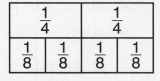

   7. _____

Name _____

8. Choose the correct comparison.

A $\frac{1}{2} < \frac{3}{4}$ **B** $\frac{1}{2} > \frac{3}{4}$

C $\frac{1}{4} = \frac{3}{4}$ **D** Not here

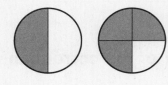

8. _____

9. Estimate the amount that is shaded.

A About $\frac{1}{4}$ **B** About $\frac{1}{2}$

C About $\frac{3}{4}$ **D** More than $\frac{3}{4}$

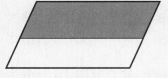

9. _____

10. Estimate the amount that is shaded.

A More than $\frac{1}{2}$ **B** About $\frac{1}{2}$

C Less than $\frac{1}{2}$ **D** About $\frac{1}{4}$

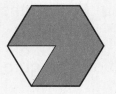

10. _____

11. Give the fraction that tells what part of the set is circled.

A $\frac{3}{5}$ **B** $\frac{3}{8}$

C $\frac{5}{8}$ **D** Not here

11. _____

12. Give the fraction that tells what part of the set is circled.

A $\frac{1}{4}$ **B** $\frac{1}{3}$

C $\frac{2}{3}$ **D** Not here

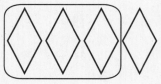

12. _____

13. Find $\frac{1}{3}$ of 6. You may draw a picture to help.

A 3   **B** 2   **C** 4   **D** Not here

13. _____

14. Find $\frac{1}{4}$ of 12. You may draw a picture to help.

A 3   **B** 4   **C** 6   **D** Not here

14. _____

15. Give a mixed number for the picture.

A $1\frac{3}{4}$ **B** $1\frac{3}{5}$

C $1\frac{2}{5}$ **D** Not here

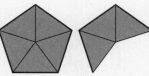

15. _____

16. Give a mixed number for the picture.

A $2\frac{1}{3}$ **B** $2\frac{1}{2}$

C $2\frac{1}{4}$ **D** Not here

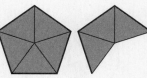

16. _____

Continued

Name _____

17. Find the sum. $\frac{3}{8} + \frac{1}{8}$

    A $\frac{4}{16}$ **B** $\frac{4}{8}$ **C** $\frac{3}{10}$ **D** Not here

17. _____

18. Find the sum. $\frac{1}{10} + \frac{5}{10}$

    A $\frac{4}{10}$ **B** $\frac{6}{20}$ **C** $\frac{5}{10}$ **D** Not here

18. _____

19. Find the difference. $\frac{3}{4} - \frac{1}{4}$

    A $\frac{2}{4}$ **B** 3   **C** $\frac{2}{8}$ **D** Not here

19. _____

20. Find the difference. $\frac{9}{10} - \frac{7}{10}$

    A $\frac{2}{10}$ **B** $\frac{3}{10}$ **C** $\frac{7}{10}$ **D** Not here

20. _____

21. Measure the worm to the nearest inch.

21. _____

    A 1 inch   **B** 2 inches   **C** 3 inches   **D** 4 inches

22. Measure the palmetto bug to the nearest inch.

22. _____

    A 1 inch   **B** 2 inches   **C** 3 inches   **D** 4 inches

23. Measure the lizard to the nearest $\frac{1}{2}$ inch.

23. _____

    A 2 inches   **B** $2\frac{1}{2}$ inches

    C 3 inches   **D** $4\frac{1}{2}$ inches

24. Measure the grasshopper to the nearest $\frac{1}{4}$ inch.

24. _____

    A $3\frac{1}{4}$ inches   **B** $2\frac{1}{4}$ inches

    C $2\frac{1}{2}$ inches   **D** $2\frac{3}{4}$ inches

25. How many inches is 3 feet?

   A 30 inches   **B** 33 inches
   C 36 inches   **D** Not here

25. _____

26. How many inches is 4 feet 4 inches?

   A 16 inches   **B** 44 inches
   C 54 inches   **D** Not here

26. _____

In 27–29, compare. Use <, >, or =.

27. 3 feet ● 36 inches

   A >   **B** <   **C** =

27. _____

28. 1 yard ● 5 feet

   A >   **B** <   **C** =

28. _____

29. 3 yards ● 100 inches

   A >   **B** <   **C** =

29. _____

30. In the final race, Vince finished second. Elizabeth came in last and Kenny finished after Jean. Name the order that the winners crossed the finish line.

   A Kenny, Vince, Jean, Elizabeth
   B Elizabeth, Vince, Jean, Kenny
   C Jean, Vince, Kenny, Elizabeth
   D Jean, Kenny, Vince, Elizabeth

30. _____

31. Alma, Frank, Sally, and Luis each ordered something different for lunch from the following choices: pizza, hot dog, hamburger, and chicken. Luis ordered pizza. Frank does not like hot dogs or hamburgers. Sally ordered her burger with cheese. Who ordered a hot dog?

   A Alma   **B** Frank   **C** Sally   **D** Luis

31. _____

32. Wynonna, Darla, Mitch, and Ernie each weighed their cats. The weights were 12, 13, 14, and 15 pounds. Darla knows her cat weighs 14 pounds. Mitch's cat weighed the least. Wynonna's cat weighs less than Ernie's. Whose cat weighs the most?

   A Wynonna's cat   **B** Darla's cat   **C** Mitch's cat   **D** Ernie's cat

32. _____

You want to make a birthday card for a friend. Think about the many ways you can fold a sheet of paper into equal parts to make a card.

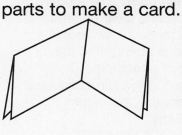 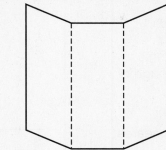

To make the card for your friend, you will use a sheet of paper that measures $8\frac{1}{2}$ inches by 11 inches. Any letters on the front of the card will be between $\frac{3}{4}$ inch and $1\frac{1}{2}$ inches tall.

a. Making Decisions How will you fold the paper to make the birthday card? Try three different ways.

b. Recording Data Measure the length and the width of the front of each card you folded to the nearest $\frac{1}{4}$ inch.

Record your measures in a table like the one below. Then find the perimeter of each card

Number of equal parts	Length of front	Width of front	Perimeter of front

c. Analyzing Data
Which card has the greatest height?
Which card has the smallest perimeter?

d. Making Decisions Choose one of the folded papers and make a card for a friend. Be sure the letters on the front of the card are the proper size.

Teacher Notes

Concepts and Skills This activity requires students to:

- make decisions using real-life experiences.
- measure to the nearest $\frac{1}{4}$ inch
- compare fractions.
- find the perimeter of a rectangle
- draw letters within a given range of measurements.

Guiding Questions

- How do you measure to the nearest $\frac{1}{4}$ inch?
- How do you find the perimeter of a rectangle?

Answers

a. Decisions will vary.
b. Answers will vary.
c. Answers will vary. Check students' answers.
d. Check students' work. Be sure that the letters on the front of the card are between $\frac{3}{4}$ inch and $1\frac{1}{2}$ inches.

Extension

Have students write a verse for the inside of their cards. Then have them find the mode number of letters for the words in their verse.

Evaluation

Level	Standard to be achieved for performance of specified level
4	**Full Achievement** The student demonstrates a clear understanding of how to measure to the nearest $\frac{1}{4}$ inch and is able to find the perimeter of a rectangle. The student can follow directions and draw letters that are within specifications.
3	**Substantial Achievement** The student demonstrates a clear understanding of how to measure to the nearest $\frac{1}{4}$ inch but may need some help in finding the perimeter of a rectangle. The student can follow directions and draw letters that are within specifications.
2	**Partial Achievement** The student demonstrates some understanding of how to measure to the nearest $\frac{1}{4}$ inch, but may need help in doing so. The student needs some help in finding the perimeter of a rectangle and may also need help in drawing letters that are within specifications.
1	**Little Achievement** The student demonstrates little if any understanding of the task at hand and needs considerable help in measuring and finding perimeter. The student makes very little attempt to draw letters that are within given specifications.

Name _____

Date _____ Score _____

In 1–2, write the equal parts of each whole.

1.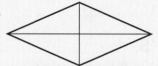

2.

1. _____

2. _____

3. _____

3. Give the fraction of the figure that is shaded.

   A $\frac{3}{8}$ **B** $\frac{3}{5}$ **C** $\frac{5}{3}$ **D** $\frac{5}{8}$

In 4–5, are the fractions equivalent or not equivalent?

4.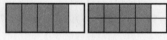

5.

4. _____

5. _____

6. Choose the correct comparison.

   A $\frac{1}{4} < \frac{1}{8}$ **B** $\frac{1}{4} > \frac{1}{8}$

   C $\frac{1}{4} = \frac{1}{8}$ **D** Not here

6. _____

7. Estimate the amount that is shaded.

   A About $\frac{1}{4}$ **B** About $\frac{1}{2}$

   C About $\frac{3}{4}$ **D** More than $\frac{1}{2}$

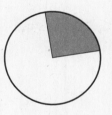

7. _____

8. Give the fraction that tells what part of the set is circled.

   A $\frac{3}{7}$ **B** $\frac{7}{10}$

   C $\frac{3}{10}$ **D** Not here

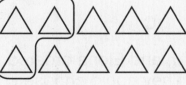

8. _____

9. Find $\frac{1}{3}$ of 18.

9. _____

10. Find $\frac{1}{5}$ of 35.

10. _____

11. Find $\frac{1}{8}$ of 16.

11. _____

12. Give a mixed number for the picture.

   A $3\frac{2}{3}$ **B** $2\frac{3}{4}$

   C $\frac{5}{6}$ **D** Not here

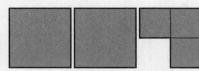

12. _____

In 13 and 14, find each sum or difference.

13. $\frac{3}{5} + \frac{1}{5}$

13. _____

14. $\frac{7}{10} - \frac{4}{10}$

14. _____

15. Measure the barrette to the nearest inch.

15. _____

16. Measure the hair pin to the nearest $\frac{1}{2}$ inch.

16. _____

17. Measure the pin to the nearest $\frac{1}{4}$ inch.

17. _____

In 18–19, compare. Use <, >, or =.

18. 10 feet ● 130 inches

A >   **B** <   **C** =

18. _____

19. 3 yards ● 9 feet

A >   **B** <   **C** =

19. _____

20. Fay, Mac, Will, and Elona ordered different toppings on their pizzas. They could choose cheese, sausage, mushroom, or pepperoni. Fay likes only cheese. Elona doesn't like sausage or pepperoni. Will's favorite is pepperoni. Which kind of pizza did each person order?

_____

21. Performance Task Explain how to find the total number of inches in 4 feet, 7 inches.

_____

_____

— Computation —

1. Find $\frac{1}{5}$ of 40.

1. _____

2. Find the sum. $\frac{1}{3} + \frac{1}{3}$

2. _____

3. Find the difference. $\frac{9}{10} - \frac{3}{10}$

3. _____

4. How many inches is 3 feet, 3 inches?

4. _____

5. Find the sum. $12.35 + 8.25$

    A $21.60   **B** $20.60   **C** $20.55   **D** Not here

5. _____

6. Find the difference. $35.00 - 18.50$

6. _____

7. 8×9

7. _____

8. $56 \div 8$

8. _____

— Concepts —

9. Give the equal parts of the whole.

    A Fourths   **B** Sixths
    C Eighths   **D** Tenths

9. _____

In 10–11, name the fraction of the figure that is shaded

10.

11.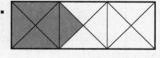

10. _____

11. _____

12. Complete. $\frac{3}{4} = \frac{\blacksquare}{8}$

    A $\frac{3}{4} = \frac{1}{8}$ **B** $\frac{3}{4} = \frac{2}{8}$
    C $\frac{3}{4} = \frac{6}{8}$ **D** Not here

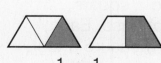

12. _____

13. Compare.
Write $<$, $>$, or $=$.

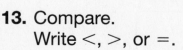

$\frac{1}{3}$ ● $\frac{1}{2}$

13. _____

14. How long was the baseball game if it began at 3:15 and ended at 5:35?

14. _____

15. Estimate the amount that is shaded.

15. _____

A More than $\frac{1}{2}$ **B** About $\frac{3}{4}$

C Less than $\frac{1}{2}$ **D** About $\frac{1}{4}$

16. Give the fraction that tells what part of the set is circled.

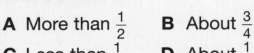

16. _____

17. Give a mixed number for the picture.

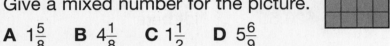

17. _____

A $1\frac{5}{8}$ **B** $4\frac{1}{8}$ **C** $1\frac{1}{2}$ **D** $5\frac{6}{9}$

18. Measure the dog biscuit to the nearest inch.

18. _____

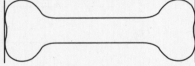

19. Measure the cat toy to the nearest $\frac{1}{2}$ inch.

19. _____

20. Compare. Write <, >, or =.   3 yards ● 6 feet   **20.** _____

── Applications ──

21. Heidi, Clarice, Shirley, and Sonia picked out pumpkins to decorate. The pumpkins weighed 9, 12, 14, and 20 pounds. Clarice's pumpkin weighed 14 pounds. Sonia's weighed the least. Shirley's weighs more than Heidi's. What is the weight of each person's pumpkin?

_____

22. Wesley wants to build a square fence around his clubhouse. Each side of the fence will measure 8 feet. How much fencing will he need?

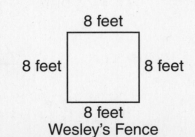

8 feet

8 feet   8 feet

8 feet
Wesley's Fence

Name _____

Date _____ Score _____

Vocabulary: In 1–3, match each with its meaning.

1. decimal

    a. symbol used to separate ones from tenths in decimals

2. decimal point

    b. one of 100 equal parts of a whole

3. hundredth

    c. a number that uses place value and a decimal point to show tenths, hundredths, and so on

1. _____

2. _____

3. _____

In 4–5, write the fraction and the decimal to name each shaded part.

4.    5.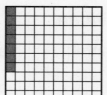

4. _____

5. _____

In 6–10, write each as a decimal.

6. eight tenths

7. one and six tenths

8. thirteen hundredths

9. $\frac{4}{10}$

10. $2\frac{28}{100}$

6. _____

7. _____

8. _____

9. _____

10. _____

In 11–12, find each sum or difference. You may use tenths grids to help.

11.   9.4
     + 3.8

12.   7.5
     − 2.8

11. _____

12. _____

In 13–15, write each as a money amount.

13. $\frac{55}{100}$ of $1.00

14. $2\frac{98}{100}$ of $1.00

15. four dollars and ninety-one cents

13. _____

14. _____

15. _____

Vocabulary: In 1–4, match each with its meaning.

1. centimeter   **a.** a metric unit of measure equal to 1,000 meters   1. _____

2. decimeter   **b.** a metric unit of measure equal to 100 centimeters   2. _____

3. meter   **c.** a metric unit of measure equal to 10 centimeters   3. _____

4. kilometer   **d.** a standard unit used to measure length in the metric system   4. _____

In 5–7, match each with its estimate.

5. length of an unsharpened pencil   **a.** 1 cm   5. _____

6. width of a piece of chalk   **b.** 2 m   6. _____

7. height of a tall bookcase   **c.** 2 dm   7. _____

In 8–11, write whether you would measure each in cm, m, or km.

8. length of a walk-a-thon   8. _____

9. length of a pillow   9. _____

10. distance of a bicycle trail   10. _____

11. length of the hallway   11. _____

12. Suppose you get on an elevator on the twelfth floor. You go up 8 floors, then down 3 floors. Then you go up 2 floors, and down 10 floors. Then you get off. On what floor do you get off?   12. _____

13. There are 8 people on the elevator on the first floor. On the third floor, 2 people get off, and 3 people get on. On the sixth floor, 7 people get off and 1 person gets on. How many people are on the elevator now?   13. _____

Vocabulary: In 1–4 match each with its meaning.

1. decimal point   **a.** a metric unit of measure equal to 1,000 meters   **1.** _____

2. centimeter   **b.** a standard unit used to measure length in the metric system   **2.** _____

3. meter   **c.** symbol used to separate ones from tenths in a decimal   **3.** _____

4. kilometer   **d.** a metric unit of measure equal to 100 centimeters   **4.** _____

In 5–6, write the fraction and the decimal to name each shaded part.

5.    **6.** 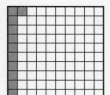   **5.** _____

6. _____

In 7–12, write each as a decimal.

7. $\frac{6}{10}$ **7.** _____

8. $3\frac{8}{10}$ **8.** _____

9. $5\frac{35}{100}$ **9.** _____

10. four hundredths   **10.** _____

11. two and fifty-two hundredths   **11.** _____

12. one tenth   **12.** _____

In 13–16, find each sum or difference.

13.   0.8
     + 0.4
14.   1.4
     + 2.9
13. _____

14. _____

15.   4.5
     − 1.3
16.   6.1
     − 3.8
15. _____

16. _____

Name _____

In 17–20, write each as a money amount.

17. $\frac{34}{100}$ of $1.00

18. $2\frac{50}{100}$ of $1.00

19. eight cents

20. one dollar and twenty-seven cents

17. _____

18. _____

19. _____

20. _____

In 21–23, match each with its estimate.

21. length of a marker   **a.** 2 cm   **21.** _____

22. length of a river   **b.** 1 dm   **22.** _____

23. width of the face of a watch **c.** 20 km   **23.** _____

In 24–26, write whether you would measure each in cm, m, or km.

24. distance of a bike ride   **24.** _____

25. length of the soccer field   **25.** _____

26. height of a small dog   **26.** _____

27. Suppose you get on an elevator on the third floor. The elevator goes up 2 floors, then up 5 more floors. It goes down 3 floors, and then up 4 floors. What floor is the elevator at now?

27. _____

28. There are 33 people on a tram. At the first stop, 2 more people get on and 4 get off. At the next stop, 8 people get off and 5 get on. At the next stop, 10 get off and 2 get on. How many people are on the tram now?

28. _____

29. Explain Your Thinking Diane shaded 4 rows of a hundredths square. Write a decimal to name the shaded part. Explain. You may use this hundredths grid to help.

_____

_____

Date _____ Score _____

Vocabulary: In 1–4 match each with its meaning.

1. decimal

a. a metric unit of measure equal to 100 centimeters

1. _____

2. decimeter

b. a metric unit of measure equal to 1,000 meters

2. _____

3. kilometer

c. a number that uses place value and a decimal point to show tenths, hundredths, and so on

3. _____

4. meter

d. a metric unit of measure equal to 10 centimeters

4. _____

In 5–6, write the fraction and the decimal to name each shaded part.

5.

6.

5. _____

6. _____

In 7–12, write each as a decimal.

7. $\frac{2}{10}$

7. _____

8. $1\frac{7}{10}$

8. _____

9. $2\frac{75}{100}$

9. _____

10. forty-five hundredths

10. _____

11. one and eighty-two hundredths

11. _____

12. two and three tenths

12. _____

In 13–16, find each sum or difference.

13. 1.4
      + 0.4

14. 0.8
      + 3.8

13. _____

14. _____

15. 3.5
      − 1.8

16. 6.6
      − 3.2

15. _____

16. _____

Name _____

In 17–20, write each as a money amount.

17. $\frac{74}{100}$ of $1.00   17. _____

18. $3\frac{80}{100}$ of $1.00   18. _____

19. seven cents   19. _____

20. two dollars and forty-eight cents   20. _____

In 21–23, match each with its estimate.

21. height of a cocoa mug   **a.** 2 m   21. _____

22. height of a tall fence   **b.** 1 cm   22. _____

23. width of a crayon   **c.** 1 dm   23. _____

In 24–26, write whether you would measure each in cm, m, or km.

24. height of a diving board from the ground   24. _____

25. distance of a train ride   25. _____

26. length of a chalkboard eraser   26. _____

27. Suppose you get on an elevator on the tenth floor. The elevator goes up 5 floors, then down 4 floors. It goes down 7 more floors, and then up 3 floors. What floor is the elevator at now?   27. _____

28. There are 18 people on a commuter train. At the first stop, 5 more people get on and 3 get off. At the next stop, 9 people get on and 2 get off. At the next stop, 12 get off and 8 get on. How many people are on the train now?   28. _____

29. **Explain Your Thinking** Will shaded 8 columns of a hundredths square. Write a decimal to name the shaded part. Explain. You may use the hundredths grid to help.

_____

_____

Give the letter of the correct answer.

1. Give the decimal that names the shaded part.

  A 0.3   **B** 0.7   **C** 1.7   **D** Not here

1. _____

2. Give the decimal that names the shaded part.

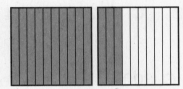

  A 1.3   **B** 1.03   **C** 0.3   **D** Not here

2. _____

In 3-6, give each as a decimal.

3. four tenths

  A 40   **B** 4   **C** 0.4   **D** 0.04

3. _____

4. three and five tenths

  A 0.35   **B** 3.5   **C** 3.05   **D** Not here

4. _____

5. $2\frac{6}{10}$

  A 0.26   **B** 2.06   **C** 2.6   **D** Not here

5. _____

6. $\frac{9}{10}$

  A 9   **B** 0.10   **C** 9.10   **D** Not here

6. _____

7. Give the decimal that names the shaded part.

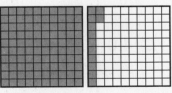

  A 0.12   **B** 1.12   **C** 1.2   **D** 112

7. _____

8. Give the decimal that names the shaded part.

  A 0.75   **B** 0.8   **C** 7.5   **D** Not here

8. _____

Name _____

In 9–13, give each as a decimal.

9. eighty-four hundredths

   A 84   **B** 8.4   **C** 0.84   **D** Not here

   9. _____

10. one and fifteen hundredths

    A 115   **B** 1.15   **C** 0.15   **D** Not here

    10. _____

11. $5\frac{92}{100}$

    A 0.592   **B** 5.092   **C** 5.92   **D** Not here

    11. _____

12. $\frac{8}{100}$

    A 0.08   **B** 0.8   **C** 800   **D** Not here

    12. _____

13. $\frac{52}{100}$

    A 0.5   **B** 52   **C** 5,200   **D** Not here

    13. _____

In 14–18, find each sum or difference. You may use the tenths grid to help.

14.   1.5
    + 4.7

    A 62   **B** 6.2   **C** 5.2   **D** 3.2

    14. _____

15.   9.4
    − 3.9

    A 13.3   **B** 12.3   **C** 6.5   **D** 5.5

    15. _____

16.   9.8
    + 4.9

    A 13.7   **B** 14.7   **C** 4.9   **D** 147

    16. _____

17.   7.3
    − 2.1

    A 42   **B** 9.4   **C** 5.2   **D** 4.2

    17. _____

18.   4.6
    + 2.3

    A 6.9   **B** 2.3   **C** 1.3   **D** 7.9

    18. _____

Continued

In 19–24, write each as a money amount.

19. $\frac{49}{100}$ of $1.00

    A $41.00   **B** $4.90   **C** $0.49   **D** Not here

19. _____

20. $\frac{18}{100}$ of $1.00

    A $1,800   **B** $1.80   **C** $1.08   **D** Not here

20. _____

21. $\frac{86}{100}$ of $1.00

    A $0.86   **B** $8.60   **C** $8,600   **D** Not here

21. _____

22. three dollars and eight cents

    A $3.80   **B** $3.08   **C** $0.38   **D** Not here

22. _____

23. seventy-one cents

    A $7.01   **B** $7.10   **C** $71.00   **D** Not here

23. _____

24. five and forty-nine hundredths of $1.00

    A $50.49   **B** $5.49   **C** $5.40   **D** Not here

24. _____

In 25–30, give the best estimate.

25. length of a staple

    A 1 cm   **B** 1 dm   **C** 5 cm   **D** 5 dm

25. _____

26. length of a glue stick

    A 1 cm   **B** 1 dm   **C** 25 cm   **D** 25 dm

26. _____

27. height of a number cube

    A 10 dm   **B** 10 cm   **C** 2 dm   **D** 2 cm

27. _____

28. height of a tall building

    A 100 m   **B** 100 km   **C** 100 cm   **D** 500 km

28. _____

29. length of a parade route

    A 5 m   **B** 5 km   **C** 50 m   **D** 50 km

29. _____

30. length of a minivan

    A 50 km   **B** 50 m   **C** 5 cm   **D** 5 m

30. _____

Name _____

In 31–35, give whether you would measure in cm, m, or km.

31. length of your shoe

    A cm   **B** m   **C** km

31. _____

32. distance between two cities

    A cm   **B** m   **C** km

32. _____

33. length of the gym

    A cm   **B** m   **C** km

33. _____

34. distance across a dinner plate

    A cm   **B** m   **C** km

34. _____

35. length of an airplane wing

    A cm   **B** m   **C** km

35. _____

36. Suppose you get on an elevator on the fourth floor. You go up 3 floors, then up 6 more floors. Then you go down 8 floors, and down 1 more floor. What floor are you on now?

    A Fifth floor   **B** First floor
    C Fourth floor   **D** Not here

36. _____

37. There are 6 people on bus. At the first stop, 3 people get on. At the next stop, 5 people get on and 1 person gets off. At the next stop, 12 people get on and 8 people get off. How many people are left on the bus?

    A 33 people   **B** 17 people
    C 16 people   **D** Not here

37. _____

38. At 8:00 A.M., the temperature was 48 degrees. One hour later it had risen 6 degrees, and it rose another 3 degrees by 10:00 A.M. At 11:00 A.M., the temperature had dropped 5 degrees. One hour later it dropped another 8 degrees. What was the temperature at noon?

    A 70 degrees   **B** 48 degrees
    C 44 degrees   **D** 36 degrees

38. _____

You decide to make friendship bracelets. You can use three or four 25-cm pieces of yarn for each bracelet.

a. Making Decisions You will not make more than 5 bracelets. Make a list of the friends you will give bracelets to and how many pieces of yarn you will need to make each bracelet.

b. Analyzing Data How many centimeters of yarn will you need in all?

Is the total length of each bracelet more or less than one decimeter?

c. Think Critically Suppose each centimeter of yarn costs one cent. Use a dollar sign and a decimal point to write how much it will cost to make each bracelet. Then write the total cost for all the bracelets.

d. Making Decisions It will take you 15 minutes to make each bracelet. You need to plan your morning so that you can complete all of the activities in the table and make the bracelets. Decide which activity you will do first, second, and so on.

Chore	Time
baby-sit	60 minutes
clean room	30 minutes
homework	45 minutes
practice piano	30 minutes

e. Recording Data Make a schedule like this one. Be sure to include all the activities.

Time	Activity

f. Analyzing Data Use your schedule.

How long will it take to make the bracelets?

How much time have you scheduled in all?

g. Explain Your Thinking Explain why you arranged your schedule in the order that you did.

Teacher Notes

Concepts and Skills This activity requires students to:
- make decisions using real-life experiences.
- add measurements.
- write money amounts as a decimal.
- add money amounts.
- find elapsed time.
- make a schedule.

Guiding Questions
- How can you use addition to find the total length of 3 pieces of yarn?
- If you have 95¢, how do you write that amount with a dollar sign and a decimal point?
- How long will it take to make 2 bracelets?
- How can you write the times in your schedule?

Answers
a. Decisions will vary.
b. Answers will vary. Each bracelet will be longer than one decimeter.
c. Check that students have written the amount in the correct format.
d. Check students' answers.
e. Check students' schedules.
f. Check students' answers.
g. Check students' answers.

Extension
Have students choose a different number of bracelets to make and decide how many pieces of yarn they will need to make them. Then have them find the cost to purchase the yarn and find how much change they would receive if they used a five-dollar bill to make their purchase.

Evaluation

Level	Standard to be achieved for performance of specified level
4	**Full Achievement** The student can compare centimeters and decimeters, and write money amounts using a dollar sign and decimal point. He or she can find the time it takes to make the bracelets and make a reasonable schedule. All computations are correct.
3	**Substantial Achievement** The student can compare centimeters and decimeters, and write money amounts using a dollar sign and decimal point. He or she can find the time it takes to make the bracelets and make a reasonable schedule. Most computations are correct.
2	**Partial Achievement** The student has some difficulty comparing centimeters and decimeters, and writing money amounts using a dollar sign and decimal point. He or she needs help to find the time it takes to make the bracelets and make a reasonable schedule. There are many errors in computations.
1	**Little Achievement** The student needs considerable help to compare centimeters and decimeters, and write money amounts using a dollar sign and decimal point. He or she cannot find the time it takes to make the bracelets and cannot make a reasonable schedule. The computation contains many errors.

Date _____ Score _____

In 1-2, write the fraction and decimal to name each shaded part.

1.   2.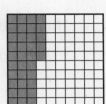

1. _____

2. _____

In 3–6, write each as a decimal.

3. $\frac{5}{10}$

4. $1\frac{92}{100}$

5. one and one tenth

6. seven hundredths

   A 700 **B** 0.7 **C** 0.07 **D** Not here

3. _____

4. _____

5. _____

6. _____

In 7–10, find each sum or difference. You may use tenths grids to help.

7.   5.3
   + 2.4

8.   9.4
   − 4.2

9.   6.2
   − 3.8

10.   3.7
   + 5.9

7. _____

8. _____

9. _____

10. _____

In 11–14, give each as a money amount.

11. $\frac{26}{100}$ of $1.00

12. four dollars and sixty cents

   A $460 **B** $4.66 **C** $4.60 **D** $4.06

13. thirty-two cents

   A $0.32 **B** $3.20 **C** $32.00 **D** Not here

14. ninety-four hundredths of $1.00

   A $9,400 **B** $94.00 **C** $9.40 **D** Not here

11. _____

12. _____

13. _____

14. _____

Name _____

In 15–18, give the best estimate.

15. height of a juice glass

    A 1 cm   **B** 1 dm   **C** 40 cm   **D** 40 dm

15. _____

16. height of a basketball hoop from the ground

    A 200 cm   **B** 1 km   **C** 3 m   **D** 3 km

16. _____

17. height of a street sign

    A 25 cm   **B** 20 m   **C** 2 m   **D** 1 km

17. _____

18. width of a postage stamp

    A 2 cm   **B** 2 dm   **C** 200 cm   **D** 200 dm

18. _____

In 19–21, write whether you would measure each in cm, m, or km.

19. distance across the Atlantic Ocean

19. _____

20. width of a stage

20. _____

21. distance across a CD

21. _____

22. Suppose you get on an elevator on the fifteenth floor. You go down 2 floors, then down 4 more floors. Then you go up 1 floor, and down 8 floors and get off. On what floor do you get off?

22. _____

23. There are 5 people on a merry-go-round. After one minute, 4 get off and 6 get on. After another minute, 3 get on and 2 get off. How many people are on the merry-go-round now?

23. _____

24. Performance Task Is 0.5 greater than $\frac{47}{100}$? Explain. You may use the hundredths grids to help.

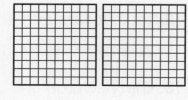

_____

_____

_____

Date _____ Score _____

— Computation —

In 1–5, find each sum or difference.

1.   0.8
     + 3.7

2.   3.2
     − 1.7

3. $\frac{1}{8} + \frac{3}{8}$

4. 232 − 187

    A 35   **B** 55   **C** 419   **D** Not here

5. $35.00 − 18.50

    A $16.50   **B** $17.50   **C** $17.00   **D** Not here

6. 16 + 43 + 85

    A 154   **B** 144   **C** 134   **D** Not here

In 7–8, find each product or quotient.

7. 18 × 7

    A 126   **B** 128   **C** 136   **D** Not here

8. 48 ÷ 8

9. How many inches is 6 feet 3 inches?

1. _____

2. _____

3. _____

4. _____

5. _____

6. _____

7. _____

8. _____

9. _____

— Concepts —

In 10–11, write the decimal to name the shaded part.

10.

11.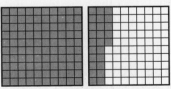

10. _____

11. _____

In 12–13, write each as a decimal.

12. three and five tenths

13. $5\frac{6}{100}$

12. _____

13. _____

Name _____

In 14–15, write each as a money amount.

14. eight dollars and twenty-six cents

A $8.06   **B** $8.20   **C** $8.26   **D** Not here

14. _____

15. seventy-nine hundredths of $1.00

15. _____

In 16–20, match each with its estimate.

16. distance traveled during a taxi ride   **a.** 5 cm   **16.** _____

17. height of a traffic signal   **b.** 15 km   **17.** _____

18. length of a butterfly   **c.** 10 m   **18.** _____

In 19–21, write whether you would measure each in cm, m, or km.

19. length of a car

19. _____

20. width of a toad

20. _____

21. distance across the state of Montana

21. _____

— Applications —

22. Ms. Hardaway wants to place a string of lights around her office building. She drew this sketch of the building. How many meters of lights will she need?

22. _____

A 19 meters
B 45 meters
C 128 meters
D 855 meters

```
              45 m
       ┌──────────────────┐
 19 m  │                  │  19 m
       └──────────────────┘
              45 m
```

23. Suppose you enter an elevator on the sixth floor. The elevator goes down 2 floors. Then it goes up 8 floors. It goes down 3 floors, and then up 5 floors where you get off. On what floor did you get off?

23. _____

24. For a newspaper headline, round 452 tickets sold to the nearest hundred.

24. _____

Vocabulary: In 1–4, match each with its meaning.

1. capacity **a.** a standard unit used to measure weight

2. milliliter **b.** a metric unit used to measure capacity

3. ounce **c.** a metric unit used to measure mass

4. gram **d.** the amount a container can hold

1. _____

2. _____

3. _____

4. _____

In 5–6, choose the best estimate for each.

5.
1 cup
1 pint
1 gallon

6.
30 mL
30 L

5. _____

6. _____

In 7–8, choose the better estimate for each.

7.
12 oz
12 lb

8.
11 g
11 kg

7. _____

8. _____

In 9–10, write each temperature using °F.

9.

10.

9. _____

10. _____

11. Which is more—1 quart or 2 cups?

11. _____

12. A horse's brain weighs about 20 ounces. Is this heavier or lighter than 1 pound?

12. _____

Vocabulary: In 1–4, match each with its definition.

1. prediction

2. possible outcomes

3. equally likely

4. likely

a. probably will happen

b. just as likely to happen as not to happen

c. a guess about what will happen

d. all results that could occur

1. _____

2. _____

3. _____

4. _____

In 5–7, decide whether each is impossible, possible, or certain.

5. You will be in kindergarten next year.

6. The sun will set tonight.

7. Your teacher will wear a blue skirt tomorrow.

5. _____

6. _____

7. _____

In 8–9, suppose you put these cubes in a bag. Predict whether you are more likely to pull out a black or a white cube.

8.

9.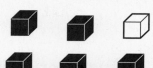

8. _____

9. _____

10. Copy and complete.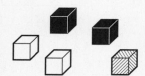

White: ■ out of 5 or $\frac{■}{5}$

Black: ■ out of 5 or $\frac{■}{5}$

Striped: ■ out of 5 or $\frac{■}{5}$

10. _____

_____

_____

In 11–12, write whether each spinner is fair or unfair.

11.

12.

11. _____

12. _____

13. Liz picked a number. Then she added 9, subtracted 2, and added 12. If Liz ended up with 27, what number did she pick?

13. _____

Vocabulary: In 1–2, write true or false.

1. Capacity is the amount an object weighs.

2. Predictions are a guess about what will happen.

1. _____

2. _____

In 3–10, write the best estimate for each.

3.
1 cup
1 quart
1 gallon

4.
1 cup
1 quart
1 gallon

3. _____

4. _____

5.
59 mL
59 L

6.
8 mL
8 L

5. _____

6. _____

7.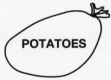
POTATOES
5 oz
5 lb

8.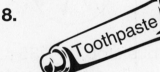
6 oz
6 lb

7. _____

8. _____

9.
14 g
14 kg

10.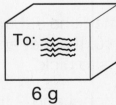
To: ≈≈≈
6 g
6 kg

9. _____

10. _____

In 11–12, write each temperature using °F.

11.

12.

11. _____

12. _____

In 13–14, decide whether each is likely or unlikely.

13. You will drive a car tomorrow.

14. Someone in your class is 9 years old.

13. _____

14. _____

In 15–16, suppose you put these cubes in a bag. Predict which color you are more likely to pull out.

15.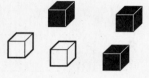

16.

15. _____

16. _____

17. Copy and complete.

White: ■ out of 6 or $\frac{■}{6}$

Gray: ■ out of 6 or $\frac{■}{6}$

Dotted: ■ out of 6 or $\frac{■}{6}$

17. _____

_____

_____

In 18–19, write whether each spinner is fair or unfair.

18.

19.

18. _____

19. _____

20. Anne needs to be at the bus stop by 7:35 A.M. It takes her 5 minutes to walk to the bus stop and 45 minutes to get ready. At what time must she get up?

20. _____

21. Janet picked a number. Then she subtracted 4, added 6, and subtracted 10. If Janet ended up with 50, what number did she pick?

21. _____

22. Explain Your Thinking Lionel and 2 friends are going to camp out in Lionel's back yard. Lionel thinks that each of the three boys will drink 1,000 mL of sports drink. He buys one 2-L bottle. Did he buy enough? Explain.

_____

_____

Vocabulary: In 1–2, write true or false.

1. You can use probability to make predictions.

2. You may use an experiment to test a prediction.

1. _____

2. _____

In 3–10, write the best estimate for each.

3.

1 cup
1 quart
1 gallon

4.

1 cup
1 quart
1 gallon

3. _____

4. _____

5.

12 mL
12 L

6.

473 mL
473 L

5. _____

6. _____

7.

7 oz
7 lb

8.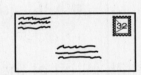

1 oz
1 lb

7. _____

8. _____

9.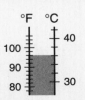

14 g
14 kg

10.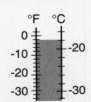

5 g
5 kg

9. _____

10. _____

In 11–12, write each temperature using °F.

11. °F °C
100
90
80
40
30

12. °F °C
0
-10
-20
-30
-20
-30

11. _____

12. _____

Name _____

In 13–14, decide whether each is likely or unlikely.

13. You will eat lunch tomorrow.

13. _____

14. Your teacher will fall asleep during class.

14. _____

In 15–16, suppose you put these cubes in a bag. Predict which color your are more likely to pull out.

15.

15. _____

16.

16. _____

17. Complete.

White: ■ out of 5 or $\frac{\blacksquare}{5}$

17. _____

Black: ■ out of 5 or $\frac{\blacksquare}{5}$

_____

Dotted: ■ out of 5 or $\frac{\blacksquare}{5}$

_____

In 18–19, write whether each spinner is fair or unfair.

18.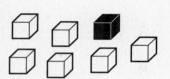

19.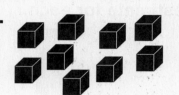

18. _____

19. _____

20. Che has a rope. He cuts 25 in. off of the rope. Then he cuts the rest of the rope into 5 equal pieces. Each piece is 15 in. long. How long was the original rope?

20. _____

21. Lilia gave 4 stamps to Eric and 3 stamps to Otis. She bought 8 more stamps. Now she has 9 stamps. How many stamps did she start with?

21. _____

22. Explain Your Thinking Florinda and 3 friends are going on a hike. Each of the four girls has a water bottle that holds 1 L of water. Will 4,200 mL of water fill all the bottles? Explain.

_____

_____

Give the letter of the correct answer.

In 1–9, give the best estimate for each.

1.

   A 1 pint   **B** 1 quart   **C** 1 gallon

   1. _____

2.

   A 1 cup   **B** 1 quart   **C** 1 gallon

   2. _____

3.

   A 1 cup   **B** 1 pint   **C** 1 gallon

   3. _____

4.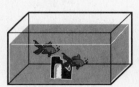

   A 5 mL   **B** 5 L   **C** 17 mL   **D** 17 L

   4. _____

5.

   A 15 mL   **B** 15 L   **C** 100 mL   **D** 100 L

   5. _____

6.

   A 4 oz   **B** 4 lb   **C** 40 oz   **D** 40 lb

   6. _____

Continued

7.

    A 6 oz   **B** 16 lb   **C** 60 oz   **D** 60 lb

7. _____

8.

    A 2 g   **B** 2 kg   **C** 25 g   **D** 25 kg

8. _____

9.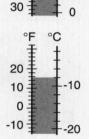

    A 1 g   **B** 1 kg   **C** 10 g   **D** 10 kg

9. _____

10. What temperature is shown?

    A 10°F   **B** 10°C
    C 55°C   **D** 55°F

10. _____

11. What temperature is shown?

    A 16°F   **B** 16°C
    C 10°F   **D** 10°C

11. _____

In 12–14, decide whether each is impossible, possible, or certain.

12. It will rain cats and dogs next week.

    A Certain   **B** Possible   **C** Impossible

12. _____

13. The sun will rise before 9:00 A.M. tomorrow.

    A Certain   **B** Possible   **C** Impossible

13. _____

14. You will play with friends this Saturday.

    A Certain   **B** Possible   **C** Impossible

14. _____

Continued

Name _____

In 15–16, decide whether each is likely or unlikely.

15. You will dig a hole 8 feet deep.

    A Likely   **B** Unlikely

15. _____

16. Someone in your class has a birthday this month.

    A Likely   **B** Unlikely

16. _____

In 17–18, suppose you put the cubes in a bag.
Predict which color you are more likely to pull out.

17.

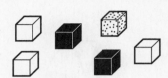

    A White   **B** Striped   **C** Dotted   **D** Not here

17. _____

18.

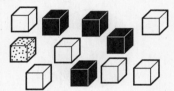

    A Black   **B** Striped   **C** Dotted   **D** Not here

18. _____

In 19–21, use the spinner to complete each statement.

19. Black: ■ out of 6 or $\frac{■}{6}$

    A 1 out of 6 or $\frac{1}{6}$ **B** 3 out of 6 or $\frac{3}{6}$

    C 4 out of 6 or $\frac{4}{6}$ **D** Not here

19. _____

20. Dotted: ■ out of 6 or $\frac{■}{6}$

    A 1 out of 6 or $\frac{1}{6}$ **B** 3 out of 6 or $\frac{3}{6}$

    C 4 out of 6 or $\frac{4}{6}$ **D** Not here

20. _____

21. Striped: ■ out of 6 or $\frac{■}{6}$

    A 1 out of 6 or $\frac{1}{6}$ **B** 3 out of 6 or $\frac{3}{6}$

    C 4 out of 6 or $\frac{4}{6}$ **D** Not here

21. _____

© Scott Foresman Addison Wesley 3

22. Which spinner is fair?

A   B

C   D

22. _____

23. Which spinner is unfair?

A   B

C   D

23. _____

24. Is this spinner fair or unfair?

A Fair   **B** Unfair

24. _____

25. Ivan cut 48 in. off of a rope. The he cut the rest of the rope into 5 equal pieces. Each piece was 24 in. long. How long was the original piece of rope?

A 168 in.   **B** 120 in.   **C** 72 in.   **D** Not here

25. _____

26. Joan picked a number to start with. Then she added 18, subtracted 5, and added 8. If Joan ended up with 38, what number did she start with?

A 7   **B** 27   **C** 17   **D** Not here

26. _____

27. Kate has a dental appointment at 9:15 A.M. It will take her 20 minutes to get to the dentist's office and 40 minutes to get ready in the morning. What time should Kate wake up?

A 10:15 A.M.   **B** 8:15 A.M.   **C** 7:15 A.M.   **D** Not here

27. _____

At the school carnival, you try the measurement game. You have to decide which outcome is most likely. Then draw a picture of something that shows that measurement.

a. Making Decisions Decide which outcome is most likely for each spinner.

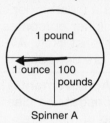

Spinner A

Spinner B

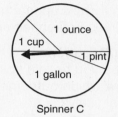

Spinner C

b. Recording Data Draw a picture of something that represents the measurement you would be most likely to spin for each spinner. For example, if 2 L is the most likely outcome on the spinner, you might draw a 2-L soda bottle as shown below.

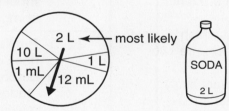

c. Analyzing Data Use the spinners.

Which measurement is least likely to happen for each spinner? Explain.

d. Making Decisions Estimate the temperature outside your school today. Write measurements in °F on Spinner D below so the most likely outcome shows your estimate.

Estimate the temperature outside your school on a day in January. Write measurements in °C on Spinner E below so the most likely outcome shows your estimate.

Spinner D

Spinner E

Teacher Notes

Concepts and Skills This activity requires students to:
- determine the most likely outcome.
- identify appropriate capacity measures in the customary and the metric system.
- identify appropriate weight/mass measures in the customary and the metric system.
- identify appropriate temperatures in degrees Fahrenheit and degrees Celsius.

Guiding Questions
- When you have a spinner, how do you know which outcome is most likely? Least likely?
- Which is more, 1 liter or 1 milliliter? 1 pound or 1 ounce? 1 cup or 1 quart?
- Which is warmer, 20°F or 20°C?

Answers
a. Spinner A, 1 pound; Spinner B, 1 gram; Spinner C, 1 gallon.
b. Drawings will vary. Check students' answers.
c. Spinner A: You cannot tell which is least likely to occur because there are two parts the same size.
Spinner B: 1 kilogram is least likely because it has the smallest area.
Spinner C: 1 pint is least likely because it has the smallest area.
d. Answers will vary. Check students' answers.

Extension
Have students order the measurements from least to greatest for each spinner. Tell them they are ordering the measurements, not the areas that they are in.

Evaluation

Level	Standard to be achieved for performance of specified level
4	**Full Achievement** The student demonstrates a clear understanding of measures of capacity, mass, and temperature. Drawings show appropriate measures. The student demonstrates a clear understanding of whether spinner outcomes are most likely or least likely. All comparisons are correct.
3	**Substantial Achievement** The student demonstrates a clear understanding of measures of capacity, mass, and temperature. The student may need some help in making drawings to show appropriate measures. The student demonstrates a clear understanding of whether spinner outcomes are most likely or least likely. Most comparisons are correct.
2	**Partial Achievement** The student has some difficulty deciding which outcome is most/least likely. The student also may have difficulty making appropriate drawings to represent the given measures. Errors may occur when making spinners showing temperatures.
1	**Little Achievement** The student demonstrates little if any understanding of the task at hand and needs considerable help identifying most likely and least likely outcomes. The student's drawings contain many errors and measurement concepts are not grasped.

Name _____

Date _____ Score _____

1. Give the best estimate.

A 1 cup   **B** 1 quart   **C** 1 gallon

2. Compare. Use <, >, or =.
4 quarts ■ 1 gallon

3. Give the best estimate.

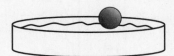

A 12 mL   **B** 12 L   **C** 120 mL   **D** 120 L

4. Paula added 750 mL of water to her aquarium. How much more or less than 1 L did she add?

A 250 mL more   **B** 150 mL more
C 150 mL less   **D** Not here

In 5–7, write the better estimate.

5.

10 oz or 10 lb

6.

2 oz or 2 lb

7.

A 5 g   **B** 5 kg   **C** 565 g   **D** 565 kg

8. Which is heavier, a 2-kilogram kitten or a 1,500-gram kitten?

In 9–10, write each temperature using °F.

9.

10.

1. _____

2. _____

3. _____

4. _____

5. _____

6. _____

7. _____

8. _____

_____

9. _____

10. _____

Name _____

In 11–12, decide whether each is impossible, possible, or certain.

11. You will eat 40,000 lb of broccoli tomorrow.

    A Impossible   **B** Possible   **C** Certain

11. _____

12. It is night time somewhere in the world.

    A Impossible   **B** Possible   **C** Certain

12. _____

In 13–14, suppose you put these cubes in a bag. Predict whether you are more likely to pull out a black cube or a white cube.

13.    **14.**

13. _____

14. _____

In 15–16, write whether each spinner is fair or unfair.

15.   **16.**

15. _____

16. _____

17. Chane picked a number. Then he added 15 to it, subtracted 8, and added 3. If Chane ended up with 35, what number did he pick?

17. _____

18. Performance Task Complete to find each probability. Which outcome are you most likely to spin? Which outcome are you least likely to spin? Explain.

Gray ■ out of 6 or $\frac{■}{6}$

White ■ out of 6 or $\frac{■}{6}$

Striped ■ out of 6 or $\frac{■}{6}$

18. _____

_____

_____

_____

_____

— Computation —

1. Find 63 ÷ 9.

2. Find 8 × 7.

In 3–5, add or subtract.

3. 4,700 − 1,650

4. $15.45 − $9.75

    A $25.20   **B** $24.20   **C** $6.70   **D** $5.70

5. $\frac{1}{5} + \frac{1}{5}$

    A $\frac{1}{5}$ **B** $\frac{2}{5}$ **C** $\frac{7}{5}$ **D** 12

— Concepts —

In 6–9, write the best estimate.

6.

1 cup
1 quart
1 gallon

7.

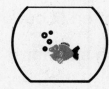

5 mL
5 L

8.

2 oz or 2 lb

9.

1 g or 1 kg

10. How many ounces is 3 pounds of fruit salad?

    A 30 oz   **B** 36 oz   **C** 48 oz   **D** 3,000 oz

11. Round 963 to the nearest hundred.

    A 900   **B** 960   **C** 970   **D** 1,000

1. _____

2. _____

3. _____

4. _____

5. _____

6. _____

7. _____

8. _____

9. _____

10. _____

11. _____

Name _____

12. What temperature is shown?

A 22°C **B** 22°F **C** 70°F **D** Not here

12. _____

13. Is it likely or unlikely that a spider will crawl up your leg today?

13. _____

In 14–15, suppose you put these cubes in a bag. Predict which color you are more likely to pull out.

14.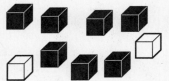

15.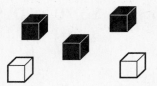

14. _____

15. _____

16. Copy and complete.

Black ■ out of 8 or $\frac{■}{8}$

White ■ out of 8 or $\frac{■}{8}$

Dotted ■ out of 8 or $\frac{■}{8}$

16. _____

_____

In 17–18, write whether each spinner is fair or unfair.

17.

18.

17. _____

18. _____

▬ Applications ▬

19. Megan drank four 300-mL containers of water. How much more or less than 1 L did she drink?

19. _____

20. The temperature was 48°F at 8:00 A.M. By noon, it was 64°F. How much did the temperature rise?

20. _____

21. Larry cut 30 in. off of a piece of molding. Then he cut the remaining piece into 3 equal pieces. Each of these pieces was 12 in. long. How long was the original piece of molding?

21. _____

Give the letter of the correct answer.

1. Use the bar graph to find how many more students prefer red than blue.

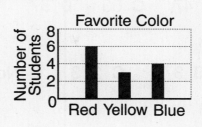

A 6 students   **B** 4 students
C 3 students   **D** 2 students

1. _____

2. Give four hundred seventy-five in standard form.

A 4,075   **B** 475   **C** 457   **D** 400,075

2. _____

3. Compare: 546 ● 564. Use <, >, or =.

A <   **B** >   **C** =

3. _____

4. Eleanor began studying at 4:15 P.M. and finished 40 minutes later. What time did she finish?

A 5:00 P.M.   **B** 5:05 P.M.   **C** 4:55 P.M.   **D** Not here

4. _____

5. Estimate the sum of 36 and 23 by rounding.

A 20   **B** 70   **C** 50   **D** 60

5. _____

In 6–9, add.

6. 47 + 38

A 75   **B** 85   **C** 83   **D** Not here

6. _____

7. 265 + 351

A 514   **B** 516   **C** 616   **D** Not here

7. _____

8. 25 + 16 + 31

A 62   **B** 72   **C** 82   **D** Not here

8. _____

9. $6.75
     + 2.31

A $8.06   **B** $8.16   **C** $9.16   **D** Not here

9. _____

In 10–14, subtract.

10. 81 − 34

    A 43   **B** 47   **C** 53   **D** 57

10. _____

11. 426 − 153

    A 333   **B** 373   **C** 273   **D** Not here

11. _____

12. 805 − 123

    A 782   **B** 722   **C** 682   **D** 662

12. _____

13.   5,437
    − 2,671

    A 2,766   **B** 3,246   **C** 3,786   **D** 2,866

13. _____

14. $15.28
    − 12.39

    A $3.11   **B** $2.89   **C** $3.99   **D** $3.89

14. _____

15. David buys a dinosaur puzzle for $3.59. He gives the clerk $10.00. How much change does he receive?

    A $13.59   **B** $6.41   **C** $1.41   **D** Not here

15. _____

16. Norma put 5 glasses on each party table. There are 7 tables. How many glasses are there in all? Choose the number sentence that gives the answer.

    A 7 − 5 = 2   **B** 7 + 5 = 12
    C 7 × 5 = 35   **D** Not here

16. _____

In 17–19, multiply.

17. 9 × 5

    A 45   **B** 54   **C** 40   **D** 36

17. _____

18. 4 × 6

    A 36   **B** 28   **C** 21   **D** Not here

18. _____

19. 7×8

    A 36   **B** 42   **C** 56   **D** 63

19. _____

In 20–22, find each quotient.

20. $35 \div 5$

    A 7   **B** 9   **C** 5   **D** 6

20. _____

21. $24 \div 3$

    A 4   **B** 5   **C** 6   **D** 8

21. _____

22. $28 \div 7$

    A 6   **B** 5   **C** 4   **D** 3

22. _____

23. Give the name for these lines

    A Parallel lines
    B Intersecting lines
    C Line segments

23. _____

In 24–25, use the coordinate grid.

24. What is the ordered pair for point X?

    A (1, 3)   **B** (2, 3)
    C (3, 1)   **D** (1, 4)

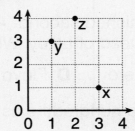

24. _____

25. Which letter is located at (2, 4)?

    A X   **B** Y   **C** Z

25. _____

In 26–27, find each product. Regroup if needed.

26.   46
   $\times$ 3

    A 128   **B** 124   **C** 138   **D** 144

26. _____

27. $5.62
   $\times$ 3

    A $15.86   **B** $16.86   **C** $17.46   **D** Not here

27. _____

In 28–29, find each quotient and remainder.

28. 3$\overline{)25}$

    A 3 R1   **B** 4 R1   **C** 5 R1   **D** 8 R1

28. _____

29. 38 ÷ 9

    A 4 R2   **B** 6 R2   **C** 8 R2   **D** 9 R2

29. _____

30. Estimate the amount that is shaded.

    A More than $\frac{1}{2}$

    B About $\frac{1}{2}$

    C Less than $\frac{1}{2}$

    D About $\frac{3}{4}$

30. _____

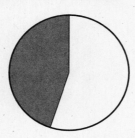

31. Give the fraction that tells what part of the set is circled.

    A $\frac{1}{4}$ **B** $\frac{1}{2}$

    C $\frac{2}{3}$ **D** $\frac{3}{4}$

31. _____

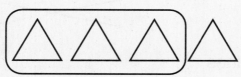

32. In a relay race, Dale finished second. Al finished after Leroy. Floyd finished ahead of Leroy. Who finished first?

    A Dale   **B** Al   **C** Leroy   **D** Floyd

32. _____

33. Give two and thirty-five hundredths as a decimal.

    A 235   **B** 2.35   **C** 2.05   **D** 0.23

33. _____

In 34–36, choose the better estimate.

34. Width of a door

    A 1 meter   **B** 1 kilometer

34. _____

35. A dose of liquid cough medicine

    A 40 mL   **B** 40 L

35. _____

36. Is a bowling ball less than or more than a kilogram?

    A Less than   **B** More than

36. _____

Table of Contents for Answer Forms

Answer Forms

Using Answer Forms

The answer forms in the *Assessment Sourcebook* can be used by students to answer test questions. There are two types of answer forms included in the sourcebook, Answer Form for Multiple-Choice Tests and Answer Form for Student-Produced Answers. Although both are formatted for machine scoring, they are easy to score by hand. The form for multiple-choice answers can be used for items with as many as four answer choices. The form for student-produced answers allows students to record numerical answers up to four digits, or up to three digits with decimal points and division bars. Using both these forms gives students practice in recording answers in the machine-scorable format that they will encounter when they take standardized tests.

Answer Form for Multiple-Choice Tests

Students use this form to record answers for multiple-choice tests with as many as 60 items. Have students fill in the correct information in the first three items at the top of the form before they begin the test. Make sure they know what the name of the test is. After tests are scored, you or the student can record the score in the fourth blank.

Be sure students understand that the numbers on the form next to the letter choices correspond to the numbers of the test items on the test. The letters in the circles correspond to the answer choices on the test. When fewer than four letter choices appear for a given test item, students should ignore the extra choices on the answer form. Explain that students are to mark each answer by filling in the lettered circle that corresponds to the answer they choose. They should use a number 2 pencil.

Explain to students that once they have completed the last item of the test, they should leave the rest of the item choices on the form blank.

Before students begin the test, you might want to guide them through the process of completing the form. Have students record the answer to a practice item in the row labeled Practice at the top of the form. Use this Practice item to make sure students understand how to mark their answers.

Caution students to:
- mark the answer in the correct row for each test item;
- fill in only one circle for each test item;
- fill in the answer circle completely.

Answer Form for Student-Produced Answers

This form is for recording numerical answers to problems that students calculate. The format is used for machine-score tests. Many standardized tests such as the SATs use this type of answer form.

Because students write their answers in the spaces at the top of each answer block, this form is also easily hand-scored.

The form can be used for answers expressed as decimals and fractions, as well as for whole numbers. However, it can only accommodate answers with four or fewer digits.

Have students fill in the correct information in the first three items at the top of the form before they begin the test. Make sure they know what the name of the test is. After tests are scored, you or the student can record the score in the fourth blank.

Make sure students understand that the number beside each answer block corresponds to the number of a test item. Then explain how to use the form, referring to the sample answer blocks on the next page. There are two steps to recording each answer as they calculate.

Example 1: Whole Numbers
Suppose the answer is 114.

Step 1: Write the answer in the empty row of marked spaces at the top of the appropriate answer block, one digit to a space. The digit farthest right in the answer goes in the farthest right space, and so on. Write 4 in the rightmost space, 1 in the second space from the right, and 1 in the third. For whole numbers, the space farthest left is the thousands place and the space farthest right is the ones place.

Step 2: Fill in the oval that corresponds to each digit in the column below it. Fill in oval 4 in the righthand column, oval 1 in the second column from the right, and oval 1 in the third column.

Explain that because the answer in Example 1 has only three digits, the leftmost space and the column below it are not marked.

Make sure students understand how to use the form to record answers in fractions and decimals.

Example 2: Decimals
Suppose the answer is 2.34.

Step 1: Write the digits of the answer in the empty spaces, as before, but also write the decimal point in the correct space. Stress to students that a decimal point uses one space. For 2.34, write 2 in the first space, a decimal point in the second space, 3 in the third space, and 4 in the last space as shown.

Step 2: Fill in the oval that corresponds to each digit, as before. For the decimal point, fill in the oval with the decimal point in the column under the space in which the decimal point appears.

Example 3: Fractions
Suppose the answer is $\frac{2}{13}$.

Step 1: Write the digits and the division bar in order in the empty spaces, allowing a full space for the division bar.

Step 2: Fill in the oval that corresponds to the division bar and to each digit.

Explain to students that once they have completed the last item of the test, they should leave the rest of the form blank.

Remind students to:
- write the answer in the correct answer block for each test item;
- carry out both steps 1 and 2 in recording their answers;
- fill in ovals for the decimal point and division bars where appropriate;
- fill in the ovals completely;
- make sure filled-in ovals correspond to the answer they have written above.

Answer Form for Multiple-Choice Tests

Student _____   Date _____

Name of Test _____   Score _____

Practice. Ⓐ Ⓑ Ⓒ Ⓓ

1. Ⓐ Ⓑ Ⓒ Ⓓ   21. Ⓐ Ⓑ Ⓒ Ⓓ   41. Ⓐ Ⓑ Ⓒ Ⓓ
2. Ⓐ Ⓑ Ⓒ Ⓓ   22. Ⓐ Ⓑ Ⓒ Ⓓ   42. Ⓐ Ⓑ Ⓒ Ⓓ
3. Ⓐ Ⓑ Ⓒ Ⓓ   23. Ⓐ Ⓑ Ⓒ Ⓓ   43. Ⓐ Ⓑ Ⓒ Ⓓ
4. Ⓐ Ⓑ Ⓒ Ⓓ   24. Ⓐ Ⓑ Ⓒ Ⓓ   44. Ⓐ Ⓑ Ⓒ Ⓓ
5. Ⓐ Ⓑ Ⓒ Ⓓ   25. Ⓐ Ⓑ Ⓒ Ⓓ   45. Ⓐ Ⓑ Ⓒ Ⓓ

6. Ⓐ Ⓑ Ⓒ Ⓓ   26. Ⓐ Ⓑ Ⓒ Ⓓ   46. Ⓐ Ⓑ Ⓒ Ⓓ
7. Ⓐ Ⓑ Ⓒ Ⓓ   27. Ⓐ Ⓑ Ⓒ Ⓓ   47. Ⓐ Ⓑ Ⓒ Ⓓ
8. Ⓐ Ⓑ Ⓒ Ⓓ   28. Ⓐ Ⓑ Ⓒ Ⓓ   48. Ⓐ Ⓑ Ⓒ Ⓓ
9. Ⓐ Ⓑ Ⓒ Ⓓ   29. Ⓐ Ⓑ Ⓒ Ⓓ   49. Ⓐ Ⓑ Ⓒ Ⓓ
10. Ⓐ Ⓑ Ⓒ Ⓓ   30. Ⓐ Ⓑ Ⓒ Ⓓ   50. Ⓐ Ⓑ Ⓒ Ⓓ

11. Ⓐ Ⓑ Ⓒ Ⓓ   31. Ⓐ Ⓑ Ⓒ Ⓓ   51. Ⓐ Ⓑ Ⓒ Ⓓ
12. Ⓐ Ⓑ Ⓒ Ⓓ   32. Ⓐ Ⓑ Ⓒ Ⓓ   52. Ⓐ Ⓑ Ⓒ Ⓓ
13. Ⓐ Ⓑ Ⓒ Ⓓ   33. Ⓐ Ⓑ Ⓒ Ⓓ   53. Ⓐ Ⓑ Ⓒ Ⓓ
14. Ⓐ Ⓑ Ⓒ Ⓓ   34. Ⓐ Ⓑ Ⓒ Ⓓ   54. Ⓐ Ⓑ Ⓒ Ⓓ
15. Ⓐ Ⓑ Ⓒ Ⓓ   35. Ⓐ Ⓑ Ⓒ Ⓓ   55. Ⓐ Ⓑ Ⓒ Ⓓ

16. Ⓐ Ⓑ Ⓒ Ⓓ   36. Ⓐ Ⓑ Ⓒ Ⓓ   56. Ⓐ Ⓑ Ⓒ Ⓓ
17. Ⓐ Ⓑ Ⓒ Ⓓ   37. Ⓐ Ⓑ Ⓒ Ⓓ   57. Ⓐ Ⓑ Ⓒ Ⓓ
18. Ⓐ Ⓑ Ⓒ Ⓓ   38. Ⓐ Ⓑ Ⓒ Ⓓ   58. Ⓐ Ⓑ Ⓒ Ⓓ
19. Ⓐ Ⓑ Ⓒ Ⓓ   39. Ⓐ Ⓑ Ⓒ Ⓓ   59. Ⓐ Ⓑ Ⓒ Ⓓ
20. Ⓐ Ⓑ Ⓒ Ⓓ   40. Ⓐ Ⓑ Ⓒ Ⓓ   60. Ⓐ Ⓑ Ⓒ Ⓓ

Answer Form for Student-Produced Answers

Student _____   Date _____

Name of Test _____   Score _____

1.

2.

3.

4.

5.

6.

7.

8.

9.

10.

11.

12.

Table of Contents for Answers

Answers

Top Left — Chapter 1 Test Form A

Name _____

Date _____ Score _____

Vocabulary: In 1–3, match each with its meaning.

1. key   **a.** a graph that uses bars to show data   1. ___b___

2. pictograph   **b.** part of a pictograph that tells what each symbol shows   2. ___c___

3. bar graph   **c.** a graph that uses pictures, or symbols, to show data   3. ___a___

In 4–5, use the pictograph.

4. What is the least popular sport?   ___Tennis___

5. How many students chose soccer?   ___6 students___

In 6–7, use the bar graph.

6. What subject has 20 votes?   ___Math___

7. How many more students prefer math than science?   ___5 students___

In 8–9, use the line graph.

8. How many books did Joe read in Week 3?   ___2 books___

9. How many more books did Joe read in Week 3 than in Week 1?   ___1 book___

Chapter 1 Test Form A   *Continued*   37

Top Right — Chapter 1 Test Form A (continued)

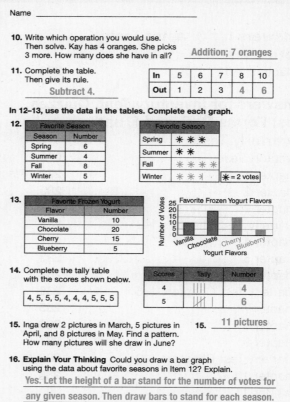

Name _____

10. Write which operation you would use. Then solve. Kay has 4 oranges. She picks 3 more. How many does she have in all?   **Addition; 7 oranges**

11. Complete the table. Then give its rule.   ___Subtract 4.___

In	5	6	7	8	10
Out	1	2	3	4	6

In 12–13, use the data in the tables. Complete each graph.

12.

Favorite Season	
Season	Number
Spring	6
Summer	4
Fall	8
Winter	5

13.

Favorite Frozen Yogurt	
Flavor	Number
Vanilla	10
Chocolate	20
Cherry	15
Blueberry	5

14. Complete the tally table with the scores shown below.

4, 5, 5, 5, 4, 4, 4, 5, 5, 5

Scores	Tally	Number
4	||||	4
5		6

15. Inga drew 2 pictures in March, 5 pictures in April, and 8 pictures in May. Find a pattern. How many pictures will she draw in June?   15. ___11 pictures___

16. **Explain Your Thinking** Could you draw a bar graph using the data about favorite seasons in Item 12? Explain.   Yes. Let the height of a bar stand for the number of votes for any given season. Then draw bars to stand for each season.

38   Chapter 1 Test Form A

Bottom Left — Chapter 1 Test Form B

Name _____

Date _____ Score _____

Vocabulary: In 1–3, match each with its meaning.

1. pictograph   **a.** a graph that uses bars to show data   1. ___c___

2. bar graph   **b.** numbers that show the units used on a bar graph   2. ___a___

3. scale   **c.** a graph that uses pictures, or symbols, to show data   3. ___b___

In 4–5, use the pictograph.

4. What is the most popular fruit?   ___Apples___

5. How many students chose oranges?   ___6 students___

In 6–7, use the bar graph.

6. What color has 10 votes?   ___Green___

7. How many more students prefer green than red?   ___6 students___

In 8–9, use the line graph.

8. How many games did Don play in Week 3?   ___15 games___

9. How many more games did Don play in Week 3 than in Week 1?   ___5 games___

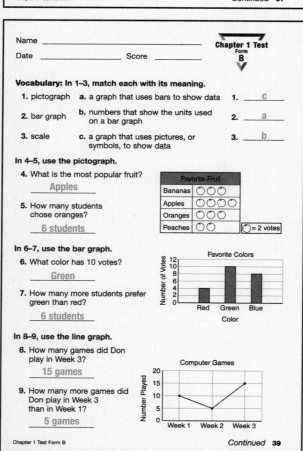

Chapter 1 Test Form B   *Continued*   39

Bottom Right — Chapter 1 Test Form B (continued)

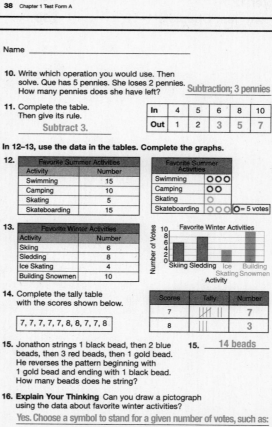

Name _____

10. Write which operation you would use. Then solve. Que has 5 pennies. She loses 2 pennies. How many pennies does she have left?   **Subtraction; 3 pennies**

11. Complete the table. Then give its rule.   ___Subtract 3.___

In	4	5	6	8	10
Out	1	2	3	5	7

In 12–13, use the data in the tables. Complete the graphs.

12.

Favorite Summer Activities	
Activity	Number
Swimming	15
Camping	10
Skating	5
Skateboarding	15

13.

Favorite Winter Activities	
Activity	Number
Skiing	6
Sledding	8
Ice Skating	4
Building Snowmen	10

14. Complete the tally table with the scores shown below.

7, 7, 7, 7, 7, 8, 8, 7, 7, 8

Scores	Tally	Number
7	|||| ||	7
8	|||	3

15. Jonathon strings 1 black bead, then 2 blue beads, then 3 red beads, then 1 gold bead. He reverses the pattern beginning with 1 gold bead and ending with 1 black bead. How many beads does he string?   15. ___14 beads___

16. **Explain Your Thinking** Can you draw a pictograph using the data about favorite winter activities?   Yes. Choose a symbol to stand for a given number of votes, such as: symbol = 2 votes. Then draw symbols to stand for each activity.

40   Chapter 1 Test Form B

Chapter 2 Test — Form A

Name _____

Date _____ Score _____

Vocabulary: In 1–3, match each with its meaning.

1. place value   a. times between midnight and noon   **1.** __b__

2. estimate   b. the value given to the place a digit has in a number   **2.** __c__

3. A.M.   c. to find a number that is close to the exact number   **3.** __a__

In 4–5, write each number in standard form.

4. 600 + 40 + 9   **4.** __649__

5. six thousand, two hundred forty-six   **5.** __6,246__

6. Write the word name for 607.   __Six hundred seven__

7. Write the word name for 5,210.   __Five thousand, two hundred ten__

In 8–9, write each missing value.

8. 90 ones = ■ tens   **8.** __9__

9. ■ tens = 5 hundreds   **9.** __50__

In 10–11, write the value of each underlined digit.

10. 379,625   **10.** __20__

11. 934,271   **11.** __900,000__

12. Carmen wants to pack 45 books in boxes that hold 10 books or 1 book. How many ways can she pack the boxes?   **12.** __5 ways__

In 13–14, compare. Use <, >, or =.

13. 435 ● 921   **13.** __<__

14. 3,215 ● 2,513   **14.** __>__

15. Order 413, 431, and 341 from greatest to least.   **15.** __431, 413, 341__

Chapter 2 Test Form A   *Continued* 59

Name _____

16. Round 87 to the nearest ten.   **16.** __90__

17. Round 315 to the nearest ten.   **17.** __320__

18. Round 245 to the nearest hundred.   **18.** __200__

19. Round 552 to the nearest hundred.   **19.** __600__

In 20–21, write each time in two ways. Possible answers:

20.   21.   **20.** __7:00__ __Seven o'clock__

21. __1:51__ __One fifty-one__

In 22–23, write each time in two ways. Write A.M. or P.M. Possible answers:

22.   23.   **22.** __6:30 P.M.__ __Six-thirty P.M.__

set dinner table   school starts   **23.** __8:15 A.M.__ __Eight-fifteen A.M.__

24. Chris cleaned for 2 hours and 5 minutes. He started at 9:00 A.M. What time did he finish?   **24.** __11:05 A.M.__

25. LaRonda had dance class from 4:00 P.M. until 5:05 P.M. How long was the class?   **25.** __1 hour, 5 minutes__

26. What is the eighth month?   **26.** __August__

27. **Explain Your Thinking** Which numbers round to 250 when rounded to the nearest ten? Which of these numbers round to 200 when rounded to the nearest hundred? Explain why your answers don't match.   __To nearest ten: 245, 246, 247, 248, 249, 250, 251, 252, 253, 254. To nearest hundred: 245, 246, 247, 248, 249. Numbers with a 5 in the tens place round to the greater hundred.__

60 Chapter 2 Test Form A

Chapter 2 Test — Form B

Name _____

Date _____ Score _____

Vocabulary: In 1–3, match each with its meaning.

1. digit   a. times between noon and midnight   **1.** __b__

2. rounding   b. 0, 1, 2, 3, 4, 5, 6, 7, 8, and 9   **2.** __c__

3. P.M.   c. replacing a number with a number that tells about how many or how much   **3.** __a__

In 4–5, write each number in standard form.

4. five hundred thirty-eight   **4.** __538__

5. 3,000 + 400 + 70 + 9   **5.** __3,479__

6. Write the word name for 649.   __Six hundred forty-nine__

7. Write the word name for 2,109.   __Two thousand, one hundred nine__

In 8–9, write each missing value.

8. 4 hundreds = ■ tens   **8.** __40__

9. ■ ones = 8 hundreds   **9.** __800__

In 10–11, write the value of each underlined digit.

10. 237,495   **10.** __400__

11. 472,839   **11.** __400,000__

12. Tony wants to pack 37 dishes in boxes that hold 10 dishes or 1 dish. How many ways can he pack the boxes?   **12.** __4 ways__

In 13–14, compare. Use <, >, or =.

13. 589 ● 256   **13.** __>__

14. 2,134 ● 2,341   **14.** __<__

15. Order 742, 427, and 472 from least to greatest.   **15.** __427, 472, 742__

Chapter 2 Test Form B   *Continued* 61

Name _____

16. Round 42 to the nearest ten.   **16.** __40__

17. Round 756 to the nearest ten.   **17.** __760__

18. Round 415 to the nearest hundred.   **18.** __400__

19. Round 675 to the nearest hundred.   **19.** __700__

In 20–21, write each time in two ways. Possible answers:

20.   21.   **20.** __10:20__ __Ten-twenty__

21. __7:42__ __Seven forty-two__

In 22–23, write each time in two ways. Write A.M. or P.M. Possible answers:

22.   23.   **22.** __7:30 A.M.__ __Seven-thirty A.M.__

get dressed   play with friends   **23.** __4:45 P.M.__ __Four forty-five P.M.__

24. Rama read for 1 hour and 40 minutes. She started at 7:00 P.M. What time did she end?   **24.** __8:40 P.M.__

25. Lonnie had soccer practice from 3:00 P.M. until 4:15 P.M. How long was the practice?   **25.** __1 hr, 15 min__

26. What is the fifth month?   **26.** __May__

27. **Extend Your Thinking** Which numbers round to 450 when rounded to the nearest ten? Which of these numbers round to 500 when rounded to the nearest hundred? Explain why your answers don't match.   __To nearest ten: 445, 446, 447, 448, 449, 450, 451, 452, 453, 454. To nearest hundred: 450, 451, 452, 453, 454. Numbers with a 5 in the tens place round to the greater hundred.__

62 Chapter 2 Test Form B

Form A (top left)

Name _____

Date _____ Score _____

Chapter 3 Test Form A

Vocabulary: In 1–3, match each with its example.

1. sum — **a.** a number that is added to find a sum
2. regroup — **b.** the number obtained when adding numbers
3. addend — **c.** to name a number in a different way

1. b
2. c
3. a

In 4, complete the number sentences.

4. $4 + 3 = \blacksquare$

$40 + \blacksquare = 70$

$\blacksquare + 300 = 700$

4. 7
30
400

In 5–6, find each sum. You may use a hundred chart to help.

5. $27 + 30$
6. $46 + 15$

5. 57
6. 61

In 7–8, find each missing number. You may use color cubes to help.

7. $14 + \blacksquare = 21$
8. $\blacksquare + 16 = 24$

7. 7
8. 8

In 9–12, find each sum. Estimate to check.

9. 57
  + 25

10. 314
  + 454

11. 3,518
  + 341

12. 17
  23
  + 45

9. 82
10. 768
11. 3,859
12. 85

Chapter 3 Test Form A   *Continued* 77

Form A (top right)

Name _____

13. Guess and check to solve. Jan has 3 more red bows than green bows. She has 15 bows in all. How many green bows does she have?

13. 6 bows

In 14–15, use mental math to find each sum.

14. $23 + 9$
15. $48 + 12$

14. 32
15. 60

In 16–17, write the total value.

16. 16. $0.58 or 58¢
17. 17. $1.28

18. Basil buys a fruit juice that costs $0.85. He pays with $5.00. Write the change in dollars and cents.

18. $4.15

In 19–20, add.

19. $3.71 + $1.25
20. $1.37 + $2.61

19. $4.96
20. $3.98

In 21–22, use rounding to estimate each sum.

21. $38 + 53$
22. $523 + 172$

21. 90
22. 700

In 23–24, use front-end estimation to estimate each sum.

23. $428 + 219$
24. $374 + 425$

23. 600
24. 700

25. **Explain Your Thinking** How much would it cost to buy 1 red pencil for $0.95, 1 black pen for $0.89, and 1 blue pen for $0.79? Explain whether you need an exact answer or an estimate.

Exact answer; $2.63

78   Chapter 3 Test Form A

Form B (bottom left)

Name _____

Date _____ Score _____

Chapter 3 Test Form B

Vocabulary: In 1–3, match each with its example.

1. regroup — **a.** a number that is added to find a sum
2. addend — **b.** the number obtained when adding numbers
3. sum — **c.** to name a number in a different way

1. c
2. a
3. b

In 4, complete the number sentences.

4. $2 + 6 = \blacksquare$

$20 + \blacksquare = 80$

$\blacksquare + 600 = 800$

4. 8
60
200

In 5–6, find each sum. You may use a hundred chart to help.

5. $29 + 8$
6. $47 + 23$

5. 37
6. 70

In 7–8, find each missing number. You may use color cubes to help

7. $19 + \blacksquare = 27$
8. $\blacksquare + 17 = 23$

7. 8
8. 6

In 9–12, find each sum. Estimate to check.

9. 46
  + 38

10. 251
  + 328

11. 2,173
  + 524

12. 12
  46
  + 31

9. 84
10. 579
11. 2,697
12. 89

Chapter 3 Test Form B   *Continued* 79

Form B (bottom right)

Name _____

13. Guess and check to solve. Carly has 4 fewer marbles than Neka. They have 12 marbles in all. How many marbles does Neka have?

13. 8 marbles

In 14–15, use mental math to find each sum.

14. $21 + 5$
15. $61 + 43$

14. 26
15. 104

In 16–17, write the total value.

16. 16. $0.51 or 51¢
17. 17. $3.33

18. Arne buys a book that costs $2.45. He pays with $5.00. Write the change in dollars and cents.

18. $2.55

In 19–20, add.

19. $2.31 + $2.14
20. $1.56 + $2.27

19. $4.45
20. $3.83

In 21–22, use rounding to estimate each sum.

21. $26 + 31$
22. $213 + 478$

21. 60
22. 700

In 23–24, use front-end estimation to estimate each sum.

23. $521 + 318$
24. $492 + 258$

23. 800
24. 600

25. **Explain Your Thinking** Suppose you have $4.00. Is this enough money to buy a hamburger for $2.25 and a drink for $0.98? Explain whether you need an exact answer or an estimate.

Estimate: Since $3 < $4, you have enough money.

80   Chapter 3 Test Form B

Form A

Name _____

Date _____ **Score** _____

Chapter 4 Test
Form
A

In 1–2, write a number sentence for each. Then solve.

1. Carlos owns 5 baseballs and 2 mitts. How many more baseballs does Carlos own than mitts?

1. 5 − 2 = 3; 3 more

2. Sue made 4 soccer goals in her first game and 6 soccer goals in her second game. How many more goals did she make in her second game?

2. 6 − 4 = 2; 2 goals

In 3–4, find each difference using mental math.

3. If 5 − 2 = 3, then 50 − 20 = ■.

3. 30

4. If 9 − 4 = 5, then 900 − ■ = 500.

4. 400

In 5–12, subtract. Check each answer.

5. 48
−21

6. 34
−18

5. 27

6. 16

7. 52 − 27

7. 25

8. 68 − 47

8. 21

9. 357
− 23

10. 219
−138

9. 334

10. 81

11. 483 − 298

11. 185

12. 725 − 367

12. 358

In 13–15, estimate each difference.

13. 35 − 21

13. 20

14. 562 − 221

14. 400

15. $4.89 − $1.76

15. $3.00

16. Regroup 1 ten for 10 ones: 78 = 6 tens ■ ones. Write the missing number.

16. 18 ones

Chapter 4 Test Form A

Continued **99**

Name _____

17. Regroup 1 hundred for 10 tens: 356 = ■ hundreds ■ tens 6 ones. Write the missing numbers.

17. 2 hundreds; 15 tens

In 18–19, subtract. Check each answer.

18. 207 − 64

18. 143

19. 404 − 38

19. 366

In 20–21, solve. Check each answer.

20. 3,786 − 1,252

20. 2,534

21. 5,703 − 1,538

21. 4,165

22. A paint brush costs $3. A set of paints costs $4. Elle bought two brushes and two sets of paints. How much more did she spend on paints than on brushes?

22. $2 more

In 23–24, write what number you would add to each in order to subtract mentally. Then subtract.

23. 37 − 19

23. 1; 18

24. 64 − 27

24. 3; 37

In 25–26, subtract.

25. $3.58 − $1.27

25. $2.31

26. $6.28 − $2.57

26. $3.71

27. Charon uses 3 drops of yellow paint for every 2 drops of blue paint. If she uses 9 drops of yellow, how many drops of blue will she use?

27. 6 drops

28. **Explain Your Thinking** Use the digits 0, 2, 4, 5, 6, and 8 to write two money amounts that you can subtract by trading 1 dime for 10 pennies. Then solve.

Possible answer: $6.54 − $2.08 = $4.46

100 Chapter 4 Test Form A

Form B

Name _____

Date _____ **Score** _____

Chapter 4 Test
Form
B

In 1–2, write a number sentence for each. Then solve.

1. Mara owns 5 baseballs and 2 bats. How many more baseballs does Mara own than bats?

1. 5 − 2 = 3; 3 more

2. Brad baked 3 apples and 7 potatoes. How many more potatoes did he bake than apples?

2. 7 − 3 = 4; 4 more

In 3–4, find each difference using mental math.

3. If 6 − 2 = 4, then 60 − 20 = ■.

3. 40

4. If 8 − 5 = 3, then 800 − ■ = 300.

4. 500

In 5–12, subtract. Check each answer.

5. 37 − 24

5. 13

6. 56 − 29

6. 27

7. 71 − 48

7. 23

8. 46 − 35

8. 11

9. 286 − 75

9. 211

10. 395 − 246

10. 149

11. 635 − 287

11. 348

12. 421 − 178

12. 243

In 13–15, estimate each difference.

13. 78 − 35

13. 40

14. 312 − 178

14. 100

15. $5.74 − $2.41

15. $4.00

16. Regroup 1 ten for 10 ones: 85 = 7 tens ■ ones. Write the missing number.

16. 15 ones

Chapter 4 Test Form B

Continued **101**

Name _____

17. Regroup 1 hundred for 10 tens: 438 = ■ hundreds ■ tens 8 ones. Write the missing numbers.

17. 3 hundreds; 13 tens

In 18–19, subtract. Check each answer.

18. 109 − 58

18. 51

19. 306 − 127

19. 179

In 20–21, solve. Check each answer.

20. 4,857 − 1,653

20. 3,204

21. 5,705 − 2,549

21. 3,156

22. Movie tickets cost $6 for adults and $3 for students. How much more does it cost for 2 adults to see a movie than it costs for 2 students?

22. $6 more

In 23–24, write what number you would add to each in order to subtract mentally. Then subtract.

23. 42 − 28

23. 2; 14

24. 65 − 36

24. 4; 29

In 25–26, subtract.

25. $2.67 − $1.35

25. $1.32

26. $5.24 − $2.67

26. $2.57

27. Michelle's mother gives her 2 pennies for every 3 dollars she saves. Michelle has saved $15. How many pennies has her mother given her?

27. 10 pennies

28. **Explain Your Thinking** Use the digits 1, 3, 4, 5, 7, and 9 to write two money amounts that you can subtract by trading 1 dollar for 10 dimes. Then solve.

Possible answer: $9.37 − $5.41 = $3.96

102 Chapter 4 Test Form B

Top Left — Chapter 5 Test Form A

Name _____

Date _____ Score _____

Chapter 5 Test Form A

Vocabulary: use 2 × 4 = 8 to answer 1–3.

1. Write the product.   1. _____ 8 _____
2. Write the factors.   2. _____ 2 and 4 _____
3. 8 is a multiple of ■.   3. _____ 2 or 4 _____

In 4–5, copy and complete.

4.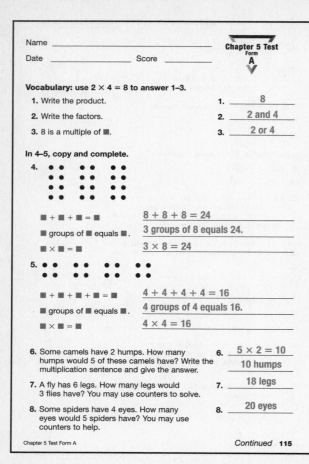

■ + ■ + ■ = ■   8 + 8 + 8 = 24
■ groups of ■ equals ■.   3 groups of 8 equals 24.
■ × ■ = ■   3 × 8 = 24

5.
■ + ■ + ■ + ■ = ■   4 + 4 + 4 + 4 = 16
■ groups of ■ equals ■.   4 groups of 4 equals 16.
■ × ■ = ■   4 × 4 = 16

6. Some camels have 2 humps. How many humps would 5 of these camels have? Write the multiplication sentence and give the answer.   6. _____ 5 × 2 = 10 _____   10 humps

7. A fly has 6 legs. How many legs would 3 flies have? You may use counters to solve.   7. _____ 18 legs _____

8. Some spiders have 4 eyes. How many eyes would 5 spiders have? You may use counters to help.   8. _____ 20 eyes _____

Chapter 5 Test Form A   *Continued* 115

Top Right — Chapter 5 Test Form A (continued)

Name _____

In 9–32, find each product.

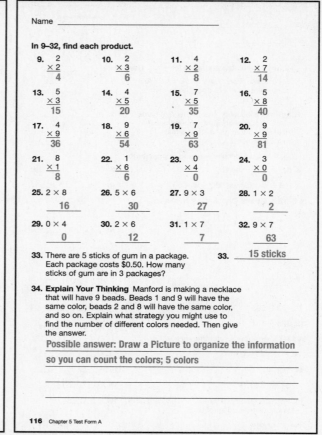

9. 2 × 2 = 4
10. 2 × 3 = 6
11. 4 × 2 = 8
12. 2 × 7 = 14
13. 5 × 3 = 15
14. 4 × 5 = 20
15. 7 × 5 = 35
16. 5 × 8 = 40
17. 4 × 9 = 36
18. 9 × 6 = 54
19. 7 × 9 = 63
20. 9 × 9 = 81
21. 8 × 1 = 8
22. 1 × 6 = 6
23. 0 × 4 = 0
24. 3 × 0 = 0
25. 2 × 8 = 16
26. 5 × 6 = 30
27. 9 × 3 = 27
28. 1 × 2 = 2
29. 0 × 4 = 0
30. 2 × 6 = 12
31. 1 × 7 = 7
32. 9 × 7 = 63

33. There are 5 sticks of gum in a package. Each package costs $0.50. How many sticks of gum are in 3 packages?   33. _____ 15 sticks _____

34. **Explain Your Thinking** Manford is making a necklace that will have 9 beads. Beads 1 and 9 will have the same color, beads 2 and 8 will have the same color, and so on. Explain what strategy you might use to find the number of different colors needed. Then give the answer.

Possible answer: Draw a Picture to organize the information so you can count the colors; 5 colors

116   Chapter 5 Test Form A

Bottom Left — Chapter 5 Test Form B

Name _____

Date _____ Score _____

Chapter 5 Test Form B

Vocabulary: use 2 × 3 = 6 to answer 1–3.

1. Write the factors.   1. _____ 2 and 3 _____
2. Write the product.   2. _____ 6 _____
3. 6 is a multiple of ■.   3. _____ 2 or 3 _____

In 4–5, copy and complete.

4.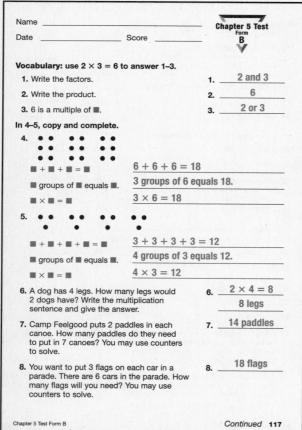

■ + ■ + ■ = ■   6 + 6 + 6 = 18
■ groups of ■ equals ■.   3 groups of 6 equals 18.
■ × ■ = ■   3 × 6 = 18

5.
■ + ■ + ■ + ■ = ■   3 + 3 + 3 + 3 = 12
■ groups of ■ equals ■.   4 groups of 3 equals 12.
■ × ■ = ■   4 × 3 = 12

6. A dog has 4 legs. How many legs would 2 dogs have? Write the multiplication sentence and give the answer.   6. _____ 2 × 4 = 8 _____   8 legs

7. Camp Feelgood puts 2 paddles in each canoe. How many paddles do they need to put in 7 canoes? You may use counters to solve.   7. _____ 14 paddles _____

8. You want to put 3 flags on each car in a parade. There are 6 cars in the parade. How many flags will you need? You may use counters to solve.   8. _____ 18 flags _____

Chapter 5 Test Form B   *Continued* 117

Bottom Right — Chapter 5 Test Form B (continued)

Name _____

In 9–32, find each product.

9. 3 × 2 = 6
10. 6 × 2 = 12
11. 2 × 7 = 14
12. 2 × 8 = 16
13. 4 × 5 = 20
14. 6 × 5 = 30
15. 8 × 5 = 40
16. 9 × 5 = 45
17. 9 × 3 = 27
18. 4 × 9 = 36
19. 6 × 9 = 54
20. 8 × 9 = 72
21. 4 × 1 = 4
22. 1 × 6 = 6
23. 7 × 0 = 0
24. 0 × 8 = 0
25. 2 × 2 = 4
26. 5 × 4 = 20
27. 9 × 3 = 27
28. 1 × 2 = 2
29. 0 × 6 = 0
30. 2 × 4 = 8
31. 1 × 6 = 6
32. 9 × 9 = 81

33. There are 2 muffins in a package. Each package costs $0.75. How many muffins are in 8 packages?   33. _____ 16 muffins _____

34. **Explain Your Thinking** Celia is making a necklace that will have 9 beads. Beads 1 and 9 will have the same color, beads 2 and 8 will have the same color, and so on. Explain what strategy you might use to find if any beads of the same color are next to each other. Then give the answer.

Possible answer: Draw a Picture to organize the information so you see no beads of the same color next to each other.

118   Chapter 5 Test Form B

Form A

Date _____ Score _____

Vocabulary: In 1–3, match each with its meaning.

1. square number   a. the product of a given whole number and any other whole number   1. ____ b

2. grouping   b. the product when both factors are the same   2. ____ c

3. multiple   c. when you multiply, you can group factors in any order and the product will be the same   3. ____ a

In 4–19, find each product.

4.   3 × 5 = 15

5.   6 × 3 = 18

6.   4 × 2 = 8

7.   9 × 4 = 36

8.   6 × 5 = 30

9.   9 × 6 = 54

10.   7 × 3 = 21

11.   5 × 7 = 35

12. 4 × 8 = 32

13. 3 × 8 = 24

14. 7 × 6 = 42

15. 6 × 2 = 12

16. 9 × 7 = 63

17. 7 × 8 = 56

18. 6 × 8 = 48

19. 8 × 8 = 64

20. Nina bought 6 packages of butter. Each package contains 4 sticks. How many sticks of butter did Nina buy?   20. __24 sticks__

21. A group of students were taking a field trip. They traveled in 7 vans with 5 students riding in each van. How many students were going on the trip?   21. __35 students__

In 22–24, write *true* or *false*. You may use a hundred chart to help.

22. 21 is a multiple of 3.   22. __True__

23. 35 is a multiple of 3.   23. __False__

24. 36 is a multiple of 6.   24. __True__

In 25–27, continue each pattern.

25. 40, 50, 60, ■, ■, ■   25. __70, 80, 90__

26. 77, 66, 55, ■, ■, ■   26. __44, 33, 22__

27. 36, 48, 60, ■, ■, ■   27. __72, 84, 96__

In 28–31, find each product.

28. 2 × 3 × 4   28. __24__

29. (3 × 2) × 8   29. __48__

30. 1 × (4 × 7)   30. __28__

31. 3 × (1 × 6)   31. __18__

32. Tim has 4 board games. Each game can have 4 players. Will Tim have enough games so that he and 23 friends can play at one time? Explain.

No. 4 × 4 = 16 and 16 < 23. So, there are not enough games.

33. Juanita is mixing pitchers of lemonade for the 29 students in her class. One pitcher will serve 4 students. How many pitchers does she need to make?   33. __8 pitchers__

34. **Explain Your Thinking** Explain how you can use the product of 4 × 3 to find 8 × 3. Then give the product.

Since 4 is half of 8, you can double the product of 4 × 3.

So, 2 × (4 × 3) = 24.

Form B

Date _____ Score _____

Vocabulary: In 1–3, match each with its meaning.

1. multiple   a. when you multiply, you can group factors in any order and the product will be the same   1. ____ c

2. grouping property   b. the product when both factors are the same   2. ____ a

3. square number   c. the product of a given whole number and any other whole number   3. ____ b

In 4–19, find each product.

4.   3 × 4 = 12

5.   9 × 3 = 27

6.   5 × 4 = 20

7.   4 × 2 = 8

8.   7 × 6 = 42

9.   6 × 3 = 18

10.   7 × 5 = 35

11.   3 × 7 = 21

12. 9 × 8 = 72

13. 5 × 8 = 40

14. 8 × 8 = 64

15. 7 × 8 = 56

16. 2 × 7 = 14

17. 6 × 8 = 48

18. 5 × 6 = 30

19. 4 × 6 = 24

20. Robin bought 3 bags of potatoes. Each bag weighs 8 pounds. How many pounds of potatoes did Robin buy?   20. __24 pounds__

21. A group of students were playing in the gym. There were 4 teams with 7 players on each team. How many students were playing in the gym?   21. __28 students__

In 22–24, write *true* or *false*. You may use a hundred chart to help.

22. 35 is a multiple of 6.   22. __False__

23. 24 is a multiple of 3.   23. __True__

24. 56 is a multiple of 6.   24. __False__

In 25–27, continue each pattern.

25. 44, 55, 66, ■, ■, ■   25. __77, 88, 99__

26. 36, 48, 60, ■, ■, ■   26. __72, 84, 96__

27. 80, 70, 60, ■, ■, ■   27. __50, 40, 30__

In 28–31, find each product.

28. 1 × 3 × 2   28. __6__

29. (2 × 4) × 6   29. __48__

30. 7 × (4 × 2)   30. __56__

31. 6 × (2 × 3)   31. __36__

32. Avril brought 7 packages of balloons to a school party. Each package had 5 balloons. There were 32 students at the party. Did Avril bring enough balloons for everyone? Explain.

Yes. 5 × 7 = 35 and 35 > 32. So, there will be enough.

33. Horace is making cookies for 49 friends. Each batch makes 8 very large cookies. How many batches will Horace need to make if each friend gets one cookie?   33. __7 batches__

34. **Explain Your Thinking** Explain how you can use the product of 2 × 6 to find 4 × 6. Then give the product.

Since 2 is half of 4, you can double the product of 2 × 6.

So, 2 × (2 × 6) = 24.

Vocabulary: In 1–4, match each with its meaning.

1. divisor   a. a whole number that has 0, 2, 4, 6 or 8 in the ones place   1. ____b____

2. quotient   b. the number by which a dividend is divided   2. ____c____

3. odd number   c. the answer to a division problem   3. ____d____

4. even number   d. a whole number that has 1, 3, 5, 7, or 9 in the ones place   4. ____a____

5. Complete the division sentence.   5. ____3____

$6 \div 2 = \blacksquare$

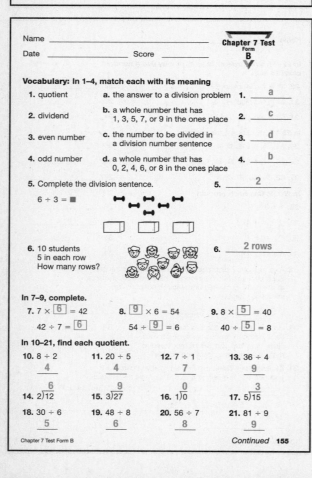

6. 8 dogs
   2 in each pen
   How many pens?   6. ____4 pens____

In 7–9, complete.

7. $8 \times \boxed{3} = 24$ 8. $7 \times \boxed{8} = 56$ 9. $\boxed{5} \times 7 = 35$
   $24 \div \boxed{3} = 8$ $56 \div 7 = \boxed{8}$ $35 \div \boxed{5} = 7$

In 10–21, find each quotient.

10. $12 \div 2$ 11. $25 \div 5$ 12. $5 \div 1$ 13. $28 \div 4$
    6   5   5   7

14. $2\overline{)16}$ 15. $3\overline{)21}$ 16. $6\overline{)0}$ 17. $5\overline{)40}$
    8   7   0   8

18. $54 \div 6$ 19. $64 \div 8$ 20. $49 \div 7$ 21. $72 \div 9$
    9   8   7   8

---

22. Ruby has 42 dollar bills. She gave 7 dollar bills to each of her nieces. How many nieces does she have?   22. ____6 nieces____

23. Victor shared 28 stickers equally with 3 friends. How many stickers did each person get? (Remember that Victor will have the same number of stickers as each of his friends.)   23. ____7 stickers____

In 24–25, write which operation you would use to solve the problem. Then solve.

24. A loaf of nut bread has 18 slices. If a serving is 3 slices, how many servings are there?   Division; 6 servings

25. Arimoto bought 9 tickets to the choir recital. Each ticket cost $5. How much money did he spend?   Multiplication; $45

26. The band has 20 members that will march in a parade. They will march in equal rows. What are all the ways the leader can arrange them?
    1 row of 20, 2 rows of 10, 4 rows of 5, 5 rows of 4, 10 rows of 2, 20 rows of 1

27. Box A has 10 cubes inside. Box B has 4 cubes inside. How many cubes are inside Box C?   27. ____6 cubes____

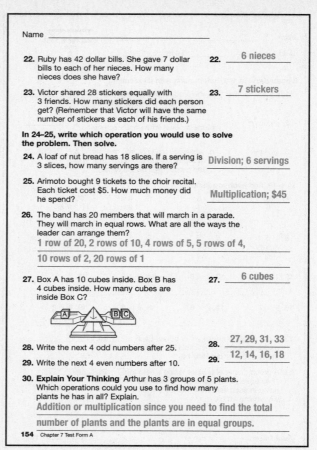

28. Write the next 4 odd numbers after 25.   28. ____27, 29, 31, 33____

29. Write the next 4 even numbers after 10.   29. ____12, 14, 16, 18____

30. **Explain Your Thinking** Arthur has 3 groups of 5 plants. Which operations could you use to find how many plants he has in all? Explain.
    Addition or multiplication since you need to find the total number of plants and the plants are in equal groups.

Vocabulary: In 1–4, match each with its meaning

1. quotient   a. the answer to a division problem   1. ____a____

2. dividend   b. a whole number that has 1, 3, 5, 7, or 9 in the ones place   2. ____c____

3. even number   c. the number to be divided in a division number sentence   3. ____d____

4. odd number   d. a whole number that has 0, 2, 4, 6, or 8 in the ones place   4. ____b____

5. Complete the division sentence.   5. ____2____

$6 \div 3 = \blacksquare$

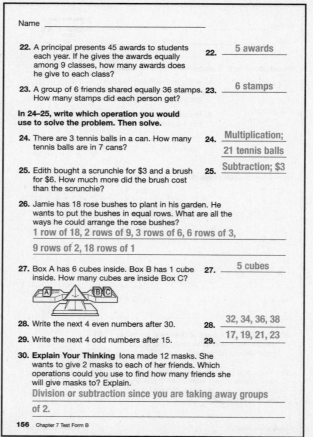

6. 10 students
   5 in each row
   How many rows?   6. ____2 rows____

In 7–9, complete.

7. $7 \times \boxed{6} = 42$ 8. $\boxed{9} \times 6 = 54$ 9. $8 \times \boxed{5} = 40$
   $42 \div 7 = \boxed{6}$ $54 \div \boxed{9} = 6$ $40 \div \boxed{5} = 8$

In 10–21, find each quotient.

10. $8 \div 2$ 11. $20 \div 5$ 12. $7 \div 1$ 13. $36 \div 4$
    4   4   7   9

14. $2\overline{)12}$ 15. $3\overline{)27}$ 16. $1\overline{)0}$ 17. $5\overline{)15}$
    6   9   0   3

18. $30 \div 6$ 19. $48 \div 8$ 20. $56 \div 7$ 21. $81 \div 9$
    5   6   8   9

---

22. A principal presents 45 awards to students each year. If he gives the awards equally among 9 classes, how many awards does he give to each class?   22. ____5 awards____

23. A group of 6 friends shared equally 36 stamps. How many stamps did each person get?   23. ____6 stamps____

In 24–25, write which operation you would use to solve the problem. Then solve.

24. There are 3 tennis balls in a can. How many tennis balls are in 7 cans?   24. Multiplication; 21 tennis balls

25. Edith bought a scrunchie for $3 and a brush for $6. How much more did the brush cost than the scrunchie?   25. Subtraction; $3

26. Jamie has 18 rose bushes to plant in his garden. He wants to put the bushes in equal rows. What are all the ways he could arrange the rose bushes?
    1 row of 18, 2 rows of 9, 3 rows of 6, 6 rows of 3, 9 rows of 2, 18 rows of 1

27. Box A has 6 cubes inside. Box B has 1 cube inside. How many cubes are inside Box C?   27. ____5 cubes____

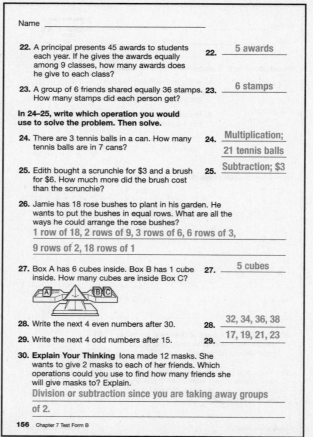

28. Write the next 4 even numbers after 30.   28. ____32, 34, 36, 38____

29. Write the next 4 odd numbers after 15.   29. ____17, 19, 21, 23____

30. **Explain Your Thinking** Iona made 12 masks. She wants to give 2 masks to each of her friends. Which operations could you use to find how many friends she will give masks to? Explain.
    Division or subtraction since you are taking away groups of 2.

Chapter 8 Test — Form A

© Scott Foresman Addison Wesley 3

Name _____

Date _____ Score _____

Chapter 8 Test
Form **A**

Vocabulary: In 1–4, match each with its example.

1. c 2. b 3. a 4. d

a. line of symmetry   b. line
c. cylinder   d. right angle

In 5–7, name the solid figure or shape that each object looks like.

5. Sphere   6. Cone   7. Triangle

8. Are these lines parallel or intersecting? — Intersecting

9. Is this angle a right angle, less than a right angle, or greater than a right angle? — Less than a right angle

In 10–12, write congruent or not congruent for each.

10. Not congruent   11. Congruent   12. Congruent

In 13–15, write slide, flip, or turn.

13. Slide   14. Turn   15. Flip

Chapter 8 Test Form A   *Continued* 169

Name _____

In 16–18, is each a line of symmetry? Write yes or no.

16. Yes   17. Yes   18. No

19. How many squares are in this design?   19. 11 squares

In 20–21, find the perimeter and the area of each figure.

20. Perimeter 16 units   Area 15 square units

21. Perimeter 12 units   Area 7 square units

In 22–24, find the volume of each.

22. 4 cubic units   23. 6 cubic units   24. 5 cubic units

In 25–26, write the ordered pair that locates each letter.

25. A (2, 3)
26. B (4, 1)
27. Which letter is located at (2, 5)? E

28. **Explain Your Thinking** Use 4 line segments to draw a polygon that has 4 right angles.

Possible Answer:

170   Chapter 8 Test Form A

Chapter 8 Test — Form B

Name _____

Date _____ Score _____

Chapter 8 Test
Form **B**

Vocabulary: In 1–4, match each with its example.

1. b   2. a   3. d   4. c

a. line segment   b. sphere
c. polygon   d. line of symmetry

In 5–7, name the solid figure or shape that each object looks like.

5. Cube   6. Cylinder   7. Circle

8. Are these lines parallel or intersecting? — Parallel

9. Is this angle a right angle, less than a right angle, or greater than a right angle? — Right angle

In 10–12, write congruent or not congruent for each.

10. Congruent   11. Not congruent   12. Congruent

In 13–15, write slide, flip, or turn.

13. Flip   14. Turn   15. Slide

Chapter 8 Test Form B   *Continued* 171

Name _____

In 16–18, is each a line of symmetry? Write yes or no.

16. No   17. No   18. Yes

19. How many squares are in this design?   19. 14 squares

In 20–21, find the perimeter and the area of each figure.

20. Perimeter 12 units   Area 8 square units

21. Perimeter 20 units   Area 13 square units

In 22–24, find the volume of each.

22. 8 cubic units   23. 3 cubic units   24. 6 cubic units

In 25–26, write the ordered pair that locates each letter.

25. A (2, 6)
26. B (3, 4)
27. Which letter is located at (6, 2)? G

28. **Explain Your Thinking** Use 4 line segments to draw a polygon that has 2 right angles and is not a rectangle.

Possible Answer:

172   Chapter 8 Test Form B

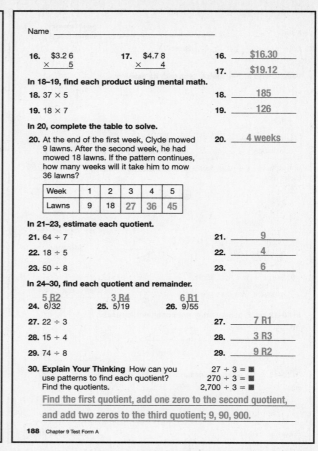

Chapter 9 Test Form A

Name _____

Date _____ Score _____

In 1–2, complete. You may use place-value blocks.

1. 9 × 1 ten = ■ tens   _9_

   9 × 10 = ■   _90_

2. 6 × 7 tens = ■ tens   _42_

   6 × 70 = ■   _420_

In 3–4, complete.

3. 7 × 5 = ■   _35_

   7 × 50 = ■   _350_

   7 × 500 = ■   _3,500_

4. 3 × 8 = ■   _24_

   3 × 80 = ■   _240_

   3 × 800 = ■   _2,400_

In 5–7, estimate each product.

5. 4 × 37   **5.** _160_

6. 6 × 92   **6.** _540_

7. 7 × 523   **7.** _3,500_

In 8–9, find each product. You may use place value blocks to help.

8. 3 × 16   3 x 10   3 x 6   **8.** _48_

9. 2 × 21   2 x 20   2 x 1   **9.** _42_

In 10–17, find each product.

10. 46 × 5   **10.** _230_

11. 28 × 6   **11.** _168_

12. 1 3 × 9   **12.** _117_

13. 2 8 × 7   **13.** _196_

14. 2 4 7 × 5   **14.** _1,235_

15. 6 0 2 × 7   **15.** _4,214_

Name _____

16. $3.2 6 × 5   **16.** _$16.30_

17. $4.7 8 × 4   **17.** _$19.12_

In 18–19, find each product using mental math.

18. 37 × 5   **18.** _185_

19. 18 × 7   **19.** _126_

In 20, complete the table to solve.

20. At the end of the first week, Clyde mowed 9 lawns. After the second week, he had mowed 18 lawns. If the pattern continues, how many weeks will it take him to mow 36 lawns?

20. _4 weeks_

Week	1	2	3	4	5
Lawns	9	18	27	36	45

In 21–23, estimate each quotient.

21. 64 ÷ 7   **21.** _9_

22. 18 ÷ 5   **22.** _4_

23. 50 ÷ 8   **23.** _6_

In 24–30, find each quotient and remainder.

24. 6)32   5 R2

25. 5)19   3 R4

26. 9)55   6 R1

27. 22 ÷ 3   **27.** _7 R1_

28. 15 ÷ 4   **28.** _3 R3_

29. 74 ÷ 8   **29.** _9 R2_

30. Explain Your Thinking How can you use patterns to find each quotient? Find the quotients.

27 ÷ 3 = ■
270 ÷ 3 = ■
2,700 ÷ 3 = ■

Find the first quotient, add one zero to the second quotient, and add two zeros to the third quotient; 9, 90, 900.

Chapter 9 Test Form B

Name _____

Date _____ Score _____

In 1–2, complete. You may use place-value blocks.

1. 4 × 2 tens = ■ tens   _8_

   4 × 20 = ■   _80_

2. 8 × 7 tens = ■ tens   _56_

   8 × 70 = ■   _560_

In 3–4, complete.

3. 7 × 6 = ■   _42_

   7 × 60 = ■   _420_

   7 × 600 = ■   _4,200_

4. 5 × 6 = ■   _30_

   5 × 60 = ■   _300_

   5 × 600 = ■   _3,000_

In 5–7, estimate each product.

5. 3 × 42   **5.** _120_

6. 8 × 93   **6.** _720_

7. 9 × 908   **7.** _8,100_

In 8–9, find each product. You may use place value blocks to help.

8. 2 × 23   2 x 20   2 x 3   **8.** _46_

9. 4 × 15   4 x 10   4 x 5   **9.** _60_

In 10–17, find each product.

10. 22 × 8   **10.** _176_

11. 54 × 3   **11.** _162_

12. 2 6 × 5   **12.** _130_

13. 8 9 × 4   **13.** _356_

14. 2 1 5 × 7   **14.** _1,505_

15. 5 3 1 × 6   **15.** _3,186_

Name _____

16. $7.5 1 × 8   **16.** _$60.08_

17. $5.9 4 × 7   **17.** _$41.58_

In 18–19, find each product using mental math.

18. 53 × 8   **18.** _424_

19. 59 × 4   **19.** _236_

In 20, complete the table to solve.

20. Cassie wrote 200 words on the first page of her journal. After the second page, she had written 400 words. If the pattern continues, how many pages will it take her to write 1,000 words?

20. _5 pages_

Pages	1	2	3	4	5
Words	200	400	600	800	1,000

In 21–23, estimate each quotient.

21. 55 ÷ 6   **21.** _9_

22. 25 ÷ 3   **22.** _8_

23. 37 ÷ 9   **23.** _4_

In 24–30, find each quotient and remainder.

24. 6)40   6 R4

25. 3)17   5 R2

26. 9)82   9 R1

27. 24 ÷ 5   **27.** _4 R4_

28. 14 ÷ 3   **28.** _4 R2_

29. 50 ÷ 9   **29.** _5 R5_

30. Explain Your Thinking How can you use patterns to find each quotient? Find the quotients.

64 ÷ 8 = ■
640 ÷ 8 = ■
6,400 ÷ 8 = ■

Find the first quotient, add one zero to the second quotient, and add two zeros to the third quotient; 8, 80, 800.

Chapter 10 Test — Form A

Name

Date _____ Score _____

Vocabulary: In 1–3, match each with its meaning.

1. unit fraction   **a.** fractions that name the same amount

2. fraction   **b.** a fraction with a numerator of 1

3. equivalent fractions   **c.** a comparison of equal parts to a whole number

1. ___b___
2. ___c___
3. ___a___

In 4–5, write the equal parts of each whole.

4.   5.

4. ___Sixths___
5. ___Fourths___

In 6–7, write the fraction of each figure that is shaded.

6.   7.

6. $\dfrac{5}{8}$
7. $\dfrac{1}{5}$

In 8–9, are the fractions equivalent or not equivalent?

8.   9.

8. ___Equivalent___
9. ___Not equivalent___

In 10–11, compare. Write <, >, or =.

10. $\dfrac{1}{2}$ $\dfrac{1}{3}$ $\dfrac{1}{3}$ $\dfrac{1}{2} \bullet \dfrac{2}{3}$

11. $\dfrac{1}{6} \bullet \dfrac{1}{3}$

10. ___<___
11. ___<___

In 12–13, estimate the amount that is shaded.

Possible answers:

12.   13.

12. About $\dfrac{3}{4}$
13. Less than $\dfrac{1}{2}$

In 14–15, solve. You may draw a picture to help.

14. Find $\dfrac{1}{4}$ of 20.

15. Find $\dfrac{1}{5}$ of 15.

14. ___5___
15. ___3___

Chapter 10 Test Form A   *Continued* 209

Name

In 16–17, write a mixed number for each picture.

16.   17.

16. $1\dfrac{5}{6}$
17. $2\dfrac{1}{4}$

18. Find the difference. $\dfrac{5}{8} - \dfrac{3}{8}$

19. Find the sum. $\dfrac{3}{10} + \dfrac{4}{10}$

18. $\dfrac{2}{8}$ or $\dfrac{1}{4}$
19. $\dfrac{7}{10}$

20. Measure the glue stick to the nearest inch.

GLUE-STICK

20. ___3 inches___

21. Measure the binder clip to the nearest $\dfrac{1}{2}$ inch.

21. $1\dfrac{1}{2}$ inches

22. Measure the pen cap to the nearest $\dfrac{1}{4}$ inch.

22. $2\dfrac{1}{4}$ inches

23. Write 1 foot 6 inches in inches.

23. ___18 inches___

In 24–25, compare. Write <, >, or =.

24. 3 yards ● 10 feet

25. 72 inches ● 2 yards

24. ___<___
25. ___=___

26. Shane, Jorie, Hoy, and Tia have different color soccer uniforms: white, yellow, blue, and red. Hoy's uniform is white. Jorie's uniform matches her red hair. Tia's uniform is the color of the sky. What color is each person's uniform?

Shane: yellow; Jorie: red; Hoy: white; Tia: blue

27. **Explain Your Thinking** Draw 6 flowers. Color some of them. Write a fraction that names how many flowers are colored. Explain what the numerator and denominator mean.

Check students' answers. Numerator is number of colored flowers. Denominator is 6, total number of flowers.

210   Chapter 10 Test Form A

Chapter 10 Test — Form B

Name

Date _____ Score _____

Vocabulary: In 1–3, match each with its meaning.

1. equivalent fractions   **a.** a comparison of equal parts to a whole number

2. unit fraction   **b.** a fraction with a numerator of 1

3. fraction   **c.** fractions that name the same amount

1. ___c___
2. ___b___
3. ___a___

In 4–5, write the equal parts of each whole.

4.   5.

4. ___Fourths___
5. ___Thirds___

In 6–7, write the fraction of each figure that is shaded.

6.   7.

6. $\dfrac{5}{6}$
7. $\dfrac{7}{10}$

In 8–9, are the fractions equivalent or not equivalent?

8.   9.

8. ___Not equivalent___
9. ___Equivalent___

In 10–11, compare. Write <, >, or =.

10. $\dfrac{1}{3}$ $\dfrac{1}{2}$ $\dfrac{1}{3} \bullet \dfrac{1}{2}$

11. $\dfrac{1}{5} \bullet \dfrac{1}{10}$

10. ___<___
11. ___>___

In 12–13, estimate the amount that is shaded.

Possible answers:

12.   13.

12. More than $\dfrac{1}{4}$
13. About $\dfrac{1}{2}$

In 14–15, solve. You may draw a picture to help.

14. Find $\dfrac{1}{5}$ of 30.

15. Find $\dfrac{1}{3}$ of 27.

14. ___6___
15. ___9___

Chapter 10 Test Form B   *Continued* 211

Name

In 16–17, write a mixed number for each picture.

16.   17.

16. $1\dfrac{2}{3}$
17. $2\dfrac{1}{4}$

18. Find the difference. $\dfrac{4}{5} - \dfrac{2}{5}$

19. Find the sum. $\dfrac{1}{12} + \dfrac{5}{12}$

18. $\dfrac{2}{5}$
19. $\dfrac{6}{12}$ or $\dfrac{1}{2}$

20. Measure darning needle to the nearest inch.

20. ___2 inches___

21. Measure yarn to the nearest $\dfrac{1}{2}$ inch.

21. $2\dfrac{1}{2}$ inches

22. Measure spool of thread to the nearest $\dfrac{1}{4}$ inch.

22. $1\dfrac{3}{4}$ inches

23. Write 1 foot 10 inches in inches.

23. ___22 inches___

In 24–25, compare. Write <, >, or =.

24. 2 yards ● 8 feet

25. 50 inches ● 3 feet

24. ___<___
25. ___>___

26. The winners of the sack races at the picnic were Max, Lisa, Ryan, and Kala. Max finished second. Ryan finished last. Lisa finished before Kala. Name the order that the winners crossed the finish line.

Lisa, Max, Kala, Ryan

27. **Explain Your Thinking** Draw 10 flowers. Color some of them. Write a fraction that names how many flowers are not colored. Explain what the numerator and denominator mean.

Check students' answers. Numerator is number of flowers not colored. Denominator is 10, total number of flowers.

212   Chapter 10 Test Form B

Vocabulary: In 1–4 match each with its meaning.

1. decimal point   **a.** a metric unit of measure equal to 1,000 meters   **1.** _c_

2. centimeter   **b.** a standard unit used to measure length in the metric system   **2.** _b_

3. meter   **c.** symbol used to separate ones from tenths in a decimal   **3.** _d_

4. kilometer   **d.** a metric unit of measure equal to 100 centimeters   **4.** _a_

In 5–6, write the fraction and the decimal to name each shaded part.

5.   6.

5. $1\frac{8}{10}$, 1.8

6. $\frac{11}{100}$, 0.11

In 7–12, write each as a decimal.

7. $\frac{6}{10}$ **7.** 0.6

8. $3\frac{8}{10}$ **8.** 3.8

9. $5\frac{35}{100}$ **9.** 5.35

10. four hundredths   **10.** 0.04

11. two and fifty-two hundredths   **11.** 2.52

12. one tenth   **12.** 0.1

In 13–16, find each sum or difference.

13. 0.8 + 0.4   14. 1.4 + 2.9   **13.** 1.2

14. 4.3

15. 4.5 − 1.3   16. 6.1 − 3.8   **15.** 3.2

16. 2.3

In 17–20, write each as a money amount.

17. $\frac{34}{100}$ of $1.00   **17.** $0.34

18. $2\frac{50}{100}$ of $1.00   **18.** $2.50

19. eight cents   **19.** $0.08

20. one dollar and twenty-seven cents   **20.** $1.27

In 21–23, match each with its estimate.

21. length of a marker   **a.** 2 cm   **21.** _b_

22. length of a river   **b.** 1 dm   **22.** _c_

23. width of the face of a watch   **c.** 20 km   **23.** _a_

In 24–26, write whether you would measure each in cm, m, or km.

24. distance of a bike ride   **24.** km

25. length of the soccer field   **25.** m

26. height of a small dog   **26.** cm

27. Suppose you get on an elevator on the third floor. The elevator goes up 2 floors, then up 5 more floors, then it goes down 3 floors, and then up 4 floors. What floor is the elevator at now?   **27.** Eleventh floor

28. There are 33 people on a tram. At the first stop, 2 more people get on and 4 get off. At the next stop, 8 people get off and 5 get on. At the next stop, 10 get off and 2 get on. How many people are on the tram now?   **28.** 20 people

29. **Explain Your Thinking** Diane shaded 4 rows of a hundredths square. Write a decimal to name the shaded part. Explain. You may use this hundredths grid to help.

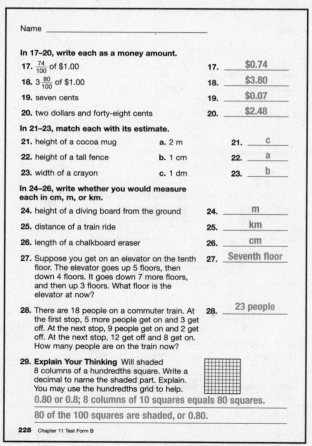

0.40 or 0.4; 4 rows of 10 squares equals 40 squares. 40 of the 100 squares are shaded, or 0.40.

Vocabulary: In 1–4 match each with its meaning.

1. decimal   **a.** a metric unit of measure equal to 100 centimeters   **1.** _c_

2. decimeter   **b.** a metric unit of measure equal to 1,000 meters   **2.** _d_

3. kilometer   **c.** a number that uses place value and a decimal point to show tenths, hundredths, and so on   **3.** _b_

4. meter   **d.** a metric unit of measure equal to 10 centimeters   **4.** _a_

In 5–6, write the fraction and the decimal to name each shaded part.

5.   6.

5. $\frac{3}{10}$, 0.3

6. $1\frac{9}{100}$, 1.09

In 7–12, write each as a decimal.

7. $\frac{2}{10}$ **7.** 0.2

8. $1\frac{7}{10}$ **8.** 1.7

9. $2\frac{75}{100}$ **9.** 2.75

10. forty-five hundredths   **10.** 0.45

11. one and eighty-two hundredths   **11.** 1.82

12. two and three tenths   **12.** 2.3

In 13–16, find each sum or difference.

13. 1.4 + 0.4   14. 0.8 + 3.8   **13.** 1.8

14. 4.6

15. 3.5 − 1.8   16. 6.6 − 3.2   **15.** 1.7

16. 3.4

In 17–20, write each as a money amount.

17. $\frac{74}{100}$ of $1.00   **17.** $0.74

18. $3\frac{80}{100}$ of $1.00   **18.** $3.80

19. seven cents   **19.** $0.07

20. two dollars and forty-eight cents   **20.** $2.48

In 21–23, match each with its estimate.

21. height of a cocoa mug   **a.** 2 m   **21.** _c_

22. height of a tall fence   **b.** 1 cm   **22.** _a_

23. width of a crayon   **c.** 1 dm   **23.** _b_

In 24–26, write whether you would measure each in cm, m, or km.

24. height of a diving board from the ground   **24.** m

25. distance of a train ride   **25.** km

26. length of a chalkboard eraser   **26.** cm

27. Suppose you get on an elevator on the tenth floor. The elevator goes up 5 floors, then down 4 floors. It goes down 7 more floors, and then up 3 floors. What floor is the elevator at now?   **27.** Seventh floor

28. There are 18 people on a commuter train. At the first stop, 5 more people get on and 3 get off. At the next stop, 9 people get on and 2 get off. At the next stop, 12 get off and 8 get on. How many people are on the train now?   **28.** 23 people

29. **Explain Your Thinking** Will shaded 8 columns of a hundredths square. Write a decimal to name the shaded part. Explain. You may use the hundredths grid to help.

0.80 or 0.8; 8 columns of 10 squares equals 80 squares. 80 of the 100 squares are shaded, or 0.80.

Form A

Name _____

Date _____ Score _____

Vocabulary: In 1–2, write true or false.

1. Capacity is the amount an object weighs.

2. Predictions are a guess about what will happen.

In 3–10, write the best estimate for each.

3.
MILK
1 cup
1 quart
1 gallon

4.
1 cup
1 quart
1 gallon

5.
Vanilla
59 mL
59 L

6.
8 mL
8 L

7.
POTATOES
5 oz
5 lb

8.
Toothpaste
6 oz
6 lb

9.
14 g
14 kg

10.
To:
6 g
6 kg

1. _____ False
2. _____ True

3. _____ 1 quart
4. _____ 1 gallon

5. _____ 59 mL
6. _____ 8 L

7. _____ 5 lb
8. _____ 6 oz

9. _____ 14 g
10. _____ 6 kg

In 11–12, write each temperature using °F.

11.
°F °C
0   -20
-10
-20   -30

12.
°F °C
30
20   -10
10

11. _____ −6°F
12. _____ 24°F

Name _____

In 13–14, decide whether each is likely or unlikely.

13. You will drive a car tomorrow.

14. Someone in your class is 9 years old.

13. _____ Unlikely
14. _____ Likely

In 15–16, suppose you put these cubes in a bag. Predict which color you are more likely to pull out.

15.

16.

15. _____ Black
16. _____ Black

17. Copy and complete.   White: ■ out of 6 or $\frac{■}{6}$

Gray: ■ out of 6 or $\frac{■}{6}$

Dotted: ■ out of 6 or $\frac{■}{6}$

17.
1 out of 6 or $\frac{1}{6}$
2 out of 6 or $\frac{2}{6}$
3 out of 6 or $\frac{3}{6}$

In 18–19, write whether each spinner is fair or unfair.

18.

19.

18. _____ Fair
19. _____ Unfair

20. Anne needs to be at the bus stop by 7:35 A.M. It takes her 5 minutes to walk to the bus stop and 45 minutes to get ready. At what time must she get up?

20. _____ 6:45 A.M.

21. Janet picked a number. Then she subtracted 4, added 6, and subtracted 10. If Janet ended up with 50, what number did she pick?

21. _____ 58

22. **Explain Your Thinking** Lionel and 2 friends are going to camp out in Lionel's back yard. Lionel thinks that each of the three boys will drink 1,000 mL of sports drink. He buys one 2-L bottle. Did he buy enough? Explain.

No, 3 × 1,000 mL = 3,000 mL, and 2 L = 2,000 mL;

3,000 > 2,000, so he didn't buy enough.

Form B

Name _____

Date _____ Score _____

Vocabulary: In 1–2, write true or false.

1. You can use probability to make predictions.

2. You may use an experiment to test a prediction.

In 3–10, write the best estimate for each.

3.
1 cup
1 quart
1 gallon

4.
O.J.
1 cup
1 quart
1 gallon

5.
12 mL
12 L

6.
SHAMPOO
473 mL
473 L

7.
7 oz
7 lb

8.
1 oz
1 lb

9.
Dog Kibble
14 g
14 kg

10.
5 g
5 kg

1. _____ True
2. _____ True

3. _____ 1 cup
4. _____ 1 quart

5. _____ 12 mL
6. _____ 473 mL

7. _____ 7 lb
8. _____ 1 oz

9. _____ 14 kg
10. _____ 5 g

In 11–12, write each temperature using °F.

11.
°F °C
100   40
90
80   30

12.
°F °C
0   20
-10
-20
-30   -30

11. _____ 96°F
12. _____ −2°F

Name _____

In 13–14, decide whether each is likely or unlikely.

13. You will eat lunch tomorrow.

14. Your teacher will fall asleep during class.

13. _____ Likely
14. _____ Unlikely

In 15–16, suppose you put these cubes in a bag. Predict which color your are more likely to pull out.

15.

16.

15. _____ White
16. _____ Black

17. Complete.   White: ■ out of 5 or $\frac{■}{5}$

Black: ■ out of 5 or $\frac{■}{5}$

Dotted: ■ out of 5 or $\frac{■}{5}$

17.
3 out of 5 or $\frac{3}{5}$
1 out of 5 or $\frac{1}{5}$
1 out of 5 or $\frac{1}{5}$

In 18–19, write whether each spinner is fair or unfair.

18.

19.

18. _____ Unfair
19. _____ Fair

20. Che has a rope. He cuts 25 in. off of the rope. Then he cuts the rest of the rope into 5 equal pieces. Each piece is 15 in. long. How long was the original rope?

20. _____ 100 in.

21. Lilia gave 4 stamps to Eric and 3 stamps to Otis. She bought 8 more stamps. Now she has 9 stamps. How many stamps did she start with?

21. _____ 8 stamps

22. **Explain Your Thinking** Florinda and 3 friends are going on a hike. Each of the four girls has a water bottle that holds 1 L of water. Will 4,200 mL of water fill all the bottles? Explain.

Yes, 4 × 1 L = 4 L, and 4 L = 4,000 mL; 4,200 > 4,000,

so there will be enough water to fill the bottles.

278

Answers

Inventory Test

1. D	**15.** A
2. A	**16.** D
3. A	**17.** B
4. D	**18.** B
5. C	**19.** B
6. B	**20.** A
7. D	**21.** A
8. B	**22.** B
9. A	**23.** A
10. C	**24.** C
11. D	**25.** C
12. B	**26.** A
13. A	**27.** A
14. A	**28.** A

Chapter 1
Quiz, Section A

1. a
2. b
3. 5 students
4. 2 students
5. Animals
6. Sports
7. 30 ounces
8. 4 weeks
9. Subtraction; 9 apples
10. Add 3.

In	2	5	8	11
Out	5	8	11	14

Quiz, Section B

1. a
2.

Scores	Tally	Number
8	卌	6
9	卌	4

3.

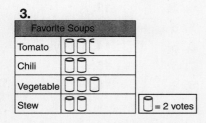

4.

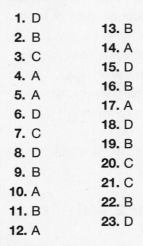

5. 10 pennies

Chapter 1 Test
Form C

1. D	**13.** B
2. B	**14.** A
3. C	**15.** D
4. A	**16.** B
5. A	**17.** A
6. D	**18.** D
7. C	**19.** B
8. D	**20.** C
9. B	**21.** C
10. A	**22.** B
11. B	**23.** D
12. A	

Chapter 1 Test
Form D

See the back of Chapter 1 Test Form D for answers.

Chapter 1 Test
Form E

1. 2 votes
2. B
3. D
4. C
5. Add 4.
6. Subtract 5.
7. A
8. Subtraction
9. Number of students
10. 30 students
11. Bikes
12. D
13. 6 hours
14. Friday
15. D

16.

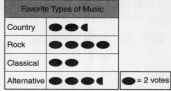

17.

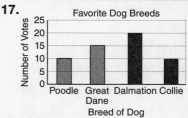

18. 7 plants
19. Possible answer: Line graph since it will show how the score changes over a period of time and allow you to compare your test performances.

Chapter 1 Test
Form F

1. 12, 14, 16	
2. 70, 80, 90	
3. 6	**9.** 3
4. 2	**10.** 4
5. 3	**11.** 4
6. 9	**12.** 7
7. 6	**13.** 9
8. 4	**14.** 1

15. 4, 5, 6; Subtract 4.
16. 6, 9, 10; Add 2.
17. 10, 11, 13; Add 3.
18. 8, 10, 12; Subtract 2.
19. Brown
20. 5 students
21. B
22. Number of votes
23. C
24. A
25. A
26. 5 books
27. 2 books
28. September
29. D
30. A

31. B

32.

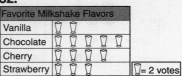

Favorite Milkshake Flavors	
Vanilla	
Chocolate	
Cherry	
Strawberry	= 2 votes

33. A

34. 4 students

35.

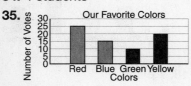

36. A

37. 5 students

38. 9 blocks

39. Circle

Chapter 2
Quiz, Section A

1. c
2. a
3. b
4. 467
5. 243
6. 9,297
7. 5,487
8. Three hundred forty-eight
9. Five thousand, six hundred forty-one
10. 90
11. 300
12. 90,000
13. 300,000
14. 4 ways

Quiz, Section B

1. b
2. c
3. a
4. >
5. >
6. <
7. =
8. 104, 401, 410
9. 5,136; 5,734; 8,542
10. 786, 687, 678
11. 7,216; 7,162; 795

12. 20
13. $50
14. 210
15. 800
16. 100
17. $500

Quiz, Section C

1. c
2. a
3. b
4. Possible answers: 2:55
   Two fifty-five
5. Possible answers: 9:12
   Nine-twelve
6. Possible answers: 7:20 A.M.
   Seven-twenty A.M.
7. Possible answers: 10:45 P.M.
   Ten forty-five P.M.
8. 6:20 P.M.
9. 1 hour, 40 minutes
10. Friday

Chapter 2 Test
Form C

1. D
2. A
3. A
4. D
5. C
6. C
7. B
8. D
9. A
10. C
11. B
12. C
13. D
14. B
15. A
16. C
17. B
18. D
19. C
20. A
21. B
22. C
23. B
24. D
25. A
26. A
27. C
28. D
29. C
30. B
31. C
32. D
33. A
34. C
35. B
36. C
37. B

Chapter 2 Test
Form D

See the back of Chapter 2 Test Form D for answers.

Chapter 2 Test
Form E

1. 724
2. 358
3. 8,406
4. 4,931
5. Two thousand, one hundred twenty-nine
6. Eighty-three thousand, ninety-four
7. C
8. A
9. 400,000
10. B
11. >
12. <
13. 325, 523, 532
14. 4,147; 4,174; 4,471
15. A
16. D
17. 400
18. 300
19. Possible answers: 7:10
   Seven-ten
20. Possible answers: 8:26
   Eight twenty-six
21. D
22. 1 hour, 45 minutes
23. C
24. Possible answer: Compare digits with the same place value, starting with the digits on the left.

Chapter 2 Test
Form F

1. 7
2. 14
3. 3
4. 15
5. 5
6. 5
7. 5
8. 2
9. 1
10. 648
11. 2,392
12. A
13. D
14. 4 ways
15. >
16. <

17. C
18. 50
19. 500
20. 200
21. Possible answers: 9:05
5 minutes past 9
22. Possible answers: 6:24
Six twenty-four
23. B
24. 5:10 P.M.
25. B
26. 450

Chapter 3
Quiz, Section A

1. c
2. a
3. b
4. 8
50
300
5. $9
$50
$400
6. 75
7. 82
8. 5
9. 7
10. 70
11. 800
12. 700

Quiz, Section B

1. b
2. c
3. a
4. 84
5. 97
6. 58
7. 81
8. 657
9. 791
10. 3,869
11. 4,697
12. 93
13. 119

14. 127
15. 21, 24

Quiz, Section C

1. b
2. c
3. a
4. 45
5. 71
6. $0.42 or 42¢
7. $1.71
8. Possible answer: two quarters, one dime, one nickel; $0.65
9. $5.98
10. 800
11. Estimate: $3 + $3 > $4; he does not have enough money.

Chapter 3 Test
Form C

1. B
2. C
3. D
4. A
5. B
6. D
7. C
8. A
9. D
10. D
11. B
12. C
13. A
14. D
15. C
16. B
17. A
18. D
19. B
20. C
21. A
22. B
23. B
24. A
25. D
26. A
27. C
28. C
29. B
30. D
31. A
32. B
33. D
34. C
35. A
36. B
37. A

Chapter 3 Test
Form D

See the back of Chapter 3 Test Form D for answers.

Chapter 3 Test
Form E

1. 72
2. 65
3. 34
4. 81
5. 869
6. 795
7. 4,796
8. 6,785
9. 78
10. 73
11. 60
12. 400
13. 8
14. 7
15. D
16. A
17. 9, 12
18. C
19. A
20. B
21. $0.38 or 38¢
22. $3.58
23. B
24. $4.84
25. 700
26. Estimate: $2 + $1 < $5; he has enough money.
27. 1 quarter, 1 dime, 1 nickel, 4 pennies

Chapter 3 Test
Form F

1. 46
2. 103
3. 875
4. 848
5. 5,748
6. 2,785
7. 88
8. 200
9. $3.78
10. $4.85
11. B
12. $2.63

13. 1 hour, 5 minutes
14. 7:00 A.M.
15. 300
16. 426
17. <
18. 2
19. 50
20. 500
21. 7
22. 13
23. 90
24. 700
25. D
26. C
27. 12 cars
28. A
29. Exact answer, $6.17

Quarterly Test
Chapters 1–3

1. B	**18.** A
2. A	**19.** C
3. C	**20.** D
4. B	**21.** C
5. C	**22.** A
6. D	**23.** D
7. B	**24.** B
8. B	**25.** B
9. D	**26.** C
10. A	**27.** B
11. D	**28.** B
12. A	**29.** C
13. C	**30.** C
14. D	**31.** A
15. C	**32.** C
16. B	**33.** A
17. A	**34.** B

Chapter 4
Quiz, Section A

1. 4 − 2 = 2; 2 more
2. 5 − 4 = 1; 1 tree
3. 5
    20
    500

4. 4
    50
    400
5. 30
6. 24
7. 37
8. 42
9. 300
10. $1.00
11. 14 ones

Quiz, Section B

1. 18
2. 47
3. 25
4. 17
5. 453
6. 526
7. 245
8. 426
9. 265
10. 438
11. 375
12. 667
13. 262
14. 218
15. 271
16. 377
17. 49 pounds
18. 19 miles per hour

Quiz, Section C

1. 2,532
2. 4,211
3. 3,406
4. 3,176
5. $7
6. $2 more
7. 1; 15
8. 4; 61
9. 1; 226
10. $2.54
11. $1.32
12. $4.35
13. 3 books

Chapter 4 Test
Form C

1. A	**19.** B
2. B	**20.** D
3. C	**21.** A
4. D	**22.** A
5. C	**23.** D
6. B	**24.** B
7. A	**25.** A
8. D	**26.** B
9. B	**27.** A
10. C	**28.** B
11. B	**29.** D
12. C	**30.** C
13. C	**31.** A
14. A	**32.** C
15. B	**33.** D
16. D	**34.** A
17. C	**35.** C
18. A	

Chapter 4 Test
Form D

See the back of Chapter 4 Test Form D for answers.

Chapter 4 Test
Form E

1. 400
2. 600
3. 41
4. 35
5. 37
6. 6 − 3 = 3; 3 more
7. 7 − 5 = 2; 2 roses
8. C
9. B
10. D
11. A
12. 231
13. 249
14. 124
15. 378
16. 2,353
17. 2,249
18. $7
19. 3; 18

20. 1; 27
21. C
22. B
23. Regroup 3 tens 1 one as
2 tens 11 ones; 13 girls

Chapter 4 Test
Form F

1. 288
2. 641
3. 21
4. 25
5. 34
6. 319
7. 721
8. 284
9. 365
10. 2,665
11. 1,248
12. $1.43
13. B
14. D
15. C
16. $6 - 3 = 3$
17. A
18. B
19. A
20. Mary
21. C
22. 10 cans
23. 4 outfits

Chapter 5 Test
Quiz, Section A

1. 2 and 5
2. 10
3. • • • • •
   • • • • •
4. $2 + 2 + 2 = 6$
   3 groups of 2 equals 6.
   $3 \times 2 = 6$
5. $5 + 5 + 5 + 5 = 20$
   4 groups of 5 equals 20.
   $4 \times 5 = 20$
6. 28 oranges

7. 24 players
8. 24 legs
9. 12 wings

Quiz, Section B

1.	multiple	11.	0
2.	12	12.	72
3.	15	13.	35
4.	36	14.	10
5.	8	15.	35
6.	4	16.	54
7.	27	17.	0
8.	6	18.	0
9.	20	19.	63
10.	16	20.	30

21. 16
22. $3.25
23. 5 students

Chapter 5 Test
Form C

1.	C	19.	D
2.	D	20.	C
3.	A	21.	B
4.	C	22.	A
5.	D	23.	D
6.	A	24.	C
7.	C	25.	D
8.	B	26.	C
9.	A	27.	C
10.	D	28.	A
11.	C	29.	D
12.	D	30.	C
13.	A	31.	B
14.	C	32.	D
15.	B	33.	C
16.	A	34.	D
17.	C	35.	D
18.	B		

Chapter 5 Test
Form D

See the back of Chapter 5
Test Form D for answers.

Chapter 5 Test
Form E

1. $3 + 3 + 3 + 3 + 3 = 15$
   5 groups of 3 equals 15.
   $5 \times 3 = 15$
2. $2 + 2 + 2 + 2 = 8$
   4 groups of 2 equals 8.
   $4 \times 2 = 8$

3.	B	12.	8
4.	C	13.	3
5.	C	14.	0
6.	D	15.	54
7.	8	16.	27
8.	16	17.	6
9.	35	18.	40
10.	15	19.	A
11.	0	20.	C

21. No, because Conrad is
standing between them.
22. Possible answer: 9×9
has one more group of
nine objects than does
9×8. So, you can add 9
to 72. Since $9 + 72 = 81$,
$9 \times 9 = 81$.

Chapter 5 Test
Form F

1. $3 + 3 = 6$
   2 groups of 3 equals 6.
2. 6
3. 40
4. 0
5. 36
6. 7
7. 16
8. 54
9. 30
10. 12
11. 15
12. 63
13. 7
14. D
15. A
16. B

17. D
18. D
19. B
20. 27 pens
21. B
22. 18 beads
23. B

Chapter 6
Quiz, Section A

1. 18
2. 12
3. 15
4. 24
5. 16
6. 32
7. 28
8. 36
9. 54
10. 30
11. 24
12. 42
13. 21
14. 40
15. 56
16. 72
17. 49
18. 63
19. 35
20. 14
21. 16
22. 48
23. 64
24. 40
25. 24 eggs
26. 63 marigolds
27. 32 wheels
28. 48 bottles

Quiz, Section B

1. a
2. b
3. False
4. True
5. False
6. 66, 77, 88
7. 60, 50, 40
8. 60, 72, 84
9. 24
10. 42
11. 0
12. 5 cakes
13. 4 seats

Chapter 6 Test
Form C

1. A	22. B
2. B	23. A
3. C	24. C
4. C	25. D
5. D	26. B
6. A	27. C
7. C	28. A
8. D	29. B
9. C	30. A
10. B	31. B
11. A	32. A
12. D	33. C
13. B	34. B
14. C	35. D
15. D	36. C
16. A	37. B
17. B	38. D
18. C	39. C
19. D	40. A
20. D	41. C
21. B	

Chapter 6 Test
Form D

See the back of Chapter 6
Test Form D for answers.

Chapter 6 Test
Form E

1. 9
2. 15
3. 24
4. 28
5. 36
6. 24
7. 42
8. 54
9. 18
10. 21
11. 35
12. 63
13. 16
14. 48
15. 32
16. 56
17. 16
18. 36
19. 49
20. 64
21. 36 students
22. B
23. True
24. False
25. 70, 80, 90
26. 44, 33, 22
27. 36, 24, 12
28. C
29. B
30. C
31. D
32. B
33. 5 coops
34. 8 wallets
35. You know 5×4 because changing the order of the factors does not change the product.

$$4 \times 5 = 5 \times 4$$
$$20 \qquad 20$$

Chapter 6 Test
Form F

1. 21	**15.** 32
2. 36	**16.** 20
3. 12	**17.** D
4. 40	**18.** B
5. 63	**19.** 616
6. 20	**20.** 273
7. 24	**21.** $2.21
8. 18	**22.** $1.74
9. 18	**23.** 78
10. 72	**24.** C
11. 24	**25.** False
12. 9	**26.** True
13. 28	**27.** A
14. 56	**28.** C

29. Possible answers: 6:15 P.M.
Six fifteen P.M.

30. 3 packages

31. 55 minutes

32. 12 books

Quarterly Test
Chapters 1–6

1. D	**20.** A
2. D	**21.** C
3. D	**22.** C
4. A	**23.** D
5. A	**24.** D
6. C	**25.** C
7. D	**26.** A
8. A	**27.** C
9. D	**28.** B
10. B	**29.** B
11. D	**30.** D
12. C	**31.** B
13. B	**32.** B
14. C	**33.** D
15. A	**34.** C
16. D	**35.** A
17. C	**36.** C
18. B	**37.** B
19. D	

Chapter 7
Quiz, Section A

1. 5

2. 3

3. 4 groups

4. 6 windows

5. 2 cards

6. 5 pages

7. 3 aunts

8. 4 stickers

9. 3 days

Quiz, Section B

1. c

2. a

3. d

4. b

5. 4×7

6. $5 \times 6 = 30; 30 \div 5 = 6$
$6 \times 5 = 30; 30 \div 6 = 5$

7. 8

8. 9

9. 9

10. 7

11. 8

12. 9

13. 5

14. 6

15. 3

16. 0

17. 4

18. 1

19. Division; 4 necklaces

20. Addition; 7 balloons

Quiz, Section C

1. b	**8.** 5
2. a	**9.** 8
3. 7×9	**10.** 5
4. 7	**11.** 4
5. 8	**12.** Even
6. 8	**13.** Odd
7. 4	**14.** Odd

15. 1 row of 12, 2 rows of 6,
3 rows of 4, 4 rows of 3,
6 rows of 2, 12 rows of 1

16. 6 marbles

Chapter 7 Test
Form C

1. A	**16.** C
2. B	**17.** D
3. C	**18.** D
4. D	**19.** D
5. B	**20.** A
6. B	**21.** B
7. C	**22.** C
8. D	**23.** D
9. B	**24.** C
10. B	**25.** A
11. A	**26.** C
12. C	**27.** B
13. A	**28.** D
14. C	**29.** D
15. B	**30.** C

Chapter 7 Test
Form D

See the back of Chapter 7
Test Form D for answers.

Chapter 7 Test
Form E

1. A

2. 5 flashlights

3. 3 sacks

4. 8 girls

5. C

6. $3 \times 1 = 3; 3 \div 1 = 3$
$1 \times 3 = 3; 3 \div 3 = 1$

7. 3

8. 9

9. 9

10. 6

11. 0

12. 6

13. 9

14. 8

15. 7

16. 4

17. 4

18. 6

19. Addition; 14 worms

20. Division; 2 servings

21. C
22. A
23. RB, RT, GB, GT
24. 1 row of 8, 2 rows of 4, 4 rows of 2, and 8 rows of 1
25. B
26. Odd, because 18 ÷ 2 = 9, and 9 is an odd number.

Chapter 7 Test
Form F

1. B
2. 54
3. 9
4. 0
5. 4
6. 4
7. 9
8. 7
9. 8
10. 7
11. A
12. 4 buckets
13. >
14. A
15. $9 \times 5 = 45$; $5 \times 9 = 45$
    $45 \div 9 = 5$; $45 \div 5 = 9$
16. 23, 25, 27, 29
17. 10, 12, 14, 16
18. Subtraction; $2.96
19. B
20. C
21. 1 row of 10, 2 rows of 5, 5 rows of 2, 10 rows of 1
22. D
23. B

Chapter 8
Quiz, Section A

1. c
2. d
3. a
4. b
5. Cone
6. Pyramid
7. Rectangular Prism

8. 4 sides
9. 3 sides
10. No sides
11. Intersecting
12. Flip
13. No
14. Right angle
15. 8 squares

Quiz, Section B

1. b
2. d
3. c
4. a
5. 14 units
   12 square units
6. 18 units
   14 square units
7. 6 cubic units
8. 4 cubic units
9. 9 cubic units
10. (2, 4)
11. (4, 3)
12. E

Chapter 8 Test
Form C

1. B   14. C
2. D   15. D
3. B   16. A
4. C   17. B
5. C   18. D
6. A   19. A
7. A   20. B
8. A   21. B
9. C   22. C
10. A   23. B
11. B   24. C
12. C   25. D
13. C

Chapter 8 Test
Form D

See the back of Chapter 8 Test Form D for answers.

Chapter 8 Test
Form E

1. Pyramid
2. Cone
3. Rectangle
4. 3 sides
5. B
6. Parallel
7. 4 right angles
8. 2 right angles
9. No right angles
10. Turn
11. Slide
12. Flip
13. Congruent
14. Yes
15. Yes
16. B
17. A
18. D
19. B
20. C
21. (1, 3)
22. (3, 2)
23. B
24. Possible answer: Add the measures of each side.
    $5 + 6 + 3 + 2 + 2 + 8 = 26$; 26 in.

Chapter 8 Test
Form F

1. $12.24
2. 1,176
3. 45
4. 30
5. A
6. 4 sides
7. 30
8. B
9. A
10. Greater than a right angle.
11. Not congruent
12. Yes
13. 11 rectangles

14. D
15. 8 cubic units
16. (2, 4)
17. (1, 2)
18. Slide
19. 26 feet
20. C
21. A

Chapter 9
Quiz, Section A

1. 6, 60
2. 16, 160
3. 15; 150; 1,500
4. 28; 280; 2,800
5. 400
6. 630
7. 120
8. 350
9. 4,200
10. 560
11. 360
12. 640
13. 39
14. 48

Quiz, Section B

1. 190
2. 168
3. 376
4. 96
5. 300
6. 230
7. 2,430
8. 2,910
9. 2,191
10. 5,418
11. $7.50
12. $10.26
13. 104
14. 195
15. 30 rooms

Quiz, Section C

1. False
2. 6, 60, 600
3. 4, 40, 400
4. 20
5. 60
6. 40 students
7. 8
8. 6
9. 4
10. About 9 cups
11. 3 R2
12. 4 R2
13. 8 R2
14. 3 R1
15. 6 R3
16. 8 R8

Chapter 9 Test Form C

1. B
2. B
3. A
4. D
5. B
6. B
7. C
8. C
9. C
10. D
11. B
12. D
13. A
14. C
15. D
16. C
17. C
18. A
19. B
20. A
21. B
22. C
23. C
24. C
25. B
26. C
27. D
28. A
29. C
30. B
31. B
32. D

Chapter 9 Test Form D

See the back of Chapter 9 Test Form D for answers.

Chapter 9 Test Form E

1. 24, 240
2. 45, 450

3. A
4. C
5. 350
6. 540
7. B
8. 204
9. 198
10. 195
11. 1,662
12. 2,992
13. $20.22
14. $30.03
15. 276
16. C
17. 5, 50, 500
18. D
19. B
20. 7 R1
21. 4 R2
22. 5 R4
23. 6 R2
24. 3 × 16 = 48;
48 newspapers

Chapter 9 Test Form F

1. D
2. 378
3. 132
4. 270
5. 1,974
6. 4,734
7. $66.08
8. $47.25
9. 6 R3
10. 5 R7
11. 6 R3
12. 7 R4
13. <
14. <
15. B
16. C
17. A
18. C
19. 326, 362, 623
20. 72; 720; 7,200

21. 8, 80, 800

22. A

23. 600

24. Five thousand, six hundred one

25. Odd digits

26. 42 students

27. 75, 100, 125, 150, 5 months

Quarterly Test
Chapters 1–9

1. B	**19.** C
2. C	**20.** D
3. A	**21.** C
4. C	**22.** D
5. C	**23.** A
6. D	**24.** D
7. B	**25.** A
8. C	**26.** A
9. A	**27.** A
10. B	**28.** B
11. B	**29.** C
12. D	**30.** D
13. C	**31.** C
14. D	**32.** A
15. C	**33.** B
16. C	**34.** D
17. D	**35.** C
18. D	**36.** B

Chapter 10 Test
Quiz, Section A

1. d

2. a

3. b

4. c

5. Eighths

6. Halves

7. $\frac{5}{6}$

8. $\frac{1}{4}$

9. Not equivalent

10. Equivalent

11. <

12. >

13. About $\frac{1}{4}$

14. More than $\frac{1}{2}$

Quiz, Section B

1. $\frac{2}{5}$	**8.** $2\frac{1}{3}$
2. $\frac{5}{8}$	**9.** $\frac{3}{8}$
3. 6	**10.** $\frac{7}{10}$
4. 3	**11.** $\frac{3}{5}$
5. 2	**12.** $\frac{9}{12}$ or $\frac{3}{4}$
6. 8	**13.** $\frac{6}{10}$ or $\frac{3}{5}$
7. $1\frac{3}{4}$	**14.** $\frac{7}{12}$

Quiz, Section C

1. True

2. True

3. False

4. 2 inches

5. 4 inches

6. $2\frac{1}{2}$

7. $3\frac{1}{4}$

8. 24 inches

9. 64 inches

10. <

11. >

12. =

13. Molly, Wapy, Mosi, Amber

Chapter 10 Test
Form C

1. C	**17.** B
2. B	**18.** D
3. A	**19.** A
4. D	**20.** A
5. D	**21.** C
6. A	**22.** B
7. C	**23.** B
8. A	**24.** D
9. B	**25.** C
10. A	**26.** D
11. C	**27.** C
12. D	**28.** B
13. B	**29.** A
14. A	**30.** C
15. B	**31.** A
16. A	**32.** D

Chapter 10 Test
Form D

See the back of Chapter 10 Test Form D for answers.

Chapter 10 Test
Form E

1. Fourths

2. Halves

3. D

4. Equivalent

5. Not Equivalent

6. B

7. A

8. C

9. 6

10. 7

11. 2

12. B

13. $\frac{4}{5}$

14. $\frac{3}{10}$

15. 3 inches

16. $1\frac{1}{2}$ inches

17. $2\frac{3}{4}$ inches

18. B

19. C

20. Fay: cheese; Mac: sausage; Will: pepperoni; Elona: mushroom

21. 1 foot is 12 inches, so multiply 4 feet by 12 and then add 7 to the product. $4 \times 12 + 7 = 55$; 4 feet, 7 inches = 55 inches

Chapter 10 Test
Form F

1. 8

2. $\frac{2}{3}$

3. $\frac{6}{10}$ or $\frac{3}{5}$

4. 39 inches

5. B

6. $16.50

7. 72

8. 7

9. D

10. $\frac{4}{6}$ or $\frac{2}{3}$

11. $\frac{5}{12}$

12. C

13. <

14. 2 hr, 20 min

15. C

16. $\frac{3}{5}$

17. A

18. 2 inches

19. $2\frac{1}{2}$ inches

20. =

21. Heidi: 12; Clarice: 14; Shirley: 20; Sonia: 9

22. 32 feet

Chapter 11
Quiz, Section A

1. c

2. a

3. b

4. $\frac{2}{10}$, 0.2

5. $\frac{7}{100}$, 0.07

6. 0.8

7. 1.6

8. 0.13

9. 0.4

10. 2.28

11. 13.2

12. 4.7

13. $0.55

14. $2.98

15. $4.91

Quiz, Section B

1. d

2. c

3. b

4. a

5. c

6. a

7. b

8. km

9. cm

10. km

11. m

12. Ninth floor

13. 3 people

Chapter 11 Test Form C

1. B

2. A

3. C

4. B

5. C

6. D

7. B

8. A

9. C

10. B

11. C

12. A

13. D

14. B

15. D

16. B

17. C

18. A

19. C

20. D

21. A

22. B

23. D

24. B

25. A

26. B

27. D

28. A

29. B

30. D

31. A

32. C

33. B

34. A

35. B

36. C

37. B

38. C

Chapter 11 Test Form D

See the back of Chapter 11 Test Form D for answers.

Chapter 11 Test Form E

1. 1.4

2. 0.35

3. 0.5

4. 1.92

5. 1.1

6. C

7. 7.7

8. 5.2

9. 2.4

10. 9.6

11. $0.26

12. C

13. A

14. D

15. B

16. C

17. C

18. A

19. km

20. m

21. cm

22. Second floor

23. 8 people

24. Possible answer: Since 0.5 = 0.50, there would be 50 squares of a hundredths grid shaded. A grid shaded to show $\frac{47}{100}$ would have 47 squares shaded. 50 > 47, so 0.5 > $\frac{47}{100}$.

Chapter 11 Test Form F

1. 4.5

2. 1.5

3. $\frac{4}{8}$ or $\frac{1}{2}$

4. D

5. A

6. B

7. A

8. 6

9. 75 inches

10. 0.6

11. 1.25

12. 3.5

13. 5.06

14. C

15. $0.79

16. b

17. c

18. a

19. m

20. cm

21. km

22. C

23. Fourteenth floor

24. 500 tickets

Chapter 12
Quiz, Section A

1. d
2. b
3. a
4. c
5. 1 gallon
6. 30 mL
7. 12 oz
8. 11 kg
9. 54°F
10. 4°F
11. 1 quart
12. Heavier

Quiz, Section B

1. c
2. d
3. b
4. a
5. Impossible
6. Certain
7. Possible
8. White
9. Black
10. 2 out of 5 or $\frac{2}{5}$
    2 out of 5 or $\frac{2}{5}$
    1 out of 5 or $\frac{1}{5}$
11. Unfair
12. Fair
13. 8

Chapter 12 Test
Form C

1. A
2. A
3. C
4. D
5. D
6. A
7. B
8. C
9. B
10. B
11. A
12. C
13. B
14. B
15. B
16. A
17. A
18. D
19. A
20. D
21. B
22. A
23. D
24. A
25. A
26. C
27. B

Chapter 12 Test
Form D

See the back of Chapter 12 Test Form D for answers.

Chapter 12 Test
Form E

1. A
2. =
3. D
4. D
5. 10 lb
6. 2 oz
7. C
8. 2-kilogram kitten
9. 90°F
10. 42°F
11. A
12. C
13. White
14. White
15. Unfair
16. Fair
17. 25
18. 1 out of 6 or $\frac{1}{6}$;
    3 out of 6 or $\frac{3}{6}$;
    2 out of 6 or $\frac{2}{6}$
    Most likely: White because $\frac{3}{6} > \frac{1}{6}$ and $\frac{3}{6} > \frac{2}{6}$. Least likely: Gray because $\frac{1}{6} < \frac{3}{6}$ and $\frac{1}{6} < \frac{2}{6}$.

Chapter 12 Test
Form F

1. 7
2. 56
3. 3,050

4. D
5. B
6. 1 quart
7. 5 L
8. 2 oz
9. 1 g
10. C
11. D
12. D
13. Unlikely
14. Black
15. Black
16. 3 out of 8 or $\frac{3}{8}$;
    1 out of 8 or $\frac{1}{8}$
    4 out of 8 or $\frac{4}{8}$
17. Unfair
18. Unfair
19. 200 mL more
20. 16°F
21. 66 inches

Quarterly Test
Chapters 1–12

1. D
2. B
3. A
4. C
5. D
6. B
7. C
8. B
9. D
10. B
11. C
12. C
13. A
14. B
15. B
16. C
17. A
18. D
19. C
20. A
21. D
22. C
23. B
24. C
25. C
26. C
27. B
28. D
29. A
30. C
31. D
32. D
33. B
34. A
35. A
36. B

Table of Contents for Management Forms

Management Forms

Using Management Forms

There are several types of management forms included in the *Assessment Sourcebook*. Some forms can be used to record results of student assessment. Others offer at-a-glance information about content objectives. Also included is a Percent Table that provides assistance in scoring formal assessments. Each type of form is described below:

Item Analysis for Individual Assessment: Inventory Test

The inventory test can be used as a baseline assessment at the beginning of the school year. The Item Analysis form for this test can be used to plan activities and assignments that address the strengths and weakness of individual students.

> *"Together, assessment and instruction can build on students' understanding, interest, and experiences."*
>
> —*NCTM Assessment Standards for School Mathematics*

Item Analysis for Individual Assessment: Chapters 1–12

Item Analysis forms for the variety of chapter tests can be used to evaluate student understanding of specific objectives. The forms can also be used to look for patterns in class performance on specific objectives.

These Item Analysis forms also provide suggestions for Review Options for specific objectives. Options from the Student Edition are listed, along with pages from the Practice and Reteaching components.

Item Analysis for Individual Assessment: Quarterly Tests

Quarterly Test Item Analysis can be used to assess student and group performance and plan instruction for the following quarter.

Class Test Record Form

This two-page form may be used for recording chapter test scores and quarterly test scores for the whole class for an entire year.

Item Analysis for Individual Assessment

Grade 3 Inventory Test

Student Name _____

See page 327 for scoring.

Place a ✔ in the column if the student has answered some or all of the questions correctly.

Objectives from Grade 2	Test Item	✔ if correct	Practice (pages)	Reteaching (pages)
	Inventory Test		**Review Options in Grade 2 Supplements**	
Solve problems by collecting, organizing, and using data.	1		P(11)	R(9)
Find differences from 12 by counting back 1 and 2; or by substituting 0.	2		P(23)	R(17)
Solve problems by determining whether to add or subtract and then writing a number sentence.	2		P(27)	R(21)
Solve related addition and subtraction stories.	3		P(40)	R(30)
Apply and determine an addition and subtraction rule.	4		P(52-53)	R(38-39)
Record tens and ones as two-digit numbers.	5		P(58)	R(42)
Compare numbers using *greater than/less than* and *greatest/least.*	6		P(67)	R(49)
Find the value of a group of dimes, nickels, and pennies through 99¢. Identify quarters and other coins.	7		P(73-74)	R(53-54)
Determine the number of hrs. that have gone by.	8		P(87)	R(63)
Identify time to 30-min. intervals.	9		P(93)	R(67)
Determine when regrouping is needed to add a one-digit to a two-digit number.	10		P(103)	R(75)
Add a one-digit number to a two-digit number.	10		P(104)	R(76)
Find the sum of 2 two-digit numbers with or without regrouping. Add two-digit numbers.	11		P(107)	R(77-78)
Determine when regrouping is needed to subtract a one-digit number from a two-digit. Subtract and record.	12		P(118-119)	R(85-86)
Find the difference of 2 two-digit numbers with or without regrouping.	13		P(124)	R(90)
Find the difference of 2 two-digit numbers.	13		P(125)	R(91)
Subtract money amounts to find differences.	12		P(127)	R(93)
Compare three-digit numbers using <, >, and =.	14		P(135)	R(99)
Order numbers to 1000.	15		P(136)	R(100)
Add three-digit numbers without regrouping. Find the sum.	16		P(141-142)	R(103-104)
Find the difference of 2 three-digit numbers with or. without regrouping.	17		P(144)	R(106)
Estimate and measure lengths to the nearest inch, foot, or yard.	18		P(151)	R(111)
Estimate and determine whether objects weigh more or. less than one pound.	19		P(157)	R(115)

continued on next page

Place a ✔ in the column if the student has answered some or all of the questions correctly.

Objectives from Grade 2	Inventory Test		Review Options in Grade 2 Supplements	
	Test Item	✔ if correct	Practice (pages)	Reteaching (pages)
Estimate whether objects weight more than, less than, or about one kilogram.	20		P(158)	R(116)
Identify the number of faces, corners, and edges for solid figures.	21		P(165)	R(121)
Count the number of sides and corners of shapes.	23		P(167)	R(123)
Identify the movement of a shape as a slide, flip, or turn.	22		P(169)	R(125)
Identify and create symmetrical shapes. Solve problems.	23		P(170-171)	R(126-127)
Identify fractions and unit fractions by determining the number of equal and colored parts.	24		P(175-176)	R(129-130)
Identify and write fractions of a set.	25		P(178-179)	R(132-133)
Add or multiply to find the number of objects in equal groups.	26		P(188)	R(137)
Write multiplication facts in vertical form.	27		P(188)	R(140)
Divide objects into equal groups.	28		P(193)	R(143)

Item Analysis for Individual Assessment: Grade 3, Chapter 1

Chapter 1: Data, Graphs, and Facts Review

Student Name _____

Place a ✔ in the column if the student has answered some or all of the questions correctly. For Test Form D, check all the objectives that are reflected in the student's response.

Quiz or Test Form	Score	Date

Review Options in Student Edition

- Section A Review and Practice, page 24
- Section B Review and Practice, page 42
- Chapter 1 Review/Test, page 44
- Chapter 1 Performance Assessment, page 45

Quizzes and Tests from the Assessment Sourcebook

Lesson	Objectives	Quizzes Items	✔	Chapter Test Form A Items	✔	Chapter Test Form B Items	✔	Chapter Test Form C Items	✔	Chapter Test Form D Items	✔	Chapter Test Form E Items	✔	Chapter Test Form F Items	✔	Review Options in Supplements — Practice and Reteaching Masters (pages)
Section A																
1-1	Read a pictograph.	3-4		1-2, 4-5		1, 4-5		1-4				1-4		19-20		P(1); R(1)
1-2	Read a bar graph.	1, 5-6		3, 6-7		2-3, 6-7		7-10				9-12		20-24		P(2); R(2)
1-3	Read a line graph.	2, 7-8		8-9		8-9		13-15				13-14, 19		26-28		P(3); R(3)
1-4	Solve problems by using a guide.	4		7, 9		7, 9		4, 10, 15				4, 12		24, 27		P(4); R(4)
1-5	Solve problems by choosing an operation.	9		10		10		11-12				7-8		21, 25		P(5); R(5)
1-6	Explore algebra by looking for patterns to find a rule.	10		11		11		5-6				5-6		15-18		P(6); R(6)
Section B																
1-7	Explore organizing data.	1-2		14		14		18, 23				15		29		P(8); R(7)
1-8	Explore making pictographs.	3		12, 16		12, 16		19-20				16		30, 32-34		P(9); R(8)
1-9	Explore making bar graphs.	4		13, 16		13, 16		21-22				17		31, 35-37		P(10); R(9)
1-10	Solve problems by collecting and analyzing data.															P(11); R(10)
1-11	Solve problems by finding a pattern.	5		15		15		16-17				18		39		P(12); R(11)
	Prior objectives													1-14, 38		

Chapter 2: Place Value and Time

Student Name

Review Options in Student Edition

- Section A Review and Practice, page 62
- Section B Review and Practice, page 72
- Section C Review and Practice, page 86
- Chapter 2 Review/Test, page 88
- Chapter 2 Performance Assessment, page 89

Quiz or Test Form	Score	Date

Place a ✔ in the column if the student has answered some or all of the questions correctly. For Test Form D, check all the objectives that are reflected in the student's response.

Lesson	Objectives	Quizzes Items	✔	Chapter Test Form A Items	✔	Chapter Test Form B Items	✔	Chapter Test Form C Items	✔	Chapter Test Form D Items	✔	Chapter Test Form E Items	✔	Chapter Test Form F Items	✔	Practice and Reteaching Masters (pages)
Section A																
2-1	Read an write numbers in the hundreds.	1-2, 4-5, 8		1, 4, 6		1, 4, 6		1-3				1-2		10		P(15); R(12)
2-2	Explore place-value relationships.	10-11		8-9		8-9		4-5				7-8		12		P(16); R(13)
2-3	Read and write numbers through thousands.	6-7, 9		5, 7		5, 7		6-8				3-5		11		P(17); R(14)
2-4	Read and write numbers through hundred thousands.	3, 12-13		10-11		10-11		9-11				6, 9		13		P(18); R(15)
2-5	Solve problems by making an organized list.	14		12		12		12-13				10		14		P(19); R(16)
Section B																
2-6	Compare numbers.	1, 4-7		13-14		13-14		14-16				11-12		15-16		P(21); R(17)
2-7	Order numbers.	8-11		15		15		17-19				13-14, 24		17		P(22); R(18)
2-8	Round 2-digit and 3-digit numbers to the nearest 10.	2-3, 12-14		2, 16-17, 27		2, 16-17, 27		20-22				15-16		18, 26		P(23); R(19)
2-9	Round numbers to the nearest hundred.	15-17		18-19, 27		18-19, 27		23-25				17-18		19-20		P(24); R(20)

Quizzes and Tests from the Assessment Sourcebook — *Review Options in Supplements*

Continued on next page.

Chapter 2 (continued)

Lesson	Objectives	Quizzes and Tests from the Assessment Sourcebook														Review Options in Supplements
		Quizzes		Chapter Test Form A		Chapter Test Form B		Chapter Test Form C		Chapter Test Form D		Chapter Test Form E		Chapter Test Form F		Practice and Reteaching Masters (pages)
		Items	✓	Items	✓	Items	✓	Items	✓	Items	✓	Items	✓	Items	✓	
	Section C															
2-10	Tell time to the nearest 5 minutes.	4		20		20		26-27				19		21		P(26); R(21)
2-11	Explore time to the nearest minute.	5		21		21		28-29				20		22		P(27); R(22)
2-12	Tell time to the nearest half hour and quarter hour.	1-2, 6-7		3, 22-23		3, 22-23		30-31				21		23		P(28); R(23)
2-13	Find ending time and the time between events.	8, 9		24-25		24-25		32-34				22		24		P(29); R(24)
2-14	Read a calendar and ordinal numbers.	3, 10		26		26		35-37				23		25		P(30); R(25)
2-15	Solve problems by making decisions about a schedule.															P(31); R(26)
	Prior objectives													1-9		

Item Analysis for Individual Assessment: Grade 3, Chapter 3

Chapter 3: Adding Whole Numbers and Money

Student Name _____

Place a ✔ in the column if the student has answered some or all of the questions correctly. For Test Form D, check all the objectives that are reflected in the student's response.

Review Options in Student Edition

- Section A Review and Practice, page 104
- Section B Review and Practice, page 114
- Section C Review and Practice, page 140
- Chapter 3 Review/Test, page 142
- Chapter 3 Performance Assessment, page 143

Quiz or Test Form	Score	Date

Lesson	Objectives	Quizzes Items	✔	Chapter Test Form A Items	✔	Chapter Test Form B Items	✔	Chapter Test Form C Items	✔	Chapter Test Form D Items	✔	Chapter Test Form E Items	✔	Chapter Test Form F Items	✔	Practice and Reteaching Masters (pages)
	Section A															
3-1	Explore addition patterns.	1, 4-5		1, 4		3-4		1, 2				11-12		19-20		P(34); R(27)
3-2	Explore adding on a hundred chart.	6-7		5-6		5-6		3-5				1-4		1-2		P(35); R(28)
3-3	Explore algebra by finding missing numbers.	8-9		7-8		7-8		6-7				13-14		21-22		P(36); R(29)
3-4	Use rounding to estimate sums.	2-3, 10-12		3, 21-22		2, 21-22		8-11				15-16		23		P(37); R(30)
	Section B															
3-5	Explore addition with regrouping.	1, 4-5		2, 9		1, 9		4-5				2-4		1-2		P(39); R(31)
3-6	Add 2-digit numbers.	6-7		5-6, 9		5-6, 9		3-5				1-4		1-2		P(40); R(32)
3-7	Add 3-digit numbers.	8-9		10		10		12-14				5-6		3-4		P(41); R(33)
3-8	Add 4-digit numbers.	10-11		11		11		15-16				7-8		5-6		P(42); R(34)
3-9	Find the sum of more than 2 addends.	12-14		12		12		17-18				9-10		7-8		P(43); R(35)
3-10	Solve problems by guessing and checking.	15		13		13		19-20				17		27		P(44); R(36)

Quizzes and Tests from the Assessment Sourcebook

Review Options in Supplements

Continued on next page.

© Scott Foresman Addison Wesley 3

Chapter 3 (continued)

Lesson	Objectives	Quizzes		Chapter Test Form A		Chapter Test Form B		Chapter Test Form C		Chapter Test Form D		Chapter Test Form E		Chapter Test Form F		Review Options in Supplements — Practice and Reteaching Masters (pages)
		Items	✓	Items	✓	Items	✓	Items	✓	Items	✓	Items	✓	Items	✓	
Section C																
3-11	Use mental math to find sums.	4-5		14-15		14-15		21-23				18-20		25-26		P(46); R(37)
3-12	Find the value of groups of coins.	1, 6		16		16		24-25				21, 27		11		P(47); R(38)
3-13	Write money amounts in dollars and cents.	2, 7		17		17		26-27				22		12		P(48); R(39)
3-14	Explore making change.	8		18		18		28-30				23, 27		28		P(49); R(40)
3-15	Add money amounts.	9		19-20		19-20		31-33				24		9-10, 29		P(50); R(41)
3-16	Estimate using front-end estimation.	3, 10		23-24		23-24		34-35				25		24		P(51); R(42)
3-17	Solve problems needing exact answers or estimates.	11		25		25		36-37				26		29		P(52); R(43)
	Prior objectives													13-18		

Item Analysis for Individual Assessment: Grade 3, Chapter 4

Chapter 4: Subtracting Whole Numbers and Money

Student Name _____

Place a ✔ in the column if the student has answered some or all of the questions correctly. For Test Form D, check all the objectives that are reflected in the student's response.

Review Options in Student Edition
- Section A Review and Practice, page 160
- Section B Review and Practice, page 178
- Section C Review and Practice, page 194
- Chapter 4 Review/Test, page 196
- Chapter 4 Performance Assessment, page 197

Quiz or Test Form	Score	Date

Lesson	Objectives	Quizzes Items	✔	Chapter Test Form A Items	✔	Chapter Test Form B Items	✔	Chapter Test Form C Items	✔	Chapter Test Form D Items	✔	Chapter Test Form E Items	✔	Chapter Test Form F Items	✔	Practice and Reteaching Masters (pages)
Section A																
4-1	Review the meaning of subtraction.	1-2		1-2		1-2		1-2				6-7		15-16		P(55); R(44)
4-2	Explore subtraction patterns.	3-4		3-4		3-4		3-4				1-2		13-14		P(56); R(45)
4-3	Explore subtraction on a hundred chart.	5-8		5-8		5-8		5-10				3-5		3-5		P(57); R(46)
4-4	Estimate differences using rounding.	9-10		13-15		13-15		11-14				8-9		17		P(58); R(47)
4-5	Explore grouping.	11		16-17		16-17		15-16				10-11, 23		18		P(59); R(48)
Section B																
4-6	Explore subtracting 2-digit numbers.	1-4		5-8		5-8		5-10				3-5		3-5		P(61); R(49)
4-7	Subtract 2-digit numbers.	1-4, 17		5-8		5-8		5-10				3-5		3-5		P(62); R(50)
4-8	Explore subtracting 3-digit numbers.	5-8, 15		9-10		9-10		17-21				12-13		6-7		P(63); R(51)
4-9	Subtract 3-digit numbers.	5-11, 15		9-12		9-12		17-21				12-13		6-7		P(64); R(52)

Quizzes and Tests from the Assessment Sourcebook

Review Options in Supplements

Continued on next page.

© Scott Foresman Addison Wesley 3

Chapter 4 (continued)

Lesson	Objectives	Quizzes		Chapter Test Form A		Chapter Test Form B		Chapter Test Form C		Chapter Test Form D		Chapter Test Form E		Chapter Test Form F		Review Options in Supplements Practice and Reteaching Masters (pages)
		Items	✓	Items	✓	Items	✓	Items	✓	Items	✓	Items	✓	Items	✓	
Section A																
4-10	Subtract with 2 regroupings.	9-11, 16		11-12, 19, 21		11-12, 19, 21		20-21, 28-29				13,15		7, 9, 11		P(65); R(53)
4-11	Subtract across zeros.	12-14, 18		18-19		18-19		22-24				14-15		8-9		P(66); R(54)
Section C																
4-12	Subtract 4-digit numbers.	1-4		20-21		20-21		25-26				16-17		10-11		P(68); R(55)
4-13	Solve multiple-step problems.	5-6		22		22		32-33				18		22		P(69); R(56)
4-14	Use mental math to subtract equal additions.	7-9		23-24		23-24		30-31				19-20		19		P(70); R(57)
4-15	Subtract money.	10-12		25-26, 28		25-26, 28		27-29				21-22		12		P(71); R(58)
4-16	Solve problems by using objects.	13		27		27		34-35				23		23		P(72); R(59)
	Prior objectives													1-2, 20-21		

Chapter 5: Multiplication Concepts and Facts

Student Name _____

Quiz or Test Form	Score	Date

Place a ✔ in the column if the student has answered some or all of the questions correctly. For Test Form D, check all the objectives that are reflected in the student's response.

Review Options in Student Edition
- Section A Review and Practice, page 210
- Section B Review and Practice, page 230
- Chapter 5 Review/Test, page 232
- Chapter 5 Performance Assessment, page 234

Lesson	Objectives	Quizzes Items	✔	Chapter Test Form A Items	✔	Chapter Test Form B Items	✔	Chapter Test Form C Items	✔	Chapter Test Form D Items	✔	Chapter Test Form E Items	✔	Chapter Test Form F Items	✔	Review Options in Supplements — Practice and Reteaching Masters (pages)
	Section A															
5-1	Explore multiplication.	4-5		4-5		4-5		2-3				1-2		1, 19		P(75); R(60)
5-2	Write multiplication sentences.	1-5		1-2, 4-6		1-2, 4-6		1-3, 6-7				1-4		19		P(76); R(61)
5-3	Explore multiplication stories.	6-9		6-8		6-8		4-7				3-6		20		P(77); R(62)
	Section B															
5-4	Multiply with 2 as a factor.	2, 8, 10-11, 14, 21		9-12, 25, 28, 30		9-12, 25, 28, 30		8-11, 24, 29				7-8, 17		2, 7, 10		P(79); R(63)
5-5	Multiply with 5 as a factor	3, 9, 13-15, 17, 20		13-16, 26		13-16, 26		12-15, 25				9-10, 18		3, 9, 11		P(80); R(64)
5-6	Explore patterns for 2s and 5s on a hundred chart.	1, 2, 8-11, 13-15, 17, 20-21		3, 9-16, 25-26, 28, 30		3, 9-16, 25-26		8-15, 24-25, 28, 29, 35				7-10, 17-18		2-3, 7, 9-11		P(81); R(65)
5-7	Explore patterns when multiplying with 0 and 1.	5-6, 11, 17-18		21-24, 28-29, 31		21-24, 28-29, 31		8, 20-23, 27-28				11-14		4, 6, 13		P(82); R(66)
5-8	Multiply with 9 as a factor.	4, 7, 12, 16, 19		17-20, 27, 32		16-20, 27, 32		11, 15, 19, 26, 29				15-16, 22		5, 8, 12		P(83); R(67)

Quizzes and Tests from the Assessment Sourcebook

Continued on next page.

Chapter 5 (continued)

Lesson	Objectives	Quizzes and Tests from the Assessment Sourcebook														Review Options in Supplements
		Quizzes		Chapter Test Form A		Chapter Test Form B		Chapter Test Form C		Chapter Test Form D		Chapter Test Form E		Chapter Test Form F		Practice and Reteaching Masters (pages)
		Items	✔	Items	✔	Items	✔	Items	✔	Items	✔	Items	✔	Items	✔	
	Section B (continued)															
5-9	Solve problems by making decisions about which information is important and by identifying what information is missing.	22		33		33		30-31				19-20		21		P(84); R(68)
5-10	Solve problems by drawing a picture.	23		34		34		32-34				21		22		P(85); R(69)
	Prior objectives													14-18, 23		

Item Analysis for Individual Assessment: Grade 3, Chapter 6

Chapter 6: More Multiplication Facts

Student Name

Quiz or Test Form	Score	Date

Place a ✔ in the column if the student has answered some or all of the questions correctly. For Test Form D, check all the objectives that are reflected in the student's response.

Review Options in Student Edition
- Section A Review and Practice, page 252
- Section B Review and Practice, page 266
- Chapter 9 Review/Test, page 268
- Chapter 9 Performance Assessment, page 269

Lesson	Objectives	Quizzes Items	✓	Chapter Test Form A Items	✓	Chapter Test Form B Items	✓	Chapter Test Form C Items	✓	Chapter Test Form D Items	✓	Chapter Test Form E Items	✓	Chapter Test Form F Items	✓	Review Options in Supplements — Practice and Reteaching Masters (pages)
	Section A															
6-1	Multiply with 3 as a factor.	1-4, 13,		4-5, 10, 13		4-5,9, 11, 20		1-3, 16, 21				1-3, 9-10		1, 7, 9, 12		P(88); R(70)
6-2	Multiply with 4 as a factor.	2, 5-8, 11, 25, 27		6-7, 12, 20, 34		4, 6-7, 19, 21, 34		1, 4-6, 13, 17, 20 22-23, 25, 39				4-6, 15, 17, 21, 35		2, 6, 11, 13, 15-16		P(89); R(71)
6-3	Multiply with 6 as a factor.	1, 9-12, 22, 25, 28		5, 8-9, 14-15, 18, 20		8-9, 17-19, 34		7-9, 16, 18-20, 26				6-9, 14, 18, 22		3, 9, 11		P(90); R(72)
6-4	Multiply with 7 and 8 as factors.	7, 12-24, 26-28		1, 10-14, 16-19, 21, 34		3, 8, 10-17, 20-21		2, 5, 7, 10-15, 19, 24, 27				3-4, 7, 10-16, 19-20, 22		1, 4-5, 7, 10, 13-15		P(91); R(73)
6-5	Solve problems by making a table.															P(92); R(74)
	Section B															
6-6	Explore patterns for 3s and 6s on a hundred chart.	1, 3-5		3, 22-24		1, 22-24		28-31				23-24		25-26		P(94); R(75)
6-7	Explore patterns on a fact table.	6-8		25-27		25-27		32-34				25-27		24		P(95); R(76)

Continued on next page.

Chapter 6 (continued)

Lesson	Objectives	Quizzes		Quizzes and Tests from the Assessment Sourcebook												Review Options in Supplements
				Chapter Test Form A		Chapter Test Form B		Chapter Test Form C		Chapter Test Form D		Chapter Test Form E		Chapter Test Form F		Practice and Reteaching Masters (pages)
		Items	✔	Items	✔	Items	✔	Items	✔	Items	✔	Items	✔	Items	✔	
	Section B (continued)															
6-8	Multiply with 3 factors.	2, 9-11		2, 28-31		2, 28-31		35-38				28-32		17-18		P(96); R(77)
6-9	Solve problems by comparing different strategies to solve the same problem.	12-13		32-33		32-33		40-41				33-34		30		P(97); R(78)
	Prior objectives													8, 19-23, 27-29, 31-32		

Chapter 7: Division Concepts and Facts

Student Name _____

Place a ✓ in the column if the student has answered some or all of the questions correctly. For Test Form D, check all the objectives that are reflected in the student's response.

Quiz or Test Form	Score	Date

Review Options in Student Edition

- Section A Review and Practice, page 282
- Section B Review and Practice, page 298
- Section C Review and Practice, page 312
- Chapter 7 Review/Test, page 314
- Chapter 7 Performance Assessment, page 315

Lesson	Objectives	Quizzes Items	✓	Chapter Test Form A Items	✓	Chapter Test Form B Items	✓	Chapter Test Form C Items	✓	Chapter Test Form D Items	✓	Chapter Test Form E Items	✓	Chapter Test Form F Items	✓	Practice and Reteaching Masters (pages)	✓
	Section A																
7-1	Explore division as sharing.	1-2		5		5		1-2				1		11		P(100); R(79)	
7-2	Explore division as repeated subtraction.	3-4		6		6		3-4				2		12		P(101); R(80)	
7-3	Explore division stories.	5-9		22-23		22-23		5-6				3-4		20		P(102); R(81)	
	Section B																
7-4	Use multiplication to divide.	1-6		1-2, 7-9		1-2, 7-9		7-8				5-6		15		P(104); R(82)	
7-5	Divide by 2.	7, 9, 13, 18		10, 14		10, 14		9, 12				7, 14		3		P(105); R(83)	
7-6	Divide by 5.	10-11, 15		11, 17		11, 17		6, 10				8, 18		6, 20		P(106); R(84)	
7-7	Divide by 3 and 4.	8, 12, 14, 19		13, 15		13, 15		5, 11, 13				9-10		5		P(107); R(85)	
7-8	Explore 0 and 1 in division.	16-18		12, 16		12, 16		14-15				11-12		4		P(108); R(86)	
7-9	Solve problems by choosing an operation.	19-20		24-25, 30		24-25, 30		22-23, 27, 30				19-20		18		P(109); R(87)	

Quizzes and Tests from the Assessment Sourcebook

Review Options in Supplements

Continued on next page.

Chapter 7 (continued)

Lesson	Objectives	Quizzes Items	✓	Chapter Test Form A Items	✓	Chapter Test Form B Items	✓	Chapter Test Form C Items	✓	Chapter Test Form D Items	✓	Chapter Test Form E Items	✓	Chapter Test Form F Items	✓	Practice and Reteaching Masters (pages)
																Review Options in Supplements
	Section C															
7-10	Divide by 6 and 7.	3-5, 7-8		18, 20		18, 20		16-17, 20				13, 15		7-8		P(111); R(88)
7-11	Divide by 8 and 9.	6, 9-11		19, 21		19, 21		18-19				4, 16-17		9		P(112); R(89)
7-12	Explore even and odd numbers.	1-2, 12-14		3-4, 28-29		3-4, 28-29		24-25				21-22, 26		16-17		P(113); R(90)
7-13	Solve problems by comparing strategies.	15		26		26		26				23-24		21		P(114); R(91)
7-14	Explore algebra by balancing scales.	16		27		27		28-29				25		19		P(115); R(91)
	Prior objectives													1-2, 13-14, 22-23		

Quizzes and Tests from the Assessment Sourcebook

Item Analysis for Individual Assessment: Grade 3, Chapter 8

Chapter 8: Using Geometry

Student Name _____

Place a ✔ in the column if the student has answered some or all of the questions correctly. For Test Form D, check all the objectives that are reflected in the student's response.

Quiz or Test Form	Score	Date

Review Options in Student Edition

- Section A Review and Practice, page 338
- Section B Review and Practice, page 350
- Chapter 8 Review/Test, page 352
- Chapter 8 Performance Assessment, page 353

Quizzes and Tests from the Assessment Sourcebook

Lesson	Objectives	Quizzes Items	✓	Chapter Test Form A Items	✓	Chapter Test Form B Items	✓	Chapter Test Form C Items	✓	Chapter Test Form D Items	✓	Chapter Test Form E Items	✓	Chapter Test Form F Items	✓	Review Options in Supplements — Practice and Reteaching Masters (pages)
Section A																
8-1	Explore solids.	5-7		1, 5-6		1, 5-6		1-2				1-2		5		P(118); R(93)
8-2	Explore connecting solids and shapes.	8-10		7, 28		7, 28		3-4				3-4		6		P(119); R(94)
8-3	Identify lines, line segments, rays, parallel lines, and intersecting lines.	4, 11		2, 8, 28		2, 8, 28		5-7				5-6		9		P(120); R(95)
8-4	Explore angles.	1, 3, 14		4, 9, 28		4, 9, 28		8-9				7-9		10		P(121); R(96)
8-5	Explore slides, flips, and turns.	2, 12		10-15		10-15		10-12				10-13		11, 18		P(122); R(97)
8-6	Explore symmetry.	13		3, 16-18		3, 16-18		13				14-15		12		P(123); R(98)
8-7	Solve problems by solving simpler problems and finding patterns.	15		19		19		14-15				16		13		P(124); R(99)
Section B																
8-8	Explore perimeter.	1, 4-6		20-21		20-21		16-18				17, 24		19, 21		P(126); R(100)
8-9	Explore area.	2, 5-6		20-21		20-21		19-20				18-19		20		P(127); R(101)
8-10	Solve problems by making decisions about area.															P(128); R(102)

Continued on next page.

Chapter 8 (continued)

Lesson	Objectives	Quizzes		Chapter Test Form A		Chapter Test Form B		Chapter Test Form C		Chapter Test Form D		Chapter Test Form E		Chapter Test Form F		Review Options in Supplements / Practice and Reteaching Masters (pages)
		Items	✓	Items	✓	Items	✓	Items	✓	Items	✓	Items	✓	Items	✓	
	Section B (continued)															
8-11	Explore volume.	3, 7-9		22-24		22-24		21-22				20		15		P(129); R(103)
8-12	Find and name points on a coordinate grid.	10-12		25-27		25-27		23-25				21-23		16-17		P(130); R(104)
	Prior objectives													1-4, 7-8, 14		

Item Analysis for Individual Assessment: Grade 3, Chapter 9

Chapter 9: Multiplying and Dividing

Student Name _____

Place a ✔ in the column if the student has answered some or all of the questions correctly. For Test Form D, check all the objectives that are reflected in the student's response.

Quiz or Test Form	Score	Date

Review Options in Student Edition

- Section A Review and Practice, page 368
- Section B Review and Practice, page 388
- Section C Review and Practice, page 402
- Chapter 9 Review/Test, page 404
- Chapter 9 Performance Assessment, page 405

Quizzes and Tests from the Assessment Sourcebook

Review Options in Supplements

Lesson	Objectives	Quizzes Items	✓	Chapter Test Form A Items	✓	Chapter Test Form B Items	✓	Chapter Test Form C Items	✓	Chapter Test Form D Items	✓	Chapter Test Form E Items	✓	Chapter Test Form F Items	✓	Practice and Reteaching Masters (pages)
Section A																
9-1	Explore multiplying tens.	1-2		1-2		1-2		1-2				1-2		22		P(133); R(105)
9-2	Explore multiplication patterns.	3-6		3-4		3-4		3-5				3-4		20		P(134); R(106)
9-3	Estimate products.	7-12		5-7		5-7		6-8				5-6		15-16		P(135); R(107)
9-4	Explore multiplication with arrays.	13-14		8-9		8-9		9-10				7		1		P(136); R(108)
Section B																
9-5	Multiply using partial products.	1-6		10-13		10-13		11-12, 17				8-10		2-4		P(138); R(109)
9-6	Multiply 2-digit numbers with regrouping.	1-6		10-13		10-13		11-12, 17				8-10		2-4		P(139); R(110)
9-7	Multiply 3-digit numbers.	7-10		14-15		14-15		13-14				11-12		5-6		P(140); R(111)
9-8	Multiply money.	11-12		16-17		16-17		15-16, 18				13-14		7-8		P(141); R(112)
9-9	Use mental math to multiply.	13-14		18-19		18-19		19-21				15		26		P(142);R(113)
9-10	Make a table to help solve problems.	15		20		20		22-23				16		27		P(143); R(114)
Section C																
9-11	Explore division patterns.	2-6		31		31		24-26				17		21		P(145);R(115)

Continued on next page.

Chapter 9 (continued)

Lesson	Objectives	Quizzes		Quizzes and Tests from the Assessment Sourcebook												Review Options in Supplements
				Chapter Test Form A		Chapter Test Form B		Chapter Test Form C		Chapter Test Form D		Chapter Test Form E		Chapter Test Form F		Practice and Reteaching Masters (pages)
		Items	✓	Items	✓	Items	✓	Items	✓	Items	✓	Items	✓	Items	✓	
	Section C (continued)															
9-12	Estimate quotients.	7-10		21-23		21-23		27-28				18-19		17-18		P(146); R(116)
9-13	Explore division with remainders.	1, 11-17		24-30		24-30		29-32				20-24		9-12		P(147); R(117)
9-14	Divide to find quotients and remainders.	11-17		24-30		24-30		29-32				20-24		9-12		P(148); R(118)
9-15	Solve problems by making decisions.															P(149); R(119)
	Prior objectives													13-14, 19, 23-25		

Item Analysis for Individual Assessment: Grade 3, Chapter 10

Chapter 10: Fractions and Customary Linear Measurement

Student Name _____

Place a ✔ in the column if the student has answered some or all of the questions correctly. For Test Form D, check all the objectives that are reflected in the student's response.

Quiz or Test Form	Score	Date

Review Options in Student Edition

- Section A Review and Practice, page 422
- Section B Review and Practice, page 434
- Section C Review and Practice, page 446
- Chapter 10 Review/Test, page 448
- Chapter 10 Performance Assessment, page 449

Quizzes and Tests from the Assessment Sourcebook

Lesson	Objectives	Quizzes Items	✔	Chapter Test Form A Items	✔	Chapter Test Form B Items	✔	Chapter Test Form C Items	✔	Chapter Test Form D Items	✔	Chapter Test Form E Items	✔	Chapter Test Form F Items	✔	Practice and Reteaching Masters (pages)
Section A																
10-1	Explore equal parts.	5-6		4-5		4-5		1-2				1-2		9		P(152); R(120)
10-2	Name and write fractions.	1-3, 7-8		2, 6-7		3, 6-7		3-4				3		10-11		P(153); R(121)
10-3	Explore equivalent fractions.	4, 9-10		3, 8-9		1, 8-9		5-6				4-5		12		P(154); R(122)
10-4	Explore comparing and ordering fractions.	11-12		1, 10-11		2, 10-11		7-8				6		13		P(155); R(123)
10-5	Estimate fractional amounts.	13-14		12-13		12-13		9-10				7		15		P(156); R(124)
Section B																
10-6	Find a fraction of a set.	1-2		27		27		11-12				8		16		P(158); R(125)
10-7	Explore finding a fraction of a number.	3-6		14-15		14-15		13-14				9-11		1		P(159); R(126)
10-8	Write fractions greater than 1.	7-8		16-17		16-17		15-16				12		17		P(160); R(127)
10-9	Explore adding and subtracting fractions.	9-14		18-19		18-19		17-20				13-14		2-3		P(161); R(128)
10-10	Solve problems by drawing pictures and making decisions.															R(162); R(129)

Continued on next page.

Chapter 10 (continued)

Lesson	Objectives	Quizzes Items	✓	Chapter Test Form A Items	✓	Chapter Test Form B Items	✓	Chapter Test Form C Items	✓	Chapter Test Form D Items	✓	Chapter Test Form E Items	✓	Chapter Test Form F Items	✓	Review Options in Supplements Practice and Reteaching Masters (pages)
	Section C (continued)															
10-11	Explore length.	1, 4-5		20		20		21-22				15		18		P(164); R(130)
10-12	Measure to the nearest $\frac{1}{2}$ and $\frac{1}{4}$ inch.	6-7		21-22		21-22		23-24				16-17		19		P(165); R(131)
10-13	Explore length in feet and inches.	2, 8-9		23		23		25-26				21		4		P(166); R(132)
10-14	Estimate and compare measurement in inches, feet, yards, and miles.	3, 10-12		24-25		24-25		27-29				18-19		20		P(167); R(133)
10-15	Solve problems by using logical reasoning.	13		26		26		30-32				20		21		P(168); R(134)
	Prior objectives													5-8, 11 22		

Item Analysis for Individual Assessment: Grade 3, Chapter 11

Chapter 11: Decimals and Metric Linear Measurement

Student Name _____

Place a ✔ in the column if the student has answered some or all of the questions correctly. For Test Form D, check all the objectives that are reflected in the student's response.

Quiz or Test Form	Score	Date

Review Options in Student Edition
- Section A Review and Practice, page 468
- Section B Review and Practice, page 476
- Chapter 11 Review/Test, page 478
- Chapter 11 Performance Assessment, page 479

Quizzes and Tests from the Assessment Sourcebook / Review Options in Supplements

Lesson	Objectives	Quizzes Items	✓	Chapter Test Form A Items	✓	Chapter Test Form B Items	✓	Chapter Test Form C Items	✓	Chapter Test Form D Items	✓	Chapter Test Form E Items	✓	Chapter Test Form F Items	✓	Practice and Reteaching Masters (pages)
Section A																
11-1	Explore tenths.	1-2, 4, 6-7, 9		1, 5, 7-8, 12, 29		1, 5, 7-8, 12, 29		1-6				1, 3, 5		10, 12		P(171); R(135)
11-2	Name and write hundredths as decimals.	3, 5, 8, 10		6, 9-11, 29		6, 9-11, 29		7-13				2, 4, 6, 24		11, 13		P(172); R(136)
11-3	Explore adding and subtracting decimals.	11-12		13-16		13-16		14-18				7-10		1-2		P(173); R(137)
11-4	Connect decimals and money amounts.	13-15		17-20		17-20		19-24				11-14		14-15		P(174); R(138)
11-5	Solve problems by making decisions.															P(175); R(139)
Section B																
11-6	Explore centimeters and decimeters.	1-2, 5-6, 9		2, 21, 23, 26		2, 21, 23, 26		25-27, 31, 34				15, 18, 21		18, 20		P(177); R(140)
11-7	Estimate and compare measurement in meters and kilometers.	3-4, 7-8, 10-11		3-4, 22, 24, 25		3-4, 22, 24, 25		28-30, 32-33, 35				16-17, 19-20		17-18, 19, 21		P(178); R(141)
11-8	Solve problems by using objects and drawing pictures.	12-13		27-28		27-28		36-38				22-23		23		P(179); R(142)
	Prior objectives													3-9, 22		

© Scott Foresman Addison Wesley 3

Item Analysis for Individual Assessment: Grade 3, Chapter 12

Chapter 12: Measurement and Probability

Student Name _____

Place a ✔ in the column if the student has answered some or all of the questions correctly. For Test Form D, check all the objectives that are reflected in the student's response.

Review Options in Student Edition

- Section A Review and Practice, page 498
- Section B Review and Practice, page 512
- Chapter 12 Review/Test, page 514
- Chapter 12 Performance Assessment, page 515

Quiz or Test Form	Score	Date

Lesson	Objectives	Quizzes Items	✓	Chapter Test Form A Items	✓	Chapter Test Form B Items	✓	Chapter Test Form C Items	✓	Chapter Test Form D Items	✓	Chapter Test Form E Items	✓	Chapter Test Form F Items	✓	Practice and Reteaching Masters (pages)	✓
Section A																	
12-1	Explore capacity in customary units.	1, 5, 11		1, 3-4		3-4		1-3				1-2		6		P(182); R(143)	
12-2	Estimate and compare measurements in liters and milliliters.	2, 6		5-6, 22		5-6, 22		4-5				3-4		7, 19		P(183); R(144)	
12-3	Explore weight in customary units.	3, 7, 12		7-8		7-8		6-7				5-6		8, 10		P(184); R(145)	
12-4	Estimate and compare measurement in grams and kilograms.	4, 8		9-10		9-10		8-9				7-8		9		P(185); R(146)	
12-5	Estimate and compare measurement in degrees of Fahrenheit and Celsius.	9-10		11-12		11-12		10-11				9-10		12, 20		P(186); R(147)	
12-6	Solve problems by making decisions about what to carry on a backpacking trip.															P(187); R(148)	
Section B																	
12-7	Explore likelihood.	4-7		13-14		13-14		12-16				11-12, 18		13		P(189);R(149)	
12-8	Explore predictions.	1-2, 8-9		2, 15-16		2, 15-16		17-18				13-14		14-15		P(190); R(150)	

Continued on next page.

Lesson	Objectives	Quizzes Items	✓	Chapter Test Form A Items	✓	Chapter Test Form B Items	✓	Chapter Test Form C Items	✓	Chapter Test Form D Items	✓	Chapter Test Form E Items	✓	Chapter Test Form F Items	✓	Practice and Reteaching Masters (pages)
						Quizzes and Tests from the Assessment Sourcebook										Review Options in Supplements
	Section B (continued)															
12-9	Explore probability.	10		17		1, 17		19-21				18		16		P(191); R(151)
12-10	Explore fairness.	3, 11-12		18-19		18-19		22-24				15-16		17-18		P(192); R(152)
12-11	Solve problems by working backward.	13		20-21		20-21		25-27				17		21		P(193); R(153)
	Prior objectives													1-5, 11		

Item Analysis for Individual Assessment

Grade 3 Quarterly Test, Chapters 1–3

Student Name _____   See page 327 for scoring.

Place a ✔ in the column if the student has answered some or all of the questions correctly.

Objectives	Lesson	Quarterly Test Chapters 1–3		Review Options in Supplements	
		Test Item	✔ if correct	Practice (pages)	Reteaching (pages)
Read a line graph.	1-3	1-3		P(3)	R(3)
Solve problems by using a guide.	1-4	3		P(4)	R(4)
Solve problems by choosing an operation.	1-5	4		P(5)5	R(5)
Solve problems by finding a pattern.	1-11	5		P(12)	R(11)
Read and write numbers through thousands.	2-3	6		P(17)	R(14)
Read and write numbers through hundred thousands.	2-4	7		P(18)	R(15)
Compare numbers.	2-6	8		P(21)	R(17)
Order numbers.	2-7	9		P(22)	R(18)
Round 2-digit and 3-digit numbers to the nearest ten.	2-8	10		P(23)	R(19)
Round numbers to the nearest hundred.	2-9	11		P(24)	R(20)
Tell time to the nearest 5 minutes.	2-10	12		P(26)	R(21)
Find ending time and the time between events.	2-13	13		P(29)	R(24)
Read a calendar and ordinal numbers.	2-14	14, 15		P(30)	R(25)
Use rounding to estimate sums.	3-4	16-18		P(37)	R(30)
Add 2-digit numbers.	3-6	19-21		P(40)	R(32)
Add 3-digit numbers.	3-7	22-24		P(41)	R(33)
Find the sum of more than 2 addends.	3-9	25, 26		P(42)	R(34)
Solve problems by guessing and checking.	3-10	27		P(44)	R(44)
Use mental math to find sums.	3-11	28		P(46)	R(46)
Write money amounts in dollars and cents.	3-13	29		P(48)	R(39)
Add money amounts.	3-15	3, 31		P(50)	R(50)
Estimate using front-end estimation.	3-16	32, 33		P(51)	R(51)
Solve problems needing exact answers or estimates.	3-17	34		P(52)	R(52)

Item Analysis for Individual Assessment

Grade 3 Quarterly Test, Chapters 1–6

Student Name _____   See page 327 for scoring.

Place a ✔ in the column if the student has answered some or all of the questions correctly.

Objectives	Lesson	Quarterly Test Chapters 1–6		Review Options in Supplements	
		Test Item	✔ if correct	Practice (pages)	Reteaching (pages)
Read a pictograph.	1-1	1,2		P(1)	R(1)
Solve problems by using a guide.	1-4	2		P(4)	R(4)
Solve problems by choosing an operation	1-5	3		P(5)	R(5)
Read and write numbers through hundred thousands.	2-4	4		P(18)	R(15)
Compare numbers	2-6	5		P(21)	R(17)
Order numbers.	2-7	6		P(22)	R(18)
Find ending time and the time between events.	2-13	7		P(29)	R(24)
Use rounding to estimate sums.	3-4	8		P(37)	R(30)
Add 2-digit numbers.	3-6	9		P(40)	R(32)
Add 3-digit numbers.	3-7	10, 11		P(41)	R(33)
Add 4-digit numbers.	3-8	12		P(42)	R(34)
Find the sum of more than 2 addends.	3-9	13		P(43)	R(35)
Add money amounts.	3-15	14		P(50)	R(41)
Estimate differences using rounding.	4-4	15		P(58)	R(47)
Subtract 2-digit numbers.	4-7	16		P(62)	R(50)
Subtract 3-digit numbers.	4-9	17		P(64)	R(52)
Subtract with 2 regroupings.	4-10	18		P(65)	R(53)
Subtract across zeros.	4-11	19		P(66)	R(54)
Subtract 4-digit numbers.	4-12	20		P(68)	R(55)
Subtract money.	4-15	21		P(71)	R(58)
Solve multiple-step problems.	4-13	22		P(69)	R(56)
Write multiplication sentences.	5-2	23		P(76)	R(61)
Explore multiplication stories.	5-3	24		P(77)	R(62)
Multiply with 2 as a factor.	5-4	25		P(80)	R(63)
Multiply with 5 as a factor.	5-5	26		P(82)	R(64)
Explore patterns when multiplying with 0 and 1.	5-7	27		P(82)	R(66)
Multiply with 9 as a factor.	5-8	25		P(83)	R(67)
Solve problems by making decisions about which information is important and by identifying what information is missing.	5-90	28		P(84)	R(68)

Continued on next page.

Place a ✔ in the column if the student has answered some or all of the questions correctly.

Objectives	Lesson	Quarterly Test Chapters 1–6		Review Options in Supplements	
		Test Item	✔ if correct	Practice (pages)	Reteaching (pages)
Multiply with 3 as a factor.	6-1	29, 32		P(88)	R(70)
Multiply with 4 as a factor.	6-2	30, 33		P(89)	R(71)
Multiply with 6 as a factor.	6-3	31, 33		P(90)	R(72)
Multiply with 7 and 8 as factors.	6-4	30-32		P(91)	R(73)
Multiply with 3 factors.	6-8	34, 35		P(96)	R(77)
Explore patterns on a fact table.	6-7	36		P(95)	R(76)
Solve problems by comparing different strategies to solve the same problem.	6-9	37		P(97)	R(78)

Item Analysis for Individual Assessment

Grade 3 Quarterly Test, Chapters 1–9

Student Name _____

See page 327 for scoring.

Place a ✔ in the column if the student has answered some or all of the questions correctly.

Objectives	Lesson	Quarterly Test Chapters 1–9		Review Options in Supplements	
		Test Item	✔ if correct	Practice (pages)	Reteaching (pages)
Read a bar graph.	1-2	1, 2		P(2)	R(2)
Solve problems by using a guide.	1-4	2		P(4)	R(4)
Compare numbers.	2-6	3		P(21)	R(17)
Find ending time and the time between events.	2-13	4		P(29)	R(24)
Add 2-digit numbers.	3-6	5		P(40)	R(32)
Add 3-digit numbers.	3-7	6		P(41)	R(33)
Find the sum of more than 2 addends.	3-9	7		P(43)	R(35)
Use mental math to find sums.	3-11	8		P(46)	R(37)
Subtract 2-digit numbers.	4-7	9		P(62)	R(50)
Subtract 3-digit numbers.	4-9	10, 11		P(64)	R(52)
Subtract with 2 regroupings.	4-10	11, 12		P(65)	R(53)
Subtract across zeros.	4-11	12		P(66)	R(54)
Use mental math to subtract equal fractions.	4-14	13		P(70)	R(57)
Solve problems by using objects.	4-16	14		P(72)	R(59)
Multiply with 2 as a factor.	5-4	15		P(79)	R(63)
Explore patterns when multiplying with 0 and 1.	5-6	16		P(81)	R(65)
Multiply with 9 as a factor.	5-8	15, 16		P(83)	R(67)
Multiply with 3 as a factor.	6-1	17		P(88)	R(70)
Multiply with 4 as a factor.	6-2	18		P(89)	R(71)
Multiply with 6 as a factor.	6-3	17		P(90)	R(72)
Multiply with 7 and 8 as factors.	6-4	18		P(91)	R(73)
Explore patterns on a fact table.	6-7	19		P(95)	R(76)
Multiply with 3 factors.	6-8	20		P(96)	R(77)
Divide by 5.	7-6	21		P(106)	R(84)
Divide by 3 and 4	7-7	22		P(107)	R(85)
Divide by 6 and 7.	7-10	23		P(111)	R(88)
Divide by 8 and 9.	7-11	24		P(112)	R(89)
Solve problems by choosing an operation.	7-9	25		P(109)	R(87)
Explore solids.	8-1	28		P(118)	R(93)
Identify lines, line segments, rays parallel lines, and intersecting lines.	8-3	26		P(120)	R(95)

Continued on next page.

© Scott Foresman Addison Wesley 3

320 Forms

Place a ✔ in the column if the student has answered some or all of the questions correctly.

Objectives	Lesson	Quarterly Test Chapters 1–9		Review Options in Supplements	
		Test Item	✔ if correct	Practice (pages)	Reteaching (pages)
Explore perimeter.	8-8	29		P(126)	R(100)
Find and name points on a coordinate grid.	8-12	27		P(130)	R(104)
Estimate products.	9-3	30		P(135)	R(107)
Multiply 2-digit numbers with regrouping.	9-6	31		P(139)	R(110)
Multiply 3-digit numbers.	9-7	32		P(140)	R(111)
Multiply money.	9-8	33		P(141)	R(112)
Estimate quotients.	9-12	34		P(146)	R(116)
Divide to find quotients and remainders.	9-14	35, 36		P(148)	R(118)

Item Analysis for Individual Assessment

Grade 3 Quarterly Test, Chapters 1–12

Student Name _____

See page 327 for scoring.

Place a ✔ in the column if the student has answered some or all of the questions correctly.

Objectives	Lesson	Quarterly Test Chapters 1–12		Review Options in Supplements	
		Test Item	✔ if correct	Practice (pages)	Reteaching (pages)
Read a bar graph.	1-2	1		2	2
Solve problems by using a guide.	1-4	1		4	4
Read and write numbers in the hundreds.	2-1	2		15	12
Compare numbers	2-6	3		21	17
Find ending time and the time between events.	2-13	4		29	24
Use rounding to estimate sums.	3-4	5		37	30
Add 2-digit numbers.	3-6	6		40	32
Add 3-digit numbers.	3-7	7		41	33
Find the sum of more than 2 addends.	3-9	8		43	35
Add money amounts	3-15	9		50	41
Subtract 2-digit numbers.	4-7	10		62	50
Subtract 3-digit numbers.	4-9	11		64	52
Subtract with two regroupings.	4-10	13, 14		65	53
Subtract across zeros.	4-11	12		66	54
Subtract 4-digit numbers	4-12	13		68	55
Subtract money.	4-15	14, 15		71	58
Write multiplication sentences.	5-2	16		76	61
Multiply with 5 as a factor.	5-5	17		80	64
Multiply with 9 as a factor.	5-9	17		84	68
Multiply with 4 as a factor.	6-2	18		89	71
Multiply with 6 as a factor.	6-3	18		90	72
Multiply with 7 and 8 as factors.	6-4	19		91	73
Divide by 5.	7-6	20		106	84
Divide by 3 and 4.	7-7	21		107	85
Divide by 6 and 7.	7-10	22		111	88
Identify lines, line segments, rays, parallel lines, and intersecting lines.	8-2	23		119	94
Find and name points on a coordinate grid.	8-12	24, 25		130	104
Multiply 2-digit numbers with regrouping.	9-6	26		139	110
Multiply money	9-8	27		141	112
Divide to find quotients and remainders.	9-14	28, 29		148	118

...inued on next page.

...Forms

Place a ✔ in the column if the student has answered some or all of the questions correctly.

Objectives	Lesson	Quarterly Test Chapters 1–12		Review Options in Supplements	
		Test Item	✔ if correct	Practice (pages)	Reteaching (pages)
Estimate fractional amounts.	10-5	30		156	124
Find a fraction of a set.	10-6	31		158	125
Solve problems by using logical reasoning.	10-15	32		168	134
Name and write hundredths as decimals.	11-2	33		172	136
Estimate and compare measurement in meters and kilometers.	11-7	34		178	141
Estimate and compare measurement in liters and milliliters.	12-2	35		183	144
Estimate and compare measurement in grams and kilograms.	12-4	36		185	146

Class Test Record Form: Chapters 1–6

Students	Chapter			Quarterly Ch. 1–3	Chapter			Quarterly Ch. 1–6
	1	2	3		4	5	6	
1.								
2.								
3.								
4.								
5.								
6.								
7.								
8.								
9.								
10.								
11.								
12.								
13.								
14.								
15.								
16.								
17.								
18.								
19.								
20.								
21.								
22.								
23.								
24.								
25.								
26.								
27.								
28.								
29.								
30.								
31.								
32.								
33.								
34.								
35.								

Class Test Record Form: Chapters 7–12

Students	Tests							
	Chapter			Quarterly	Chapter			Quarterly
	7	8	9	Ch. 1–9	10	11	12	Ch. 1–12
1.								
2.								
3.								
4.								
5.								
6.								
7.								
8.								
9.								
10.								
11.								
12.								
13.								
14.								
15.								
16.								
17.								
18.								
19.								
20.								
21.								
22.								
23.								
24.								
25.								
26.								
27.								
28.								
29.								
30.								
31.								
32.								
33.								
34.								
35.								

Percent Table for Scoring Tests

This table will help you quickly convert a raw test score to a percent score for any test containing up to 53 items.

Directions for using the table

Example: There are 28 items on a test, and a student correctly answers 22 of them.

1. Find the number of items, 28, along the left side of the table.
2. Place a rule or a strip of paper under the row for 28.
3. Find the column for 22, the number of items correctly answered.
4. Go down the column for 22 until you come to the row for 28. The number 79 is the percent score.

Number Correct

Number of Items

Items\Correct	1	2	3	4	5	6	7	8	9	10	11	12	13	14	15	16	17	18	19	20	21	22	23	24	25	26	27	28	29	30	31	32	33	34	35	36	37	38	39	40	41	42	43	44	45	46	47	48	49	50	51	52	53
1	100																																																				
2	50	100																																																			
3	33	67	100																																																		
4	25	50	75	100																																																	
5	20	40	60	80	100																																																
6	17	33	50	67	83	100																																															
7	14	29	43	57	71	86	100																																														
8	13	25	38	50	63	75	88	100																																													
9	11	22	33	44	56	67	78	89	100																																											
10	10	20	30	40	50	60	70	80	90	100																																										
11	9	18	27	36	45	55	64	73	82	91	100																																								
12	8	17	25	33	42	50	58	67	75	83	92	100																																						
13	8	15	23	31	38	46	54	62	69	77	85	92	100																																				
14	7	14	21	29	36	43	50	57	64	71	79	86	93	100																																			
15	7	13	20	27	33	40	47	53	60	67	73	80	87	93	100																																		
16	6	13	19	25	31	38	44	50	56	63	69	75	81	88	94	100																																	
17	6	12	18	24	29	35	41	47	53	59	65	71	76	82	88	94	100																															
18	6	11	17	22	28	33	39	44	50	56	61	67	72	78	83	89	94	100																														
19	5	11	16	21	26	32	37	42	47	53	58	63	68	74	79	84	89	95	100																													
20	5	10	15	20	25	30	35	40	45	50	55	60	65	70	75	80	85	90	95	100																												
21	5	10	14	19	24	29	33	38	43	48	52	57	62	67	71	76	81	86	90	95	100																											
22	5	9	14	18	23	27	32	36	41	45	50	55	59	64	68	73	77	82	86	91	95	100																										
23	4	9	13	17	22	26	30	35	39	43	48	52	57	61	65	70	74	78	83	87	91	96	100																									
24	4	8	13	17	21	25	29	33	38	42	46	50	54	58	63	67	71	75	79	83	88	92	96	100																								
25	4	8	12	16	20	24	28	32	36	40	44	48	52	56	60	64	68	72	76	80	84	88	92	96	100																							
26	4	8	12	15	19	23	27	31	35	38	42	46	50	54	58	62	65	69	73	77	81	85	88	92	96	100																						
27	4	7	11	15	19	22	26	30	33	37	41	44	48	52	56	59	63	67	70	74	78	81	85	89	93	96	100																					
28	4	7	11	14	18	21	25	29	32	36	39	43	46	50	54	57	61	64	68	71	75	79	82	86	89	93	96	100																				
29	3	7	10	14	17	21	24	28	31	34	38	41	45	48	52	55	59	62	66	69	72	76	79	83	86	90	93	97	100																		
30	3	7	10	13	17	20	23	27	30	33	37	40	43	47	50	53	57	60	63	67	70	73	77	80	83	87	90	93	97	100																	
31	3	6	10	13	16	19	23	26	29	32	35	39	42	45	48	52	55	58	61	65	68	71	74	77	81	84	87	90	94	97	100																
32	3	6	9	13	16	19	22	25	28	31	34	38	41	44	47	50	53	56	59	63	66	69	72	75	78	81	84	88	91	94	97	100															
33	3	6	9	12	15	18	21	24	27	30	33	36	39	42	45	48	52	55	58	61	64	67	70	73	76	79	82	85	88	91	94	97	100														
34	3	6	9	12	15	18	21	24	26	29	32	35	38	41	44	47	50	53	56	59	62	65	68	71	74	76	79	82	85	88	91	94	97	100													
35	3	6	9	11	14	17	20	23	26	29	31	34	37	40	43	46	49	51	54	57	60	63	66	69	71	74	77	80	83	86	89	91	94	97	100												
36	3	6	8	11	14	17	19	22	25	28	31	33	36	39	42	44	47	50	53	56	58	61	64	67	69	72	75	78	81	83	86	89	92	94	97	100											
37	3	5	8	11	14	16	19	22	24	27	30	32	35	38	41	43	46	49	51	54	57	59	62	65	68	70	73	76	78	81	84	86	89	92	95	97	100										
38	3	5	8	11	13	16	18	21	24	26	29	32	34	37	39	42	45	47	50	53	55	58	61	63	66	68	71	74	76	79	82	84	87	89	92	95	97	100									
39	3	5	8	10	13	15	18	21	23	26	28	31	33	36	38	41	44	46	49	51	54	56	59	62	64	67	69	72	74	77	79	82	85	87	90	92	95	97	100								
40	3	5	8	10	13	15	18	20	23	25	28	30	33	35	38	40	43	45	48	50	53	55	58	60	63	65	68	70	73	75	78	80	83	85	88	90	93	95	98	100							
41	2	5	7	10	12	15	17	20	22	24	27	29	32	34	37	39	41	44	46	49	51	54	56	59	61	63	66	68	71	73	76	78	80	83	85	88	90	93	95	98	100						
42	2	5	7	10	12	14	17	19	21	24	26	29	31	33	36	38	40	43	45	48	50	52	55	57	60	62	64	67	69	71	74	76	79	81	83	86	88	90	93	95	98	100					
43	2	5	7	9	12	14	16	19	21	23	26	28	30	33	35	37	40	42	44	47	49	51	53	56	58	60	63	65	67	70	72	74	77	79	81	84	86	88	91	93	95	98	100				
44	2	5	7	9	11	14	16	18	20	23	25	27	30	32	34	36	39	41	43	45	48	50	52	55	57	59	61	64	66	68	70	73	75	77	80	82	84	86	89	91	93	95	98	100			
45	2	4	7	9	11	13	16	18	20	22	24	27	29	31	33	36	38	40	42	44	47	49	51	53	56	58	60	62	64	67	69	71	73	76	78	80	82	84	87	89	91	93	96	98	100		
46	2	4	7	9	11	13	15	17	20	22	24	26	28	30	33	35	37	39	41	43	46	48	50	52	54	57	59	61	63	65	67	70	72	74	76	78	80	83	85	87	89	91	93	96	98	100	
47	2	4	6	9	11	13	15	17	19	21	23	26	28	30	32	34	36	38	40	43	45	47	49	51	53	55	57	60	62	64	66	68	70	72	74	77	79	81	83	85	87	89	91	94	96	98	100
48	2	4	6	8	10	13	15	17	19	21	23	25	27	29	31	33	35	38	40	42	44	46	48	50	52	54	56	58	60	63	65	67	69	71	73	75	77	79	81	83	85	88	90	92	94	96	98
49	2	4	6	8	10	12	14	16	18	20	22	24	27	29	31	33	35	37	39	41	43	45	47	49	51	53	55	57	59	61	63	65	67	69	71	73	76	78	80	82	84	86	88	90	92	94	96
50	2	4	6	8	10	12	14	16	18	20	22	24	26	28	30	32	34	36	38	40	42	44	46	48	50	52	54	56	58	60	62	64	66	68	70	72	74	76	78	80	82	84	86	88	90	92	94
51	2	4	6	8	10	12	14	16	18	20	22	24	25	27	29	31	33	35	37	39	41	43	45	47	49	51	53	55	57	59	61	63	65	67	69	71	73	75	76	78	80	82	84	86	88	90	92
52	2	4	6	8	10	12	13	15	17	19	21	23	25	27	29	31	33	35	37	38	40	42	44	46	48	50	52	54	56	58	60	62	63	65	67	69	71	73	75	77	79	81	83	85	87	88	90
53	2	4	6	8	9	11	13	15	17	19	21	23	25	26	28	30	32	34	36	38	40	42	43	45	47	49	51	53	55	57	58	60	62	64	66	68	70	72	74	75	77	79	81	83	85	87	89